Graham Walkhead.

ENJOYING ORNITHOLOGY

This book is for 'those naturalists whose enjoyment in watching wild life is enriched by the attempt to understand it.' DAVID LACK

'. . . pondering upon the past may give guidance in days to come . . .'
WINSTON SPENCER CHURCHILL

Enjoying Ornithology

A Celebration of Fifty Years of
The British Trust for Ornithology
1933–1983

Edited and compiled by
RONALD HICKLING

T & A D POYSER
Calton

ISBN 0 85661 036 4

First published 1983 by T & A D Poyser Ltd
Town Head House, Calton, Waterhouses, Staffordshire, England
for the British Trust for Ornithology

Text set in 10/12pt Linotron 202 Plantin,
printed and bound in Great Britain
at The Pitman Press, Bath

Contents

List of Figures

Foreword

D. A. Ratcliffe

Chief Scientist, Nature Conservancy Council

This book depicts the development of British ornithology during the twentieth century, as a science, a hobby, and a key element in nature conservation practice. The rôle of the British Trust for Ornithology has involved all three aspects. In particular it has been the means of capitalising on the fieldwork of energetic and dedicated amateur birdwatchers, and welding together much of their effort in a coordinated form that has greatly advanced the science of ornithology. The Trust has adopted a positive and promotional rôle here, catalysing and focussing the interests of the membership in a highly productive way which has been the envy of other countries. The collecting urge has been poured creatively into bird ringing and recording, with the result that the distribution, numbers, movements and biology of our avifauna are probably better known than those of any other group of organisms. A selective summary of certain themes will indicate briefly the main directions which this endeavour has taken.

The work on ringing and migration has, in conjunction with that of the Wildfowl Trust, contributed substantially to the international effort in documenting the seasonal movements of birds. It has also provided an increasingly valuable information base about longevity and mortality for many species. The Common Birds Census has given a measure of year to year changes in bird numbers within the more developed agricultural and lowland environment and exemplifies the modern development of monitoring studies designed to detect and follow population trends. It also provides information about breeding density and habitat needs for many species. The Nest Records Scheme continually enlarges knowledge of nesting biology, especially on such topics as reproductive performance. Geographical or habitat-based surveys such as the Birds of Estuaries Enquiry and the Atlas of Breeding Birds in Britain and Ireland have produced systematic, accurate and comprehensive statements of the distribution and numbers of birds in these categories. These have been complemented by individual species surveys, usually focussed on breeding distribution and population, which have given a detailed picture of the current status of some of our more localised birds. Most of the projects also serve the need for surveillance, by providing base-lines against which repeat surveys can be measured after appropriate time intervals. And many have been the means of identifying ecological relationships and pointing to useful lines of study in a variety of problems.

The outstanding feature of the British Trust for Ornithology has, indeed, been its primary concern for the advancement of knowledge through corporate research projects. There has always been the need for a full-time professional staff of trained ornithologists to organise and collate the field contributions of the Trust membership in these collective investigations. Some of the individual species surveys have been run by Trust members, but the office usually provides much background support. *Bird Study*, launched in 1954 as the journal of the Trust, has catered for publication not only of internal papers but also of a wide range of outside contributions, and has a world reputation in the science of ornithology. The editor has usually been a member of the Trust staff. The data store built up at Trust HQ has been made available to outside workers, and has been an important source of information on many aspects of bird biology and ecology.

Max Nicholson, one of the founding fathers of the Trust, and later also of the Nature Conservancy, realised the enormous potential of the organisation for supplying scientific information highly relevant to the conservation of birds. It was also advantageous to have such information submitted by a neutral research organisation whose only commitment was to the quality of its science. By means of a research contract from the Conservancy, he forged a close link between the two bodies. His vision gave stability and career prospects sufficient to attract good scientists to the Trust, enabling them to build up a permanent complement with the capacity to maintain long-term projects but yet flexible enough to develop new themes as the needs arose. In return, the Conservancy received an assured flow of ornithological information tailored to the needs of its conservation programme, particularly on the advisory side.

The research contract became, in effect, an integral part of the Conservancy's funding programme. After the splitting of the Conservancy in 1973, the Trust contract was shared for a time between the Institute of Terrestrial Ecology (the former research arm) and the new Nature Conservancy Council, but was eventually taken over wholly by the latter. The NCC has since 1973 had to obtain the bulk of its research by contract, and it has maintained its support to the Trust by this means. The Conservancy has always been mindful of the high value for money which accrues from the efforts of a large, unpaid labour force, and of the key place of birds in the overall interest of the concerned public in nature conservation. Successive Visiting Groups have endorsed the relevance and importance of the contract programme to the Conservancy on the one hand, and high quality and cost-effectiveness on the other.

To make the best use of the vast data store held by the Trust, the NCC provided a computer for Beech Grove in 1979. Under the guidance of the present Director, Dr Raymond O'Connor, this was quickly put to good use, and an enhanced flow of papers has followed the increased facility for data analysis. The Conservancy itself has made increasing use of the rapidly available print-outs of information highly relevant to topical bird conservation issues, such as up-dated counts of waders on estuaries. The capacity of the Trust to conduct conservation-oriented studies is being utilised in other ways, such as the development of management options for birds in the Lincolnshire woods which have been the subject of detailed botanical investigation by the NCC. The separate contract for the Ornithological Sites Register was designed specifically to identify and report upon all those areas known to be important for breeding birds, so that appropriate measures for their conservation could be taken. It is gratifying that increasingly the Trust staff are translating the fruits of the contract work into excellent books, such as *Estuary Birds of Britain and Ireland* by A. J. Prater and *Bird Habitats in Britain* by R. J. Fuller.

It is with the greatest pleasure that, on behalf of the Nature Conservancy Council, I extend congratulations to the British Trust for Ornithology on the occasion of its Jubilee celebration, and gratitude for the fruitful partnership which has developed between our two organisations during the second half of this period. This book is a most appropriate expression of the occasion, and the record of a fine achievement, fascinating in its historical perspective and in its breadth of scope and vision. Its title is a timely reminder – so often are we caught up in stressful conservation issues or weighed down by the heavy objectivity of science – that enjoyment is, at bottom and to most of us, what our interest in birds is all about. Not that those attending Trust functions, and the Annual Conference in particular, could ever be in doubt of this. I have the happiest memories of these events, and remember the warmth and friendliness which greeted me when, as a young fieldworker, I was invited in 1960 to organise the Peregrine enquiry for the Trust. I am glad of the opportunity to pay my own tribute to the unfailing helpfulness and dedication which have so characterised the organisation as I have known it, whether as Council, Officers or Members. And, in looking to the future, I should like to think that the world of ornithology would join in hoping that the Trust's development and success will continue to grow as they have during its first half-century.

14 March 1983

Introduction

Enjoying Ornithology has been chosen as the title of this book after a long search, because it sums up so concisely the aims and achievements of the British Trust for Ornithology. It is not of course a new title. It was used in 1965 by the late Dr David Lack for a collection of his occasional writings and broadcasts. As the earlier book has been long out of print it seemed permissible to use the title again, and Dr Elizabeth Lack readily gave her consent. It was believed that David Lack himself would have approved, for one of the most important influences he had on the Trust was to convince amateur ornithologists who were its members that research – that is 'finding out something' – was 'one of the most delightful of all pastimes'. It was this belief which inspired the far-sighted men who formed the Trust fifty years ago. Their vision has proved enduring.

The name of the British Trust for Ornithology was coined by E. M. Nicholson. He was one of the group of four ornithologists who met to set in motion the formation of the Trust, and he became its first Honorary Secretary. After a distinguished career he is still a dominant force in British ornithology, and a leader in world conservation. We are grateful that, in spite of his incredibly busy life, he has been able to write the first chapter in this book, describing the origins and early days of the Trust. The story of the Trust from 1951 to 1982 is then continued by Robert Spencer. This period saw a great change in the structure of the Trust, beginning with the staff appointment of Dr Bruce Campbell. The co-operation between a professional biologist and amateur field-workers eventually grew into the kind of research institute which we have had since 1963; the observations of members are used as the basis for analysis and research by a professional staff, led by a distinguished biologist, and with important work carried out under contract for the Nature Conservancy Council. The growth of membership during the post-war period – which has made our achievements possible – was largely dependent on the growth of the county and local ornithological societies.

Chapter Three reviews the fieldwork of the Trust, and this is followed by a remarkable contribution from Robert Spencer on the changing ranges and fortunes of British birds: it will be seen that much of the information has come from Trust enquiries. The Trust's involvement in migration research, largely through the Ringing Scheme and the bird observatory network, is then reviewed in Chapter Five. Conservation in this country has developed since the war, alongside the major growth of the Trust. However, the Trust has not sought to become directly concerned in the practice of conservation, seeing its rôle as providing objective information which can be used in planning practical conservation. Inevitably, members of the Trust are engaged in conservation work, but through specialist organisations, whose developments are reviewed in Chapter Six. This is followed by a chapter concerned with the problems which trouble our environment, the sections of which have been contributed by experts in each particular field.

Finally, there is an important appendix, which it is hoped will be of value as a constant source of reference. This shows in tabular form a substantial selection of facts and figures which have accumulated in the Trust's files over the years. The publication of the present book has provided an opportunity to analyse these records, and some from other sources, and to make them available in a way not possible before. Compilation of these tables has been a mammoth task. A temporary member of staff, Alison Gunn, was employed for this purpose, and she received much help from Christopher Mead, Robert Spencer, Robert Morgan and Dr Raymond O'Connor.

ACKNOWLEDGEMENTS

This book was planned by a Jubilee Book Panel, consisting of Dr Raymond O'Connor, Robert Spencer, Trevor Poyser, Crispin Fisher, Ronald Hickling and Michael Allen.

The Trust wishes to thank all those who have contributed to the book, and to all members of the scientific staff, who have advised and read through most of the text. Gwen Bonham and Elizabeth Murray have proved invaluable in finding books and papers, and drawing many of the figures. The editorial skills of Robert Hudson have done much to improve the book.

Most of the drawings reproduced have been taken from publications of the Trust, but others by Sir Peter Scott, Donald Watson and John Busby are used by permission of the artists. The bookjacket and title page illustration were specially drawn by Robert Gillmor.

Martin Withers prepared bromide prints for all the maps and drawings, and helped in many ways. Above all, my wife has given constant help and support.

RONALD HICKLING

1: Origins and early days

E. M. Nicholson

Ever since Gilbert White published his *Natural History of Selborne*, in 1789, growing numbers of amateur naturalists have felt an urge to contribute something to our knowledge of the wildlife of our country, with increasing attention to its birds. For more than a century their movement remained spontaneous and unorganised, and its fruits were anecdotal and fragmentary. During the nineteenth century some more serious ornithologists, including a few professional scientists inspired by Gilbert White (such as Professor Alfred Newton), came together in the British Ornithologists' Union to discuss and publish systematic studies. Many of these, however, related to distant lands. Some time later the (Royal) Society for the Protection of Birds emerged, with its interest focussed on Britain, but with a propagandist, educational and activist bias.

Those who wished to spend their time in the field in advancing knowledge of living birds found no rallying point until June 1907, when H. F. Witherby launched a new monthly publication *British Birds*. In its first issue an editorial said that there was universal agreement on the need for a magazine devoted entirely to the study of birds in this country; and it added significantly:

> We hope, with the co-operation of our readers, to embark upon a series of more systematic investigations than have hitherto been attempted, with regard to matters concerning the birds of this country. Our plan is to make organised enquiries into such questions as the extension or diminution of the breeding range of certain species, the exact status and distribution of some birds, the effects of protection in certain areas and on different species, the nature of the food of particular birds, and many kindred subjects. Could observations on such points be conducted on a common basis and made contemporaneously in different parts of the country, results of great interest and of very considerable scientific importance would be achieved.

Although this admirable idea was ably and vigorously pursued, any lasting developments to which it might have led were arrested by World War I. The volunteers who then perished included a tragic proportion of those who might have brought it to fruition. In the difficult post-war years Witherby was unable fully to revive it, but the seed had been sown and it germinated elsewhere. The Oxford Ornithological Society, launched on 10 February 1921, began by issuing model annual local reports. When I started writing articles and books on birds in the mid-1920s I demonstrated how bird censuses and other techniques could be used, and how the discoveries and opportunities of more systematic observations could be disseminated widely. When I went up to Oxford in 1926, I was quickly put to work organising the Oxford Bird Census. I also started (in 1927) a co-operative trapping station in Christ Church Meadow, which built upon the continuing pre-war ringing scheme and paved the way for a series of bird observatories. With Witherby's backing I next organised (in 1928) a national census of Heronries, which showed the validity of his earlier concept, but also showed that in order to realise it some continuing national organisation, other than a hard-pressed monthly journal, would be essential. The important opportunities, and the readiness of hundreds of ornithologists to take part, were now proved. How were they to be welded acceptably into a regular team, and efficiently serviced, to ensure that the fruits of their efforts were competently processed, published and acknowledged?

We were up against problems of funding, at one of those moments when those in charge of the British economy were busy running it into the ground. Our only hope seemed to be in taking advantage of the then widespread, if scientifically dubious, belief that (before chemical pesticides had been heard of) birds could render great services in ridding farms of invertebrate pests. For the necessary demonstration I launched a census of Rook numbers on an area of 244 square miles around Oxford. I was able to show that, if the actual

Rook population was multiplied by its seasonal consumption of planted cereals on known arable areas, the total offtake could not amount to a limiting factor on the crop, while the consumption of wireworms and other pests was substantial. Thus armed, and with the invaluable help of J. C. F. Fryer (later Secretary of the Agricultural Research Council), we persuaded the academic authorities to accept an Oxford University Research in Economic Ornithology. Then the Ministry of Agriculture and the Empire Marketing Board agreed to provide a bare minimum of funds to employ W. B. Alexander as whole-time research officer in conformity with our recommendation (1930) 'that a suitable and fully qualified biologist should be appointed and subsidised by the Ministry of Agriculture to be responsible for further research' (*Journal of Ecology* 18: 51–66).

Our hard-won success here made a start towards building up the scientific headquarters staff which we envisaged. It remained, however, to persuade a convincing number of leading British field ornithologists of the need to create a new organisation, able to take over the rôle of conducting systematic investigations which Witherby had envisaged some 23 years earlier for *British Birds*. In embarking on this we were fortunate to have the full support of Harry Witherby, who had been converted by the success of the Heron census and no longer regarded *British Birds* as a suitable agency for the task. On the Oxford side we were lucky that the Chancellor of the University, Viscount Grey of Fallodon, was a keen field ornithologist. Although now fearfully handicapped by failing sight he saw to it that the University gave the project a fair wind. Yet our base was frighteningly tenuous. Although there was no outright opposition many were sceptical either about the need for a new organisation or about the practicability of launching it in such difficult times, or (above all) the desirability of linking it with such an extraneous institution as a university – especially, in some minds, with the University of Oxford.

History shows clearly that the twinning of the embryonic British Trust for Ornithology with Oxford University was from the first unpopular and difficult to implement. Within two decades the two came apart. Was it then a mistake from the outset? I think not, despite all the pain and grief it cost me as the man in the middle. Without the prestige, facilities and research climate of Oxford it could scarcely have been possible to attain the necessary standards of performance, or publication of the results of study projects which were almost entirely the work of amateurs. Without Oxford, financial backing from the Establishment would hardly have been attainable. On the other hand without the continuous enthusiastic teamwork of the newly enrolled members, and the voluntary financial and other support which they were able to build up, the University would have baulked at launching such a far-fetched and pioneering enterprise. The eventual divorce may or may not have been inevitable or desirable; but at least it was deferred until both the Trust and the Edward Grey Institute were firmly established, within a new climate in which both could find a way to worthwhile development. The fact that both eventually proved able to stand on their own feet, separately, is no evidence that either could have become viable initially in isolation.

At the outset of the 1930s progress towards a permanent scheme proved practicable only through Oxford, where accommodation was found (within the Department of Biology) for W. B. Alexander, who was funded by grants to the University mainly from State sources. He was shortly to receive official status as the Oxford University Research in Economic Ornithology, under an Advisory Committee headed by Professor E. S. Goodrich, and which included representatives of the Ministry of Agriculture and the Oxford Ornithological Society.

A document circulated early in 1932 deplored the frustration of biological research work for lack of 'field data scientifically obtained'. It declared that 'this starvation of science is not the result of any deficiency of observers. It is due simply to a deficiency of scientific direction and organisation. Observers . . . urgently need training and guiding; otherwise they waste their time repeating trivial work that has already been done.' The essentials for progress were defined as *Concentration of Aim*, *Expert Direction*, and the *Training of Observers* (especially of young ones) in order to bring the 'quantity and value of biological data . . . nearer to the needs of biology.' After reviewing recent progress the document stated that limitations of funds were crippling activities 'and a precarious and unwholesome reliance on economic aims is unavoidable'.

The proposed remedy was 'to expand the scheme to its natural limits by abandoning its local Oxford character and making it an independent clearing house and directive centre for all kinds of ornithological field work in the United Kingdom'. This would require the formation of a 'representative national council' to take over the remodelled scheme, and of 'a chain of organised bird-watchers throughout the British Isles, with correspondents in the Empire and abroad, in order to undertake co-ordinated research on a long-term plan'. The concept would be based upon the nucleus (at or near Oxford) of 'a national headquarters for field ornithology, including a permanent address and clearing house for observations, a library of books, papers, MSS, photographs etc . . . an office for issue of a bulletin and for . . . stimulating and co-ordinating research, and as a secondary consideration a centre for continuing the intensive Oxford scheme, with University recognition.' It was envisaged as undertaking national survey operations such as the Census of Heronries (1928) and the Great Crested Grebe Enquiry (1931), and other national activities. In the depths of what was rightly named the Great Depression it conceded that some might find this 'an ill-chosen moment to embark on so large a scheme', but it warned of the withdrawal of existing funds and the throwing away of 'all the effort which has gone so far towards building up a national centre of field ornithology'. (The appeal for not less than £1,600 per annum for at least five years was equivalent to probably some

£30,000 today in real terms; it relied upon 'a far-sighted understanding of the need for preserving from extinction in a temporary time of stress, the nucleus of incalculable future scientific advance'.)

With hindsight the perspective has been shown to be valid, but its boldness and optimism in the circumstances may still be felt as breath-taking. It spelt out as a commitment those ideas which had been sketched for a 'National Society of Bird-watchers' in Chapter IV of my book *The Art of Birdwatching*, published by Witherby in November 1931. It was on a visit the following spring to Guy Charteris, at Stanway in the Cotswolds, that he and Bernard Tucker and W. B. Alexander and I set action in train, adopting the title which had suddenly occurred to me: the British Trust *for* Ornithology.

A series of meetings followed, legal advice was obtained on a constitution, and an appeal was drafted. The latter was to be signed by Viscount Grey of Fallodon, Lord Scone (later Lord Mansfield) as Chairman, H. F. Witherby, J. C. F. Fryer, the Rt Hon. Malcolm MacDonald, and such well-known ornithologists as D. A. Bannerman, the Duchess of Bedford, T. A. Coward, H. Eliot Howard, Julian Huxley, F. C. R. Jourdain, N. B. Kinnear, C. Oldham, W. L. Sclater and Miss E. L. Turner, as well as B. W. Tucker and myself. The wording followed closely that of the 1932 draft, already quoted at some length. Luckily I was on good terms with the Editor of *The Times*, who gave us a good send-off (1933); but funds and recruits came in too gradually to avert an agonisingly long struggle to achieve viability, which taxed all our pluck and endurance.

Our only early lucky break came (once more) from Harry Witherby, who concluded that he was no longer making enough use of his collection of over 9,000 skins of Palearctic birds, formed to illustrate their plumage, moults and geographical variation. Accordingly, he sold them to the British Museum (Natural History) and thus was enabled to give £1,400 to the infant British Trust for Ornithology. In making this handsome gift he observed: 'I have very carefully considered the project and I see a great future for it. It deserves all possible support and I am very glad that my collection has been the means of making a step towards its permanent foundation.'

In July 1934 Oxford was the scene of the Eighth International Ornithological Congress, where I read a paper making the case for the type of work envisaged by the Trust. It was based on the annual index of the British Heron population, showing its fluctuations during the six years since the 1928 census, and explaining its value not only for the advancement of biological knowledge but for economic ornithology and bird protection also. This was a first step towards making the Trust known internationally. We took the opportunity to hold the Trust's first Annual General Meeting at Oxford during the Congress, thus obtaining an attendance of some 50 persons. It was noted that the University had helped further by setting up a broader-based Oxford University Committee for Ornithology; but the Board of Trade had not helped by holding up the Trust's incorporation, which was not completed until 1939.

Edward Grey had died in September 1933, and suggestions were pursued for giving his name to the Institute at Oxford, and endowing it out of memorial funds. Unfortunately, divided counsels and procrastination amongst those most closely concerned confused and delayed the launching of the necessary appeal until January 1936. Although sponsored by the Prime Minister, the Archbishop of Canterbury and a posse of Establishment figures it raised a disappointing sum, only part of which came to the Edward Grey Institute. But meanwhile the Pilgrim Trust had given valuable grants of £200 each for 1935 and 1936 towards the running costs of the research programme which, despite financial stringency, had made a promising and early start.

W. B. Alexander had lost no time in following through the study of the Bird Population of an Oxfordshire Farm, which had been initiated with the Oxford Bird Census in 1927. While the results were in some ways disappointing, this was the prototype for the now-important Common Birds Census; and among its technical advances was the conversion of numbers of different-sized birds into a total biomass, which came out on average over the years at 57 kg per 50 ha in October, 46·7 kg in November and 32 kg in February. Follow-up over four more years amplified and corrected these results, which were reviewed in a BTO publication (with the same title) by W. M. M. Chapman in 1939. Alexander also repeated on a much larger scale in 1931 the census of the Rook population which had been made in 1928, and was able to throw a good deal of additional light on the problem, although he did not venture further into the actual assessment of economic impacts on agriculture.

While these studies were most valuable in developing techniques and approaches they stopped short of the deployment, supervision and training of bands of amateur birdwatchers to carry out extensive co-operative projects. For this purpose the Scientific Committee of the Trust got together a small picked group to make a trial study of the breeding bird populations of British heath and moorland, as being one of the simplest British bird habitats; 1,700 acres were covered in England, Scotland and Ireland, about a third of which was on small islands. Again, important problems of technique and evaluation arose immediately, and could be pursued in some depth owing to the exceptionally experienced and capable team of observers working under David Lack's supervision.

On a more grandiose scale, the Woodcock was chosen for a two-year nationwide investigation which eventually gathered in a thousand completed schedules; it was reinforced by a special ringing effort which more than doubled the previous level. Among the questions set at rest was the previously controversial aerial transport of chicks. The eventual Report occupied 140 pages, but its late appearance and disjointed pattern of publication (in *Ibis*) reduced the impact which it had been expected to have. Less ambitious were A. W. Boyd's 1934 inquiry on broods reared by Swallows, and David Lack's Woodland Bird Inquiry which was a follow-up to that on heathlands. More critical, and eventually decisive for protection, was Alice Hibbert-Ware's Little Owl Food Inquiry, which called for food pellets and larder contents from many districts, together with corpses of any Little Owls allegedly killed in the act. This gave rise to an unforeseen problem when the sub-postmistress at Girton, where the investigator lived, went on strike against the obnoxious contents of her mail, and arrangements had to be made to divert the flow elsewhere. Less successful were inquiries into Bud-eating and Tameness in Wild Birds, which came up against technical problems at that time unsuitable for handling in co-operative investigations.

All in all, the tedious and time-consuming job of organising and funding the Trust was not allowed to interfere with fulfilment of the more interesting functions for which it had been conceived, and which soon justified its existence. Its main reason for existence was to bring about a big advance in the quantity and quality of scientifically acceptable field observation and recording of wild birds in Britain. This was to be achieved both by organising well-conceived and well-run co-operative studies, and by promoting individual initiatives and spontaneous interchanges of ideas and experience for a fuller appreciation of the opportunities and rewards of modern ornithology. All kinds of opportunities were taken to demonstrate how ordinary observers could participate. One of the first to rally round was A. W. Boyd with his inquiry into the average size of broods of the Swallow, for which he recruited 22 helpers as far apart as Sussex, South Wales, the Yorkshire coast, Norfolk, Central Scotland, the Isle of Man and Cheshire; 644 broods were examined, averaging just over four young, the first brood usually being the largest, and much was learnt about the species' relation to domestic and other animals and to House Martins. A more opportunist study took advantage of a plague of voles to study the build-up of Short-eared Owls on the Scottish borders.

Such investigations triggered off new ideas and awareness among bird-watchers generally, and taught them the rewards of making new friends and contributing to ornithological knowledge. It also created for the Trust a clear image, distinct from and complementary to those of the British Ornithologists' Union and the Royal Society for the Protection of Birds. However, complications soon arose – for example, when the Trust was pressed to join representations over the threatened RAF bombing range at Abbotsbury (Dorset) in 1935, and then more particularly over the question of banning egg-collecting. At the Annual General Meeting in 1935 a resolution was carried unanimously reaffirming the aims of the Trust 'to be the encouragement and carrying on of bird studies and the impartial provision of common services for the benefit of ornithologists', and further declaring it 'to be contrary to these aims for the Trust to imperil its impartial status by taking sides or making general pronouncements upon controversial matters'. This resolution was made, as the Trust's Second Report records, 'because of the campaign of a small number of men – not members of the Trust – who sought to misrepresent it as being in favour of egg-collecting because it refused to be driven by outside intrigues into a declaration on the subject which would falsify its character as a service institution'. Since the press campaign was continued by the same persons, the Trust's Chairman (Lord Mansfield), the Vice-Chairman (H. F. Witherby), the Hon. Treasurer (B. W. Tucker) and the Hon. Secretary (E. M. Nicholson) issued in March 1936 a statement on *Why the Trust Makes No Statement About Egg Collecting.* It pointed out the healthy tendency to become too keen on watching or photographing wild birds in the field to have any time for such destructive pursuits as had rent British ornithology into warring sections. The BTO, created to foster and assist this tendency, and having already attracted over a thousand observers to join in its field inquiries, could claim to be fulfilling a need; for bird protection, other appropriate bodies existed and no new forum was needed. It ended full-bloodedly:

> As a fact-finding body the Trust will, with the approval of its members, continue to leave them to express their views on matters of policy through the organisations appropriate for that purpose, as many of them already do. The Trust will express no opinion on the ethics either of egg-collecting or of shooting, game preservation and similar issues. In view, however, of the tactics which have been adopted it is necessary to point out that any statement or suggestion that the Trust in any way 'favours' egg-collecting must be treated as slanderous.

This disposed of the matter. It is worth quoting because of its plain insistence on the principles that ornithological bodies should stick to their own fields of competence, and should not be misled into dabbling in a bit of everything. Now that so many bodies concerned with nature are able to work so confidently together in the assurance that mutual respect and consultation will be the order of the day, it is salutary to recall that the establishment of this assurance did not occur without an effort of leadership.

Another area in which the Trust's early efforts have borne lasting fruit has been that of public information and enlightenment. This was in any case demanded by the Appeal, but it was pursued further when the British Broadcasting Corporation agreed 'to allocate in April 1936 a series of three twenty-minute evening radio talks to explaining the ideas behind the Trust's co-operative field work and something of the aims and progress of current inquiries'. At a time when the Trust's individual membership totalled only 215, plus a dozen societies and corporate bodies, this ambitious and self-assured approach offered the only hope of reaching an income level of £1,000 a year and beyond, the sum for 1935 having amounted to only £786 19s 3d.

Yet already other assets were being secured, such as a library of bird books 'already amongst the most complete in England', thanks to a series of generous gifts. Anxiety was expressed 'to avert the threatened destruction or dispersal of sets of bird photographs, MSS, notes, field diaries and bird literature of any kind, which may prove difficult or impossible to replace'. This Second Report, issued on 22 May 1936, ended with a warning that in the absence of increased subscriptions the progress in carrying on a substantial field programme and creating enduring assets for British ornithology 'on a Trust income which must be considered beggarly' could not be maintained.

In the *Transactions of the South-Eastern Union of Scientific Societies* for 1936 I spelt out ten ways in which the BTO aimed to help the field observer. I reported that the Trust was already functioning effectively on two of these: getting experts to work at defining what needs finding out and giving a clear lead on what to look for and how; and secondly, organising teams of observers who could tackle successfully problems which no isolated individual could cope with. Encouraging progress had also been made on a third aim – building up a central library for observers of books, photographs, films, maps, diaries and MSS notes.

Resources were still insufficient to lend books, to offer grants, to answer questions about what work had been done on particular problems, or to keep track of who was working on each subject with a view to putting each in touch with the others. The other three aims were more general: the issuing of information (especially of methods), helping observers to improve their knowledge and experience, and helping to promote and co-ordinate (in association with other national and local bodies) the advancement of field ornithology, experimental investigations and education. An indication of the growing acceptance of the Trust was also afforded in 1936 by a request from regional and local bird societies for it to choose species which their members might concentrate on investigating nationwide. The first three to be selected were the Little Owl, Lesser Redpoll and Grey Wagtail, all apparently experiencing widespread changes in status at the time. P. A. D. Hollom's partial repeat of the 1931 census of Great Crested Grebes indicated an increase of about 3% in population, although breeding pairs had fallen during the 1934 drought by about 6%. Breeding pairs of Herons had recovered to just above the 1928 level. The Trust's efforts were enabling reliable data to be made available nationally for the first time on what was happening to at least some sectors of the bird population, and sound conclusions to be reached accordingly.

A further step in bringing ornithologists together fruitfully was made by following the Annual General Meeting in November 1936 with a dinner; this was accompanied by a specially prepared programme of gramophone records of bird song (Ludwig Koch's first public hearing in England), a film on the life of the Hobby, and various exhibits and papers. Appreciation of this kind of service was given by, among others, a member who wrote: 'I have decided to increase my subscription to two guineas for two main reasons. Firstly the dinner gave one a much better idea of the usefulness of the Trust and the work it is doing in both scientific and protective directions: and secondly I have derived such pleasure from helping with the Little Owl investigation that it has taken the place of other less useful but more expensive pastimes.' Such responses gave immense encouragement to the small dedicated band of promoters of the Trust, who had believed that somewhere 'out there' such potential supporters must exist but who had paid a heavy price for their temerity in acting on that assumption.

Growing awareness of the Trust led to many inquiries, one of which (from New York) asked whether the Birdless Grove at Goodwood is really birdless, and if so why! It so happened that this tall beechwood, almost devoid of ground cover, had been one of those covered in the Trust's Woodland Bird Inquiry, thus enabling the American enquirer to be informed at once which species lived in the Birdless Grove and in what numbers (the avifauna being poor but not absent).

The range of investigations was widened (emphasising habitat) by the Lapwing Habitat Enquiry of 1937. This sought not only to obtain valuable information but to help in building up a trained corps of observers able to tackle a broader range of ornithological questions.

Among the pioneering practices of the Trust, now very widely adopted, was a rule that no Council member should be eligible for re-election indefinitely, a term of six years being set as the limit. This rule began to bite as three eminent founder members – Harry Witherby, Percy Lowe and F. C. R. Jourdain – retired at the 1936 AGM. Some confusion followed, for the new Hon. Treasurer (N. B. Kinnear) had to give up after a short period, as did the leading businessman (J. Spedan Lewis) on whose contribution high hopes had been set. As a result I had to function temporarily both as Hon. Secretary and Treasurer, but I was lucky in obtaining an outstanding Hon. Assistant Secretary in James Fisher, who was to be my successor before too long.

There followed other important developments which were to complete the pre-war build-up of the Trust. With effect from 1 June 1937 the national bird-ringing scheme was taken over from *British Birds*, with premises and an address at the British Museum (Natural History) which enhanced its international status, and with its own budget and dedicated Hon. Secretary, Miss E. P. Leach. The new scheme was directed by a special Bird-Ringing Committee under the Chairmanship of (Sir) Arthur Landsborough Thomson. Thus in these early days the Trust enjoyed the services of two future Presidents of International Ornithological Congresses, and a galaxy of other outstanding talents whose unstinting efforts set it on course for success.

In 1938 W. B. Alexander, who had in the previous year been reinforced by Averil Morley (later married to Frank Fraser Darling), was rewarded for his dogged staying power by at last becoming Director of a formally established Edward Grey Institute of Field Ornithology within Oxford University. Rent-free accommodation was provided in Museum Road, and some fresh financial resources from the Viscount Grey Memorial Fund, although not nearly enough to cover capital and running costs. Under complicated constitutional arrangements the Institute was administered by an eminent Committee, including the Vice-Chancellor and Proctors, three Oxford professors and representatives of the BTO, the BOU and the Oxford Ornithological Society, with a joint standing supervisory committee whose name (in deference to Oxford views on English grammar) was changed from Scientific Advisory Committee to Advisory Scientific Committee.

In 1939 the Trust at last became incorporated by a licence from the Board of Trade. Individual membership had now risen to 458, and the keenness of support was shown by the attendance at the 1938 Annual Dinner; at 247, this was said to be 'probably the largest meeting of ornithologists in this country other than the International Ornithological Congress in 1934'. Nevertheless its last pre-war Report (in 1939) commented on the 'great difficulties . . . caused by the burden of financing even a limited range of services on so narrow a base.' The Trust was still too poor to pay for even one staff secretary of its own, or a room for an office. The term 'cost effectiveness' had not yet been coined, but comparing the infant Trust's performance with its budget the reality was surely there. Another index of members' activity was the record ringing total for 1939 of 55,817 birds.

The outbreak of World War II led to many changes, among them my relinquishment of the key post of Hon. Secretary to my energetic successor, James Fisher. Under him and despite all the wartime difficulties, the membership went on rising and passed the thousand mark in 1944, and with Jane Priestley as Treasurer the financial situation became somewhat stronger. Thus the Trust was able to increase its grant to the Edward Grey Institute. Taking advantage of extensive wartime practice flights by RAF Coastal Command, the Trust was enabled to build up (through one of its members who was also an Air Vice-Marshal) a collection of remarkable photographs of outstanding bird colonies such as St Kilda, Sula Sgeir and Ailsa Craig; these enabled the presence of Gannets, Fulmars and other species to be established at previously unrecorded sites. Major investigations were commissioned officially by the Agricultural Research Council on the economic status of the Rook and the Woodpigeon, the latter following a report by W. B. Alexander (at the request of the Royal Agricultural Society of England) which contained a series of recommendations on control. The fuller Woodpigeon Report was published in abridged form in 1951 as no. 10 in the *Agricultural Research Council Report Series*. No formal report on the Rook investigation by James Fisher was ever published.

The Trust's Council, under Landsborough Thomson, continued to function effectively throughout the war, and R. S. R. Fitter (who took over as Treasurer) reported that 'with all the difficulties of wartime movements and the problems of tracing members, our subscriptions are only 6% in arrears' for that grim year of 1943. By 1944 government contracts were running at nearly £4,000 a year, the money going through the BTO to the EGI, and representing an official vote of confidence in both. Council reminded members 'that much of our post-war activity will be influenced and shaped by the research which is going on at present' – a forecast which has been well borne out. Council expressed concern at 'having heard very little from our members about our policy' – although there had been some interested and mostly friendly criticism from outside, including the point that 'there is a little too much of London and Oxford about the Trust'. In response the practice was begun of listing the locations of Council and Committee members; it was pointed out that there were Trust members in every county of England, all but two of Wales, and all but ten of Scotland. The death of Witherby in December 1943 underlined the break which the war had already made with the Trust's origins, and its confrontation with the impending post-war world.

New investigations, such as the important Hatching and Fledging Enquiry and the Black Redstart Enquiry, catered for a wider range of collaborators. Membership not only expanded but brought in many recruits of a new and active type, largely from the Services. The bird observatories persuaded the Trust to set up, under W. B. Alexander (who retired as Director of the Edward Grey Institute in October 1945), a special committee to co-ordinate their work and standardise their methods of keeping records. The EGI moved to large new premises and obtained valuable field research facilities on the University's newly acquired Wytham Wood Estate. The reference library and the lending library were considerably expanded. David Lack took over as EGI Director. In 1947, after a long interruption on war service, I returned to an active role as Chairman. There was much to be done, especially in fitting out the Trust for an expanded post-war programme. Boldly we appointed a full-time Secretary, Dr Bruce Campbell, from 1 October 1948, after doubling the annual subscription to members. They took it much better than the more timid members of Council had feared. Although 200 lapsed during the year, we attracted 423 new members, and set a wildly ambitious target for 1949 of 2,000; but even with the aid of James Fisher's persuasive Pelican series books we ended up with only 1,663. Yet foundations for growth were laid by launching a nationwide scheme of regional representation, with the aim that every Trust member should be able to make personal contact with a Trust representative not too far away. Sixty-six Regional Representatives were appointed and over forty of them attended a first meeting. A drive was also started to develop closer collaboration with a wide range of kindred bodies, county and regional, national and international – an annotated list of which occupied eight pages of the Sixteenth Report for 1948. The latter also contained illustrations and a map, as well as an attractive cover design of Black Terns by Eric Ennion and the new Gannet symbol, drawn by Peter Scott. The Chairman's Foreword stated:

> The Trust is not simply a society composed of individuals but is also a society of societies, to which many other bird organisations are affiliated or linked, and above all it is a Trust for the advancement of ornithology in the British Isles . . . More broadly still, we are faced by such fundamental issues as the successful absorption of large numbers of people who are keen to become bird-watchers,

A page of sketches by Sir Peter Scott for his original design for the Gannet emblem.

> but have very little experience or background, while at the same time we have to strive to raise standards of accuracy and scientific worth. Even better contact and even closer harmony are needed within the expanding world of ornithology, and constant vigilance is called for against debasements of standards or the re-appearance of sterile conflicts and rivalries. Nor can we rest content with the relatively limited scope of current fieldwork when so many equally important problems await intelligent attack; and when increasing diversity of research can do so much to enrich ornithology.

Not surprisingly this robust forward policy caused expenditure to exceed income in 1949, at which point A. W. Boyd took over as Chairman, with B. W. Tucker and myself as his Vice-Chairmen. The year was distinguished by a great increase in the number of meetings up and down the country, including four joint occasions in Scotland and one in Dublin. Five scientific meetings were held in London during the winter of 1949/50, one of which was a joint meeting with the British Ornithologists' Union; the average attendance was sixty. Regional Representatives met at Bridlington, followed by a visit to Spurn Bird Observatory. There were many other meetings, including two by the Bird Observatories Committee, at York and Edinburgh.

Bernard Tucker, who should have become Chairman at this stage, died on 19 December 1950. In the Seventeenth Report I wrote:

> He has deserved always to be honoured by the Trust as one of its principal founders, who personified its mission of bringing together systematic 'museum' ornithology and bird-watching, academic study and field observation, and teamwork with individual research. His conscientiousness matched his enthusiasm, and both outran his strength.

This seems the appropriate point to divide between the early and the modern history of the Trust.

2: The Trust from 1951 to 1982

Robert Spencer

> The real test of any ornithological organisation lies not so much in what its members can get out of it as in what contributions they can themselves put in.
>
> K. G. SPENCER, *19th Annual Report*

The Annual Report for 1951 implies that, in the eyes of officers of the Trust, it was a year of consolidation rather than of new projects. Compared with 1948, which saw the launching of the network of Regional Representatives and the appointment of Dr Bruce Campbell as the Trust's first full-time Secretary, the developments were perhaps of a less dramatic nature, but progress was continuous.

The Edward Grey Institute, which had so kindly housed the Trust office, was ordered to move to new premises in the Botanic Garden where it would be unable to find accommodation for the Trust. So it came about that on 15 June 1951 the headquarters of the Trust were established at 2 King Edward Street, Oxford. If the address sounds mildly regal, the premises did not exactly live up to the impression conveyed, being somewhat small and cramped and reached by a steep and narrow staircase. For all that, they did represent independence; yet the move was not entirely straightforward, as the following *Bulletin* announcement reveals:

> *Appeal for furniture* When the Trust moved office it was found that it possessed practically no furniture of its own, and it is subsisting at present on a generous loan from the Edward Grey Institute. But these articles will be required by the Institute when it moves in the near future.

Tony Norris, later to be intimately involved in the transfer of RSPB headquarters from London to Sandy, and of the Trust from Oxford to Beech Grove, was the Hon. Treasurer of the day and hence responsible for the economics of the move. Fifteen years of inflation have so blunted our sensibilities that we are apt to pass lightly over an excess of income above expenditure of £250, until we notice that the total income was under £2,500. 'In early Reports', we are told, '1,000 members was regarded as the figure which would bring the millenium of British ornithology'. In 1951, for the first time, the even more potent figure of 2,000 members was surpassed. The report acknowledges that, as had been the case for some years, James Fisher's Pelican books continued to be the major source of recruitment. Even so, personal recommendation by existing members was thought to be of particular value in recruitment, and one must acknowledge that the Trust of the day had much to offer.

Under the enthusiastic spare-time leadership of John Gibb the Nest Record Scheme was going from strength to strength, with an increase from 4,000 completed cards in 1950 to 8,500 in 1951. Nowadays, with a membership of 7,000, we complete some 25,000 cards annually, so the position has altered relatively little over a period of thirty years. Yet the comparison is not a straightforward one for in those days one paid for the privilege of completing nest record cards for the Trust, at the rate of a shilling for 20 cards. Concerned that this charge might be inhibiting members from completing cards, Council voted many years ago to lift it. We shall never know whether this caution was necessary – bearing in mind that the Trust is an organisation skilled in making even a little extra money go a long way.

Then, as now, the programme of field investigations consisted of two different types. There were the so-called 'permanent' investigations, represented by the Ringing Scheme (it was generally referred to as the *National* Ringing Scheme), the Nest Record Scheme and the annual sample census of heronries. The remaining enquiries were of a more short-term nature, although even some of these were repeated annually for several years or at fairly regular intervals. The Black Redstart Enquiry, for example, was nearing its end as a special Trust fieldwork study, and it was announced that the further spread of the species henceforth would be documented by a careful search of the county bird reports. (Even so, in 1977 it was felt that the time had come for another comprehensive field survey.)

The fifth and final watch for migrant Swifts was held in 1951, from the date of first arrival until the middle of May. It could not be argued that it produced results of major and continuing significance, but it was exciting in a way which we may perhaps miss in many of our present-day, more disciplined enquiries. The enthusiasm was captured in a contemporary report to members:

> A. Darlington continued his ingenious and successful attempts to trace the actual course of migrating Swifts. Motor coaches were used to deploy large numbers of Schoolboy helpers, whilst trios of cyclists acted as flying squads in the Cambridge area. . . . The course of Swifts, even of individual birds, was traced northwards across a watershed by means of 'walkie-talkie' apparatus.

Although the formal founding of the BTO took place in 1933, so that this volume celebrates the golden jubilee in 1983, the Council of the day appears to have been keen to reach the landmark of a twenty-first birthday, which was celebrated in 1952, on the grounds that the first meeting of the provisional Council of the as yet unborn Trust was held in the autumn of 1932. Four pages of a specially enlarged annual report contained birthday greetings from home and abroad. That from the Rt Hon. Lord Forester, Chairman of the RSPB, included the thoughtful comment: 'in recent years it has become obvious to all serious ornithologists that conservation is in itself a scientific problem'. Few ordinary members of the RSPB were at that time ready to make so daring a leap across the boundary which, it was often imagined, separated the warm-hearted Society members from the cool-headed 'scientists' of the Trust. Dr J. M. Winterbottom, Hon. Secretary of the South African Ornithological Society, expressed simply the gist of many messages when he wrote of the SAOS that 'it would like to place on record its debt to the Trust for the inspiration of its enquiries and methods, repercussions of which have made themselves felt even in this remote end of a distant continent.' Such kindly remarks recharged out batteries with a zeal and a spirit of enterprise which saw us safely through the 1950s.

In retrospect 1953 can be seen as a particularly significant year for the Trust. The problem was described succinctly by the Hon. Treasurer, Tony Norris:

> . . . there can be no doubt that the work of organising and co-ordinating the permanent enquiries . . . is no longer within the capacity of part-time voluntary work, nor is it within the financial resources of the Trust to pay adequately for this kind of work from our own unaided income.

That remains the position today, and the solution negotiated in that anxious year remains substantially true:

> By undertaking for the time being the financial responsibility for this the Nature Conservancy is earning the gratitude of everyone who is in any way interested in the study of ornithology, and especially members of the Trust.

From that day to this the greater portion of the scientific work of the Trust has been largely financed by the Nature Conservancy, and its successor the Nature Conservancy Council. Even so, it would be wrong to give the impression that it was all charity. For example, the contract negotiated in

1953 included an undertaking that the Trust, through its members, would assess the ornithological value of existing and potential nature reserves. This was an early use of the Sites Register technique, and the funds raised enabled the Trust to give Bruce Campbell the support of an assistant, John Burton.

A second contract, negotiated by Sir Landsborough Thomson, provided the necessary funds to employ a full-time officer in the Ringing Office. At that time the work was still undertaken in a voluntary capacity by Miss E. P. Leach. She was a lady of great dedication, integrity and firmness; on first acquaintance a little forbidding until one became aware of the twinkle in her vivid blue eyes. Despite the rather stern exterior she would go to infinite trouble to help people and, if not to her face, was widely and affectionately known as Elsie. Her MBE in the 1954 Birthday Honours was earned by many years of service, and meant a great deal to her, as did the brooch subscribed for by members on her retirement, and the Donald Watson painting presented to her by the SOC in recognition of her services. She did not, in fact, immediately disappear from the Ringing Office. For several years she continued to be responsible for the handling of all foreign bird rings reported in Britain and Ireland, and, whilst keeping discreetly in the background, was always ready to help with current problems if requested to do so.

Another key problem was being debated at length in 1953: should the Trust launch a journal of its own? As in all such debates, there were the optimistic advocates and the cautious statesmen, as a Council Minute dated 8 July 1953 reveals:

> P. E. Brown said that the Trust should take the publication of reports of investigations sponsored by it into its own hands and make the Bulletin into a scientific journal; it was a service that was due to members. Sir Landsborough Thomson said that the publication of a new scientific journal was a very serious step and that it took time to gain acceptance in other countries. R. C. Homes felt that the value of a journal in attracting new members was speculative, because he thought the period of expanding membership of ornithological societies might be coming to an end and asked whether the Trust could afford to produce a journal without counting on an increase of membership. C. A. Norris said that the Trust could afford to produce a quarterly journal of 32 pages and supported P. E. Brown's points. The Chairman said that the present considerable delay in publication of papers was an argument for a new medium. D. Lack agreed that there would be no shortage of papers, but he thought that a cautious start should be made. It was essential to begin a new series distinct from the present Bulletins and it would be a good idea to print more than the immediate demand of the first numbers, as these tended to have a much enhanced value in future years when the journal became well established. Stuart Smith wondered whether Trust members were really interested in full scientific reports and would not be content with adequate summaries. Sir Landsborough Thomson agreed, provided that such summaries were written by the authors, because in any case some papers were specially suited to certain journals and it would be quite wrong to prevent authors publishing where they liked.
>
> It was finally agreed to accept the following proposition by R. C. Homes: That the Trust raises its Bulletins to the status of a scientific publication, to

include original papers on the results of investigations sponsored by the Trust and summaries of such papers which may be published in full elsewhere.

Even at this late stage there was one further hitch. Journals require titles and Council settled on 'The Gannet'. Journals also require editors, and by common consent the ideal person was H. N. Southern, who worked at the Bureau of Animal Populations in Oxford, but was particularly noted in ornithological circles for his owl studies. He accepted the invitation, but in doing so spoke out firmly against 'The Gannet' in particular and bird-name titles in general. Thus was *Bird Study* born; the decision was announced to members in the annual report for 1953.

It will be convenient to break, briefly, the chronological approach in order to follow the early fortunes of the Trust's journal. Even though a title like *Bird Study* must largely determine the scope of what is accepted for publication, it usually takes a little while to settle on the appropriate level of contribution. This was true for the Trust, and two early papers linger particularly in the memory because of the vehemence of the response they provoked. The first, entitled 'Back Garden Ornithology', dealt enthusiastically and helpfully with the concept of carrying out serious research in one's own garden, but it has to be admitted that its missionary fervour was somewhat authoritarian as the following paragraph suggests:

There may be those who say 'But I don't want to go in for *scientific* ornithology' not realising that this is another way of saying 'But I'm quite content with the second-rate in my bird-watching'. It cannot be too strongly urged that the characteristic of the scientist is neither cold detachment nor a love of the abstruse but rather an enthusiasm so furious that he can regard no detail as unimportant and no exertion in the field or in the study as unwarrantable. Non-scientific bird-watching is not splendid and adventurous bird-watching: it is simply lazy, incompetent and slovenly bird-watching.

Of the published replies, the following perhaps carries added authority in that the author had undertaken a classic study of the House Sparrow and was thus demonstrably a serious-minded ornithologist:

Sir,
I am a scientist, though ornithology is not my subject, and hope that I have that 'enthusiasm so furious' demanded by the Rev. P. H. T. Hartley in his article on 'Back Garden Ornithology'. Even to a scientist the recording of detail may become tedious, particularly if the research is a protracted one, and it is only the discipline of scientific training that enables him to see beyond the gathering of facts to the postulation of hypothesis and theories, which are the fruits of scientific devotion.
The scientist (there is nothing professional in this title, it describes rather a way of thinking) must realise that there are other objects in watching birds as laudable as the collection of facts and the expansion of the frontiers of knowledge: their aesthetic appeal; the satisfaction of the collector's instinct in adding new species to a tally (greatly to be preferred to many other forms of collecting); relaxation to the tired mind. This is no more 'slovenly bird-watching' than going to a concert without a score is slovenly listening. While it

> is not denied that deeper satisfaction may be obtained from deeper study, many are not suited to carry out scientific studies or read scores. Should we criticise them for the pleasure they get from birds or music?
> Let us have no more of this scientific snobbishness; a real enthusiasm will have more influence in attracting others to the recording of facts than any amount of castigation.
>
> *Yours faithfully,*
> D. SUMMERS-SMITH

The second case became so famous that the correspondence continued for some time under the heading 'A walk through the woods', although the title of the paper which caused all the furore was 'The theory of line transects'. Here, the paper's summary is an adequate reflection of its contents and general level.

> SUMMARY
>
> A line transect may be used to determine the density of animals or plants by means of the formula
>
> $$D = \frac{z}{2R(\bar{u}^2 + \bar{w}^2)^{\frac{1}{2}}}$$
>
> where D is the number of organisms per unit area, z is the number of encounters between observer and organism in unit time, R is the effective radius of the organism, $\bar{u}$ is the average speed of the organism, and $\bar{w}$ that of the observer. Some of the terms in the equation are difficult to determine, but transects may be used for comparative purposes when the terms are unknown but may be assumed to be constant. Under certain conditions this assumption is probably justified.

The date of publication was June 1956, and in those days BTO readers had not yet become familiar with, or inured to, the presence of algebraic formulae in writings on birds. By present day standards the paper was scrupulously fair insofar as the long and fearsome looking formulae were consigned to an appendix. Nevertheless, there was an outcry, with threats of resignation. Of the published replies that by a veteran Cheshire ornithologist summed up the position calmly and simply:

> I think that I am voicing the opinion of many readers of *Bird Study* when I suggest that the Editor might take a hint from No. xxiv of the Articles of Religion in the Prayer Book and make sure that articles in his journal should be such as can be 'understanded of the people'. 'The Theory of Line Transects' in the June number is no doubt an able statement, which is presumably lucid and intelligible to other mathematicians, but I am convinced that it is entirely beyond the capacity of the great majority of his readers to make much of it. One ribald reader unfairly declared that the fact that the 'argument is based on the kinetic theory of gases' (p. 102) was significant. Articles in *Bird Study*, a journal so widely read by ordinary bird observers and students, should not lay themselves open to so unseemly a comment.
> *Bird Study* is surely no place for esoteric writings, which can be enjoyed by only a comparatively small number of qualified readers. There must be other journals that will welcome and whose readers will appreciate articles of this

nature. Much of the article is of such interest that the more humble readers may be excused for wishing it had been presented more simply, so that all readers of *Bird Study* could benefit more fully from it.

Yours truly,
A. W. BOYD
14 July 1956

Contemporary readers of the Trust's Annual Report for 1956 would have known exactly what weight to attach to the statement: 'Whilst some papers in the journal have provoked lively discussion, the Council feel H. N. Southern has done remarkably well in establishing *Bird Study* as a journal of recognised scientific status.'

About this time two other elements in the now-familiar framework of the BTO were fitted into place. In 1953 Guy Mountfort submitted a document to Council proposing the institution of two awards. The first was to be in silver or bronze, known as the Witherby Medal, and awarded annually for the most outstanding work by a member of the Trust. The second, a special award in gold plate, was to be known as the Edward Grey Medal, and 'to be awarded as occasion merited, with the purpose of bestowing a signal honour on a member of the Trust for an oustanding contribution or important services to field ornithology.' In Council debate a transmutation occurred. A Bernard Tucker medal was settled upon 'to give a tangible recognition for outstanding recent work by a member of the Trust as organiser or participant in field work for the Trust.' A decision on the proposed gold medal was shelved indefinitely, possibly because the name of Edward Grey was already perpetuated in the institute bearing his name. Fifteen years were to pass before Council finally settled on the Witherby Memorial Lecture to commemorate the outstanding contribution of Harry Witherby, but before that there had been a protracted but unsuccessful attempt to change the Trust's address from 'Beech Grove, Tring' to 'Witherby House, Beech Grove, Tring'.

The second now-familiar element of the Trust's year which first appeared in 1954 was the annual conference. Annual General Meetings and dinners there had long been held on a Saturday evening in London, latterly at either the Rembrandt Hotel or the zoo, but a conference was something new. It began very modestly as an annual meeting of Regional Representatives, using a different venue each year. In 1954 it was turned into a residential weekend at Grantley Hall in Yorkshire, to which gathering all local members of the Trust were invited, for apart from the committee meeting, there was a programme of lectures and outings. The formula was an instant success, and was repeated in subsequent years. But always it was a mobile conference, taking the BTO to its members – at Kent Bank (Morecambe Bay), Cheltenham, Norwich, Dumfries, Llandudno, Weymouth, Shrewsbury, Skegness and Beadnell (Northumberland), before finally coming to rest (in 1965) at Swanwick. Until 1958 it was described as the Regional Representatives Conference, but the following year, at Dumfries, for the first time it was advertised as the 'Annual Conference'. This led to the abandonment of the separate AGM in London. Much later, to compensate for the immobility of an annual conference permanently at Swanwick, a series of one-day regional conferences was introduced. Two or three of these a year have been held, allowing the Trust once again to travel to its members.

Due in no small measure to the enterprise of Bruce Campbell and a small inner circle of inspired officers, the 1950s was a decade of development. There were courses on bird biology, organised in conjunction with the Field Studies Council. There were the first worries about toxic chemicals, with a small working party under the Chairmanship of W. D. Campbell. There was a proposed BTO 'Bird Haunts Guide' – which, had it materialised, would have been a forerunner of John Gooders' *Where to Watch Birds*. With information being supplied by Regional Representatives, and the text written by Philip Brown and Peter Conder of the RSPB, it had impeccable credentials, and texts of about half the English counties were drafted. It was, alas, killed dead. Regional Representatives reported back grave misgivings that such a work would lead to unacceptable pressure on favourite sites, with George Waterston reporting particularly strong feelings from Scotland. So it was left to private enterprise.

Although they may not have been aware of it at the time, the 1950s belonged in particular to those members who were enthusiastic about migration and bird ringing. For those fanatics with strong stomachs there were voyages on weather ships, available through the Trust. The Bird Observatories Committee was voting in new members almost every year and its annual New Year conference in Oxford soon outgrew the accommodation at a small institute and moved to New College. There, with no shortage of rooms, more and more enthusiasts managed to convince a not too strict secretariat that they deserved a place. Then there was the Bird Observatories Flying Squad – a corps of experienced workers who, at least in theory, held themselves ready to rush to any observatory which was in danger of being undermanned. The concept of a big migration 'fall' was a heady one and, for whatever the reason, the decade saw some particularly spectacular mass arrivals. So there grew up in the Bird Observatories Committee a desperate resolve to have a Migration Research Officer who could spend his days drawing together and digesting the data being collected at a score of islands and promontories. An appeal went to the Trust (the Bird Observatories Committee was an independent body) and, thanks especially to the good offices of Sir Landsborough Thomson, a successful application was made to the Nuffield Foundation for the five-year funding of a Migration Research Officer. Amongst all concerned with the project it was assumed from the outset that the ideal person for the work that lay ahead would be Kenneth Williamson, who had done so much to pioneer observatory techniques while Director of Fair Isle Bird Observatory. Thus, with minimum delay he was appointed. In no time observatory logs from all over the country were being stored in microfilm at a central respository, observatory workers training courses were being organised (the forerunners of today's ringers training courses) and a new journal *Bird Migration* was spreading its wings. Nor were purely ringing matters stagnating. New-type, non-overlapping rings were being field-tested by senior ringers; the concept of ringing inquiries received an official blessing from Council, and the *Ringers' Bulletin* crept quietly past the Hon. Treasurer of the day (the first issue was on subscription at 6d. a time, but this charge was subsequently dropped). Yet there were also the first slow developments in trends which were later to challenge the success and the self confidence of the bird observatory network. Mist nets arrived on the scene, and soon the Trust was acting as the sole supplier. Hitherto, virtually the only way of catching migrating birds was in a Heligoland trap and that, in practice, meant staying at an observatory. Mist nets, with their cheapness and portability, were soon to end the supremacy of the Heligoland. About that time, too, the first radar studies on migration were being published, and the first suggestions made that the migration recorded at observatories was not representative of that which passed undetected high overhead. And as the decade neared its end Bruce Campbell moved on to a post with the BBC, to be succeeded by David Wilson.

The 1960s

If the 1950s were, as has been suggested, the decade of ringing and migration studies, it would be difficult to deny to the 1960s the epithet of the decade of census and survey. Unquestionably, some of the seeds of what was to come were sown in the second half of the 'fifties, with disturbing reports about the possible harmful effects of farm chemicals and the short paper by Dr Derek Ratcliffe about Peregrines breaking their eggs. The story has often been related of how the pigeon fanciers applied to the Nature Conservancy for a programme to reduce the numbers of Peregrines because of their predilection for homing pigeons, and of how, before reaching a decision on the subject, the Conservancy approached the Trust with a request for a census of our finest falcon. It is a familiar part of history, too, that the population was found to be at an alarmingly low level, especially in England.

If a large and fairly conspicuous species could decline so disastrously in numbers, probably because of the use of farm chemicals, it was thought equally possible that populations of many common farmland birds might have declined without the loss being noted. The Nature Conservancy wondered whether the BTO could set up any simple monitoring system to try to discover what was happening. Thus at their meeting on 12 March 1960 Council were informed that the Scientific Advisory Committee of the Trust had decided to attempt a Sample Breeding Season Census of Common Species, on a pilot scale, with selected helpers. It was, of course, the precursor of the Common Birds Census, identical in aim, but at this stage not based on a mapping technique. A more extensive trial followed the next year, under the care of K. D. Smith. Although an outstanding field ornithologist, Ken found the detailed census work uncongenial, and it fell to the young and enthusiastic Humphrey Dobinson to guide the CBC (the name was first used in a Council minute dated 5.12.61) through 1962. By the 1963 season the present day mapping technique had been settled upon. The Nuffield Grant funding of migration studies had come to an end and Ken Williamson was thus free to take up the reins. Subsequent developments of the CBC are dealt with by Michael Taylor in Chapter Three.

Apart from the CBC, two other major field projects were conceived and launched during the 1960s although both, as it happens, towards the end of the decade. The first reference to one of them is to be found in a minute of the Scientific Advisory Committee held on 24 November 1964.

> *Possibility of an Atlas of British Birds*
> The request for such a map had come from the Nature Conservancy and presumably the finished work would be similar to the recently published B.S.B.I. Botanical Atlas. It was the general opinion of the meeting that we should not just follow the botanist's methods but that we must know exactly what purpose the atlas could best serve. Densities as well as distribution was desirable . . .

At the end of their discussions the Committee decided to recommend to Council that thinking, planning and preliminary negotiations be started in preparation for an atlas or similar publication. Council accepted the recommendation at their next meeting and decided to set up a working group as soon as an application to the Nature Conservancy was completed. It was not to be so straightforward: although the Nature Conservancy had suggested an ornithological atlas, they were not in a position to offer the necessary financial support. Hence there was considerable pessimism about securing funding and pessimism too, in some quarters, about the chances of achieving adequate geographical cover.

In such a climate it is perhaps understandable that things moved slowly. More than a year passed before the first, hesitant public announcement was made in *BTO News* no. 14; but the membership's reaction to this was most encouraging. Thus, following the axiom that what pleases the members must be good for the Trust at large, Council screwed its courage to the sticking point and in the spring of 1968 embarked upon what has been called (with no false modesty) the greatest single co-operative ornithological undertaking ever. More surprisingly, especially for an organisation which has ever had to count the pennies as well as the pounds, it launched the project before it had secured funds to carry it out. It was not until August 1968 – after the first summer's fieldwork – that Council were able to announce in *BTO News*:

> We have had the good news that a grant to finance the Atlas project has been awarded to the Trust by the Leverhulme Trust Fund. The grant totals £11,720 over a period of 5½ years, and makes provision for a full-time organiser as well as allowing for the printing of forms, other clerical expenses, travel and incidentals. We hope to make an appointment later this year.

> It is most gratifying that the risk we took in launching the scheme a few months ago, before we had the necessary finances to carry it through, has in the event been justified. It is gratifying too that the launching of the Atlas has unleashed an encouraging amount of enthusiasm.

In the years which followed atlasing became for many a way of life and the term 'square bashing' acquired an entirely new meaning, but the details may be found in the introduction to the published work, and need not be pursued further here.

The other major survey to be started in the 1960s was the Birds of Estuaries Enquiry. Associated now particularly with the name of Tony Prater, it was in fact organised initially by David Glue in partnership with Philip Burton (representing the IWRB Wader Working Group). Like the Atlas, this survey became habit-forming and for some hundreds of members with access to the coast, wader count dates were entered into diaries with the same mixture of enthusiasm and determination that characterised wildfowl counters a decade earlier. Whereas the Atlas was solely a BTO concern, the BOEE is managed jointly by a working group on which are represented the RSPB, the Wildfowl Trust and the Nature Conservancy, as well as the BTO (see Chapter Three). Yet if only because the work was based at Beech Grove and the results, at times, integrated with those from other sub-disciplines, it is easy to think of it as another Trust enquiry.

From the ever-engrossing subject of research it is necessary to turn to things practical – and political. Throughout the second half of the 'fifties and all of the 'sixties the work of the Trust was growing in complexity and, thanks in particular to Nature Conservancy support, the staff was increasing to cope with the extra work. Nowhere is this better observed than in the contemporary history of the Ringing Office.

Although the Trust was formed in 1933 it was not until 1937 that Harry Witherby handed over to it responsibility for administering the national ringing scheme. Moreover, there were special conditions attached to the transfer. One was that Sir Landsborough Thomson should be Chairman of the specially-formed Bird Ringing Committee, and another was that 'it should enjoy a certain autonomy, being under the general control of Council but not responsible to the Scientific Advisory Committee.' If only because the scheme was based in London, whilst the Trust's offices were in Oxford, some degree of day-to-day autonomy was inevitable.

The Ringing Office was, in fact, a single room in that section of the Natural History Museum in South Kensington known as the Bird Room. This was the room which Miss Elsie Leach handed over to her successor, Robert Spencer, together with a part-time secretary and a list of ringers theoretically totalling about 800, of whom (in practice) fewer than 200 were active. It was a short-lived phase, for with better and cheaper rings and simplified paperwork, ringing became ever more popular. The numbers of birds ringed increased from 98,000 in 1953 to 280,000 in 1960, the number of recoveries from some 3,000 to 8,000. And as the work increased, so Council received urgent requests from Bob Spencer for extra staff. To fund additional staff was one thing, and thanks to Conservancy support and a levy on ringers it was accomplished; to house additional staff was an entirely different matter. The Ringing Office was, if truth be told, an unwelcome Cuckoo in the Bird Room nest, occupying valuable space which might otherwise have been given over to more legitimate museum activities. Nevertheless its presence was accepted with good grace and, although no extra room could be allocated, no protest was lodged when the extra Ringing Office staff, unable to squeeze into an office measuring no more than 18 ft × 18 ft, overflowed into the work benches reserved for visiting workers.

Meanwhile at Oxford, with the appointment of an MRO, Assistant Secretaries and shorthand typists, the congestion was as bad. From at least as early as 1953 Council dreamed of uniting its London and Oxford offices in Oxford, the city of its birth. There were snags: the vision was grand but the Trust's resources were pitifully small. In a succession of Council minutes, spread over nearly ten years, the twists and turns in a complex story are revealed. In January 1956 Council agreed to 'take steps to find adequate offices in Oxford to house the main office, the ringing office and the lending library, with provision for storage.' In October 1956 Council was informed that there was 'now a good possibility of the Trust being offered adequate accommodation by the university in Wytham Abbey.' In April 1961 the President, Vice-Presidents, Hon. Treasurer and Hon. Secretary were 'given power to investigate and if successful conclude purchase of property in or near Oxford.' In July 1961 Council minuted 'it was unlikely that an offer of accommodation would be made by the RSPB', but a sub-committee was authorised to look for property in the Bedford area. By December of that year unit construction prefabricated buildings costing £6,000 were being investigated, while by July 1962 'Tring Museum had been examined and was not very suitable.'

Although the minutes are seldom explicit, it is difficult to escape the conclusion that Council members were not united in their vision of the Trust's future home. Certainly there were Council members, resident in the south of England, who believed that the headquarters of a national organisation ought to be in the capital city but, if only on financial grounds, they had an uphill task. Even so they were not entirely without support in important places. A spokesman for the Nature Conservancy hoped that Council would reconsider the plan to centralise in Oxford 'because it would be much harder to get agreement to continue financial backing [for ringing] if the scheme were to move away from London.' Yet a solution was not far off, for politics is the art of the practicable. In the autumn of 1962 Christopher Mead was sent on a foray to Tring – his ancestral homeland – and there discovered Beech Grove. The then President (Tony Norris) paid a flying visit and acting with characteristic decisiveness put down a deposit; Council, meeting on 30 October, gave unanimous approval. Structural repairs and renovations were necessary; but the Ringing Office moved in the following September, the Oxford office some two months later, and the Trust was at last united.

To be under one roof had many advantages. There were obvious aspects such as the sharing of duplicating machines and the opportunity to meet crises by shifting clerical staff from one office to another. There were also more far-reaching consequences. Council feared, and perhaps not without justification, that the physical separation of the London and Oxford offices had contributed to a mental isolation, with committees and their relevant staff operating in compartments which were far too watertight. 'Cross-pollination' was the watchword, and as a part of the attempt to achieve this a three-tier committee structure was introduced. Two committees, for Populations and Surveys, and for Ringing and Migration, were to be answerable to the Scientific Advisory Committee. A Finance and General Purposes Committee was created to deal with day-to-day affairs and it, like the Scientific Advisory Committee, was directly answerable to Council.

The vision behind all this was simple and laudable. Here was the Trust with so many research strings to its bow – census work, ringing and migration work, nest recording and the like. It must surely be possible to harness all these methodologies in studies of single species or single problems. In practice there were, and probably always will be, difficulties about the realisation of this plan. To use ringing well, to make proper use of CBC or of nest records, requires an understanding of the strengths and weaknesses of each, and it is not always easy to find prospective committee members with the necessary breadth of knowledge. Apart from this problem, it seems inevitable that ad-hoc committees and working groups arise. There was, for example, a Nuffield Grant Committee to look after the five-year migration research programme. More controversially, a Research Co-ordinating Committee sprang up, with seven members and two staff; understandably, the Scientific Advisory Committee did not feel able to give their wholehearted blessing to this intrusion into their province.

Some of the earlier recruits to the BTO staff were men stronger in practical field skills than in proven academic research. As the staff grew bigger, more especially the component of the staff funded by the Nature Conservancy, there came a time when the Director-General of that body felt it necessary to protect its investment in the Trust by creating and financing the post of Director of Research, whose duties would combine both an oversight of the scientific validity of Trust work and a drawing together of the strands in co-ordinated research. Dr David Snow was the first incumbent and realised one long-standing dream of the Trust when the prestigious journal *Nature* accepted a paper on Blackbird populations dynamics which incorporated ringing, nest-record and census data.

David's reign of four years was particularly productive of papers, which must in itself have been reassuring to the Nature Conservancy, as chief paymaster. However, one of his last major responsibilities before leaving for a post as head of the Bird Room at the British Museum was to steer the Trust – both officers and staff – through the imposing but, in the event friendly, ritual of a 'visiting group' on behalf of the Natural Environment Research Council. Such visiting groups are a civil service procedure of inspection to ensure that public money is being well spent, and so it was an important occasion for the Trust. Happily, the report was very favourable and included the heart-warming comment that 'the *esprit de corps* among staff at Beech Grove and the cordial response which they and the Council succeeded in winning from the membership bespeak of good organisation and management.'

Little time was to pass before it became apparent that to be a property-owning organisation called for resources greater than the Trust had. In the first instant it was a matter of making parts of the rambling house more habitable, and at weekends working parties of volunteers helped to decorate. But quite soon, with a growing staff and with record cards and papers accumulating at an exponential rate, it was necessary to bring into use every available nook and cranny. The Trust was singularly fortunate in finding – or being found by – a local architect, Edmund Tory, who worked tirelessly and with great ingenuity to produce solutions which were within the Trust's pocket. To deepen that pocket, an appeal was made to members. They, as ever, responded magnificently, contributing over £22,000: money which helped to make the establishment rather more efficient and respectable in appearance. Yet it was clear that we would quite soon have to contemplate the addition of a new wing in order to accommodate a growing staff. The eventual solution to the problem of financing an extension came from an unexpected and indeed improbable quarter. Scattered through the minutes of both Council and F&GP over a period of more than a year were exceedingly guarded references under the heading 'Avian collection'. By 1966, when it seemed that eventual success was assured and therefore unlikely to be jeopardised by indiscreet talk, the minuting could be more specific. Thus minute 11 of a meeting of F&GP held on 7 May of that year reads:

> *Storage at Tring Museum*
> The Trust had been offered a collection of specimens which appeared to be of value, and storage had been arranged at Tring Museum. Authority was given for payment of removal charges.

Behind this still somewhat cryptic entry lay a long story. A very wealthy ornithologist, Vivian Hewitt, whose biography *Modest Millionaire* was written by William Hywel (1973), had a house on Anglesey which was crammed with ornithological specimens – both eggs and skins. On his death he left his house to his servant of many years, Mr J. H. Parry. The latter wished to make proper use of the house, and to do so it was necessary to dispose of the collection – so extensive as eventually to fill several large furniture vans. Under the terms of the Protection of Birds Acts 1954–67 it would have been a very complex procedure for him to obtain the necessary licence to sell the collection, but he could give it away. And it was to the Trust that eventually he presented it, perhaps because of sympathetic help from our Secretary, David Wilson.

Sorting the specimens occupied Kenneth Williamson's spare time over many months, but in due course some were presented to Tring Museum, which purchased others, and the bulk were sold to museums in Europe and America. At the end of one tense bargaining session between the new Director of the Trust, Dr Jim Flegg, and the director of an American museum the staff were invited to assemble in a committee room. There a relaxed and beaming Jim handed out glasses of champagne and a toast was drunk to the new extension, now made possible by the generosity of Mr Parry and the design skill of our architect, Edmund Tory.

Somewhat earlier, before attempting to raise money by appeal, Council had thought it sensible to seek professional advice from an appeal planning organisation and, because of the generosity of an anonymous Council member, were able to commission a detailed study of our prospects. In the course of this survey members were visited and soundings made. There was, it emerged, considerable confusion in the public's mind regarding the respective roles of the BTO and the RSPB, while some people who understood the differences well enough apparently thought that there would be much to be said for a merger. In the light of such advice, and without committing themselves in any way, it seemed sensible to Council to discover how the situation looked through RSPB eyes. Informal soundings were made, and equally informally the impression was conveyed from Sandy that the separate but complementary roles of the two organisations represented the best way of carrying out the multifarious range of activities necessary in the fields of research and conservation.

The Trust and the RSBP had seemed to have been moving along paths of convergent evolution to the extent that their respective images were in danger of becoming blurred in people's minds. It may be, too, that a Council statement published in the Annual Report for 1962 gave some encouragement to this thinking. It reads:

> The policy shall be: The study of the bird populations of the British Isles in respect of distribution, numbers and movements and of the ecological factors, including those of human origin, affecting them. It shall be one of the principal objects of this policy to answer the following questions:— In what ways is contemporary man affecting wild birds and, in particular, how are changes in forestry, agricultural and horticultural practice influencing bird populations?

Thus the Trust, whilst still seeking to be an impartial, fact-finding body, took a positive step in the direction of conservation. It did so because, whilst stoutly defending the position that amateurs can participate in research, and that research is fun, it was aware of a prevailing mood amongst thinking bird-watchers that more research ought to be directed explicitly towards species thought to be at risk, and about threatened habitats. 'Facts are as important as fences' was a catchphrase used in publicity of the day.

At the same time it was obviously necessary to try to foster a more distinctive image of the Trust. The 'cordial response' from members, which the NERC Visiting Group were to comment on later, had to be fostered rather than taken for granted. A F&GP minute dated 8 October 1963 neatly summed up the situation:

> Mr Norris (the President) said that the picture of any society formed by its members was almost completely based on what they received in the way of literature from that society. Members of the BTO only received *Bird Study* which was a high powered scientific journal, and an Annual Report which was at least nine months out of date. To give a true picture of the BTO these should be supplemented by a regular and up to date bulletin with news of Trust activity and information received in connection with current enquiries.

He was right in his analysis of the situation and the following January an 8-page bulletin, *BTO News* no. 1, was posted to all members.

A little later other responses followed. More than most organisations, the BTO is dependant upon a smooth and happy working relationship between members and headquarters staff. The members *are* the Trust, and because of the vast amount of time and enthusiasm they give to supporting Trust fieldwork programmes (it is not fanciful to suggest that nowadays it exceeds a million hours a year) the 'servicing' of members must always claim a high priority. When the annual conference moved to Swanwick – later to be followed by the recently-inaugurated Ringing and Migration conference and a February conference – it became possible for fifteen or twenty staff members (most of them specialists) to share the spacious accommodation for a weekend with as many as 350 members. For staff and members alike, what had once been mere names at the bottom of letters were fleshed out into faces, personalities, friends. Such was the prevailing spirit of mutual respect and understanding that it was even possible to moot the holding of a conference on the theme of bird statistics!

Any historian may be something of a butterfly, sipping nectar here and there, or a censor, ruling out some large themes in favour of others. He must strive for a degree of objective balance as he steers a course between these two extremes, especially if he is limited for space. This survey of the 1960s must end by mentioning some of the themes which have so far been neglected. Some were brief events which held the limelight for a while, such as the Trust's display at National Nature Week (under the banner *Are we losing our birds?*) and the 14th International Ornithological Congress at Oxford, during which we were able to welcome numerous distinguished overseas ornithologists to Beech Grove and to show them a little of our growing prowess. The *Torrey Canyon* disaster took but a brief moment in time, but because of the enormity of what happened, and of the even worse things that could have happened, it altered patterns of thinking and in a modest way affected the pattern of work at Beech Grove. The European Union for Bird Ringing (Euring) was born out of idealism, and of the practical need for the thirty or more ringing schemes in Europe to be able to speak a common scientific language, to standardise ring designs and recovery handling methods, and ultimately to establish a data bank in which would be housed copies of all European ringing recoveries. As far as the Ringing Office was concerned, it led to the introduction of codes, punch cards, and all the paraphernalia of automatic data processing. There was the first BTO publicity film, *Rings for Research*, made and largely financed by Odhams Press as a result of the kind interest of Mr Brian Barker.

There was an RAF Fellowship, set up specifically to study the bird risk for low-flying aircraft in Yorkshire, and a Shell Studentship to investigate the rôle of statistics in ornithology. In particular there was the Silsoe Conference, sometimes referred to as the battle of Pendley Grove. There, for the first time, conservationists and farmers came together in an exercise – almost a war game – to test the likely effects of different agricultural practices on the wildlife of a farm area. The Populations and Surveys section, with its record of detailed CBC work on both Grove and Pendley Farms, was much involved. The Trust can feel proud to have played so constructive a rôle in the activities which led to the formation of the Farming and Wildlife Advisory Group, for its work was to be one of the encouraging signs throughout the 1970s.

The 1970s

The decade began sadly for the Trust. Concerned about the slender margins by which the accounts were (generally) in the black, in 1969 Council called in a firm of business efficiency consultants; one of their representatives spent some time studying the administration and accounting systems in use at Beech Grove. Their report, delivered early in 1970, expressed the view that too large a proportion of the Trust's subscription income was being spent on administration, and that an organisation the size of the Trust ought not to require the services of a Secretary of the salary and experience range of the one employed. The firm devised a system which would be more efficient than the old one, and capable of being operated by a smaller staff. Thus with great regret Council found itself obliged to dispense with the services of David Wilson, who had served the Trust steadfastly through twelve particularly formative years.

In a way, the event was symptomatic of the 'seventies. On the one hand, in the country as a whole, the 'never had it so good' era was demonstrably coming to an end, and the money supply was to grow steadily tighter. On the other, the affairs of headquarters were marked by a growing professionalism: more of the scientific work was being carried out under closely-defined and costed contracts. Clearly, it was a time for fresh thinking, and possibly for a change of policy. Until 1970 Council had appointed as Secretaries, Assistant

Secretaries and, latterly as Administrator, people who were keen field ornithologists with a knowledge of office methods. When in 1970, as an aftermath of David Wilson's departure, Keith Clark resigned as Administrator, Council turned to the world of business and appointed, in the person of Cecil Plant, someone who claimed no knowledge of birds. It may be no more than a coincidence, with many of the knotty problems having been faced up to and solved during the previous fifteen or twenty years, but the Council minutes throughout the 1970s do give the impression of a decreasing incidence of crises and of a more orderly pattern of existence, as if the Trust were sailing into smoother waters.

There are fewer major themes for the 1970s, and it would be difficult to deny to the Atlas a claim to importance as the outstanding Trust event of the decade. With the finances on a firmer footing, thanks to the generous support of the Leverhulme Foundation, Dr J. T. R. Sharrock had been appointed in 1969 and added an extra vitality to the project. In the summer, equipped with a small caravan which the Trust had bought for the purpose, he made extended trips into squares which might otherwise not have been covered. That Scotland was covered completely was partly due to such endeavours. Then there was Ireland. The Trust announced the project as an atlas of Britain, but from the outset it was hoped that the Irish Wildbird Conservancy would throw its influence behind the project, and such was the case; David Scott, in particular, was indefatigable. At a crucial moment, too, the Irish government made a valuable financial contribution, and the project became in title what it already was in practice – a joint venture between the Trust and the IWC. The use of the word 'crucial' is a considered one, for towards the end of 1970 Council learned that the writing-up process would take not the eighteen months which had been budgeted for but a full three years. In addition, it was obvious that inflation was greatly adding to the cost of the operation. An infusion of extra money from a new source was thus reassuring. At that stage it could not be foreseen that more than four years were to pass between the completion of the fieldwork in the summer of 1972 and the eventual appearance of the published work in November 1976. The major cause of delay was the inordinate length of time it took to negotiate individually with the observers concerned the method of portraying the distribution of rarities: of securing privacy for rare birds whilst still reflecting general patterns. In the end it was a race against the clock, and Tim Sharrock was assisted in writing the text by members of Headquarters staff.

The Annual Report for 1971–72 advised members that thought was being given to the question of what fieldwork programme should follow the Atlas. It was indeed. Amongst officers and staff alike there was a strong feeling that the magnificent and dedicated task force which had grown up to survey our countryside for the Atlas should not be allowed slowly to disintegrate through want of suggestion or lack of leadership. Surely there was some worthy successor to the Atlas, if only it could be identified? Eventually it was

Dr W. R. P. Bourne – something of a Stormy Petrel in the politics of ornithology but always fertile and constructive of thought – who proposed a register of ornithological habitats. This clearly was it, the idea which Council had been seeking. Not only could it absorb the energy and skill of many thousands of field workers, but the conservation value was obviously enormous. The RSPB were quick to see this, and it is much to the credit of the Trust's sister society that it funded the early stages of the work. It is interesting to reflect that, paralleling the situation with the Atlas, the BTO Council was so sure of the rightness of the project that it launched it before it had secured the necessary long-term finance. Eventually, as on so many occasions, it was the Nature Conservancy (by that time metamorphosed into the Nature Conservancy Council of today) which provided the long-term financial support. The name of the project was changed from the Habitats Register to the Ornithological Sites Register, and it was commonly described in the Trust's publicity as an 'ornithological Domesday Book'. For a few members with long memories, both the whole concept and the juxtaposition of the words 'ornithological' and 'sites' may have had a vague familiar ring, for there already existed in print both a description, and a *raison d'être*.

> The pace of human interference and of bird adaptations to it was being speeded up and missed opportunities might mean irretrievable losses to knowledge. It was also becoming more and more urgent to have full and reliable information about all sites of special ornithological interest. If this interest was known it would often be possible to avert dangers involved in development schemes at an early stage, whereas later attempts to contest and reverse the claims or commitments of bodies, which had once got a hold on the site, were much more difficult and less likely to succeed. As a member of the Nature Conservancy he therefore wished to impress on representatives the urgent need for surveying and notifying bird sites which ought to be looked after in their regions. On the other hand it was important to discourage the use of bird arguments in aid of sites which either had no birds of sufficient interest to justify it, or where the birds were unlikely to suffer and might even gain by the change proposed. Bird protection arguments would be discounted in such negotiations if they were used indiscriminately and without full justification.

For those familiar with his writings, the words carry the unmistakable imprint of Max Nicholson. It is a cause for regret that, because of the smallness of his audience (he was addressing the third gathering of Trust Regional Representatives, at Flatford Mill) the exhortation was lost sight of, for the date was 7 October 1950. Who knows what sites of real importance might have been defended successfully against the developers had the Sites Register been launched some twenty years earlier?

Nevertheless, despite its late start the project prospered, growing in strength and value, consulted by conservationists. In the skilful hands of R. J. Fuller as organiser, the wealth of data were classified and cross-referenced, and card indices were photocopied for use by NCC staff. More than that: for as the members' observations accumulated it became clear that in addition to serving the function of documenting sites, they also provided an invaluable insight into the relationship between habitats and the bird species which tend to be associated with them. Such information was much too interesting and important to remain buried in files, so while Tony Prater (by this time an RSPB Regional Officer) was putting the finishing touches to a major volume summarising the results accumulated during the years of the estuaries survey, Rob Fuller embarked upon the long task of distillation which led to the publication in 1982 of his important book *Bird Habitats in Britain*.

The year 1971 saw the departure from the staff of Henry Mayer-Gross. A nest finder of quite remarkable skills, he had joined the staff on a Nature Conservancy contract to investigate, in so far as such matters can be investigated, the extent to which visiting nests to examine their contents for nest recording might or might not affect the successful hatching and fledging of the brood. This reassuring phase of his work had been completed for several years when it was decided that the future envisaged for the enquiry no longer called for so highly qualified a person.

Also in 1971 was a happy venture in international co-operation. Euring was quietly gathering stature and there was a small but enthusiastic International Bird Census Committee. Co-operation and standardisation were fashionable concepts in various European countries, perhaps the more so because of the growing influence and success of the EEC. Furthermore, in the world of ornithology it was possible to identify numerous areas where international agreement to standardise methodology and terminology could bring nothing but benefit. Nest recording, habitat coding, biometrical data recording and moult recording were just some of the fields of study which seemed ripe for attention. So in collaboration with the German institute Vogelwarte Radolfzell, and with generous financial support from Radolfzell's parent body the Max-Planck-Institut für Verhaltenphysiologie, and due largely to the enthusiasm of James Ferguson-Lees, a highly successful international conference was held at Green Park, near Tring.

Ever short of funds, in 1972 the Trust was fortunate to receive a generous donation, thereafter repeated annually, from the Worshipful Company of Grocers. The money amounted to £1,500 a year, and it was decided to use it on a succession of short-term posts for young people, usually of three months' duration. The system was splendidly flexible: any important project which was falling behind schedule could be given a fillip by the appointment of a temporary assistant. It was, perhaps, inevitable that these assistants should become known as 'grocer's boys' and 'grocer's girls'. It is difficult to overestimate the value of this funding from the Grocer's Company on the productivity of the Trust. The 'boys' and the 'girls' served the Trust well, some eventually being absorbed into the regular staff of the Trust.

The following year, 1973, partly because members were urging it and partly because the CBC (with its farmland and woodland emphasis) was ill-equipped to reflect the population vicissitudes of riparian species, an encouraging pilot trial was held of what became the Waterways Bird Survey. Thus another tool was added to the Trust's research potential. Less agreeably, HM Customs and Excise, deaf to arguments that at their own expense ringers were supplying recoveries to the state, ruled that bird rings must attract VAT. This was not the only problem arising from the collection of VAT, for in 1978 it was increased to 15%. Now, the contract under which the Trust works for the NCC is (alas) itself liable to VAT. Neither the Trust nor the NCC had foreseen the increase to 15%, and since the NCC was operating within a very restricted budget, it meant that something would have to be cut to raise the extra tax. The officers and Council of the Trust did everything possible to ease the circumstances, but it did mean that throughout the period of acute financial stringency posts falling vacant could not be filled. The Trust staff, for their part, were thankful to come through the period without any redundancies.

Toward the very end of 1975 Jim Flegg gave notice of his resignation as Director in order to return to his former work. This posed serious problems for Ronald Hickling, the President of the day. The ten-year contract with the NCC was due to expire in 1978. Unless or until it was sure that there would be a further contract, prospective new directors could be offered no certain future with the Trust beyond three years. Bob Spencer was appointed as Acting Director, keeping the seat warm until July 1978, by which time agreement to a new contract from the NCC made possible the appointment of Dr Raymond O'Connor.

The year 1976 was that of the long, hot summer, but for the Trust as an organisation it slipped by uneventfully. There was, it is true, another book: *Bird Observatories in Britain and Ireland*. Although the Trust had nothing to do with the writing of the work, it had throughout the history of the observatories movement provided the secretariat and the co-ordinating element of the Bird Observatories Council, and was thus able to share in the general sense of gratification that the work of the observatories had gained a more durable testimony.

Would that the calm uneventfulness had continued, for in June 1977 the Trust suffered an irreparable loss by the overnight death of Kenneth Williamson, carried away by a heart attack. Ever fertile in ideas, ever enthusiastic, ever helpful and friendly, he had become an oustanding missionary, spreading the Trust's gospel that research *is* for the amateur and is deeply satisfying. After his death there was the inevitable phase of mental readjustment, followed by the equally inevitably closing of the ranks. Robert Hudson was appointed editor of *Bird Study* in succession to Ken. L. A. Batten took over responsibility for running the Populations and Surveys section, and gradually a degree of order and normality arose.

Ken Williamson's death was a disaster for the Trust but if, as Kipling did, it is possible to link opposites, then one may also mention triumphs, of which three may be listed. Firstly, in their spare time Tony Prater and John

Marchant had spent a year or two compiling a *Guide to the Identification and Ageing of Holarctic Waders*. Part way through the project they learned that a Finn was engaged in a similar task, so they joined forces to complete a remarkable book which was published in 1977. Like Ken Williamson's warbler identification guides, it was to attract buyers in many countries, thereby enhancing the reputation of the Trust as well as contributing to its coffers.

Next, it must be confessed that from time to time over the years, there had been professional voices raised in doubt over the validity of the results of the CBC. If these critics were right, it was important to know; if they were wrong, the means must be found to convince them of that fact. It was as important to the NCC as to the Trust to establish the truth, and so for some considerable time a searching examination was carried out by members of the staffs of both the NCC and the Institute of Terrestrial Ecology. Their report, when it came, was a full vindication of the CBC, and it was sad that Ken Williamson did not live to read it. He would have been pleased, but not surprised, for there were never any doubts in his mind as to the validity of the technique he had done so much to develop and exploit.

The third triumph came in the form of a pat on the back. In the USA, Cornell University organised a conference on the theme 'The Amateur and North American Ornithology'; and they paid the Trust the compliment of inviting the then President, John McMeeking, to deliver the 'keynote' lecture on the rôle and workings of the BTO.

Raymond O'Connor, when he joined the Trust in the summer of 1978, brought with him a new and important expertise. In addition to being an ornithologist he was, to the finger tips, a computer man. This was no accident. It was apparent to both the Trust and to the NCC that the only way of deriving maximum benefit from the data which Trust members collected so steadfastly, year in year out, was by computer. So there was the man: one piece of the structure was fitted into position. Every organisation deserves an occasional stroke of good fortune, and this was the Trust's hour. Towards the end of 1978 the NCC realised that there might be a sum of money available to buy a computer if the Trust could act quickly. It had to be spent within that financial year, and with the computer would have to go the necessary programs which would be needed to turn data into results; the NCC would expect an acceptance trial before the end of the financial year. Was it possible to achieve all this in just a few months? It was, because the Trust was again fortunate. Firstly, it received a legacy which, together with the NCC funding, would cover the costs. Secondly, by the merest accident a BTO member, Dr R. G. Newell, learned of the proposed computerisation. Dick Newell was not only an experienced ornithologist and former ringer but also the director of a computer consultancy and a top-flight programmer. In no time he had recommended a particular make of computer, negotiated for the Trust an advantageous price and (with his colleagues) was hard at work writing a suite of programs which would meet the Trust's needs. In this work he was aided by Chris Mead, who had a wide familiarity with the data coupled with a mathematician's aptitude for computer thinking.

The deadline was met. The acceptance trials were a success. The Trust's ways of handling data would never be the same again. The problems, if there were any, would lie in integrating the impersonal efficiency made possible by the computer with the close personal relationships which have characterised the Trust throughout its history.

The years 1979 and 1980 were exciting ones for science and research. The new computer was installed and working at Beech Grove and, rather like a new toy, was being tried out for various purposes. In no time a computer print-out had replaced the old four-part stationery used for the preparation of ringing recoveries, and a start was made on extracting the full ornithological value from the quantities of data already housed at Beech Grove. New possibilities were constantly arising and, as is so often the case, it could be seen that a computer with a bigger memory would enable ever more complex analyses to be carried out. Papers were being prepared at a rate seldom achieved in the past; new books were planned; lectures were prepared. The urge to communicate was the ruling spirit of the day: publish or be damned the watchwords.

The winter of 1980/81 saw experimental fieldwork for a brave (or foolhardy some thought) new project: an Atlas of winter bird distribution. For long-serving officers and staff there was an uncanny feeling of *déjà vu*. Just as with the breeding season Atlas, there was considerable doubt as to the feasibility of the project. After all, participants in the enormously successful breeding season Atlas had been able to take advantage of long summer evenings, and to take summer holidays in remote parts. The problems of squeezing the fieldwork into about thirty short weekend days each winter were daunting. Would the members be willing to tackle this more demanding field work: more demanding because there would be no bird song to aid identification, and because the project called for some form of quantification?

The feedback from those who participated in pilot trials suggested that, despite some anxieties about quantification, the enthusiasm was there and that the fieldwork was both demanding and satisfying. Thus, as in 1967, the spirit of optimism prevailed and Council took the courageous decision to launch the project on a national scale in the winter of 1981/82. It was courageous in more senses than one for (as in 1967) the decision was taken in the belief that the necessary funding could and would be raised. An organiser was appointed in the person of Dr Peter Lack and, at the end of the first season (a season of atypically severe weather), it was possible to conclude that the project would be a popular was well as a scientific success. No better evidence could be found of the kind of loyalty such corporate studies evoke than the observer who spent nearly eight winter hours in his Scottish square without seeing a single bird! We are often told that negative results are as important and as interesting as positive ones, but it must take a particular quality of determination to prove that a 10 km square is singularly lacking in birds. With that kind of inspirational example, the Trust can approach its fiftieth birthday in a spirit of confidence for the future.

ENVOI

Fifty years is the better part of a human life span. In the country as a whole the fifty years covered by this volume have seen enormous changes: in the standard of living, as manifested in the way we take foreign holidays for granted, in a growing informality of dress and custom, in technical developments such as television and the electronic computer – the list could be extended almost indefinitely. For the Trust those same fifty years have seen growth from a modest club with a few hundreds of supporters, and not even a part-time secretary, to a large organisation owning its own headquarters, managing a staff which sometimes exceeds thirty, and with an international reputation for innovation.

What is this Trust of ours? It is a *charity*; the word 'Trust' in the title helps to define its role, as does article 3 of the Memorandum of Association:

> 3. Objects:
> For the benefit of the nation:—
> (i) to promote, organise, carry on and encourage study and research and particularly field work in all branches of the science of ornithology, including the investigation and publication of reports on the effects of bird life in relation to agriculture, horticulture, forestry and fisheries.

Here is the spirit of service which typifies all those organisations most worthy of the name charity.

It is also a *society*; the Concise Oxford Dictionary defines 'society' as 'a social community', and the Trust could not function unless its members co-operated in network research. But is it not more than that? Surely the words 'encourage study and resesearch' in the Memorandum of Association justify the addition of an epithet, so that, eschewing false modesty, we may think of the Trust as a *learned society*?

Nowadays the acronym 'quango' (quasi-autonomous non-governmental organisation) occurs frequently in our newspapers. Is not the Trust a *quango?* Certainly it is non-governmental, while it is also, in a sense, quasi-autonomous. Yet a BTO not in receipt of NCC research funding would of necessity employ a very much smaller headquarters staff. Such a Trust would need to be much more reliant on self-help, as in fact it already is in certain respects.

Technically, the Trust is a *company limited by guarantee*. The Council members are company directors and the President of the day is the chairman of that board of directors. To have responsibility for an annual budget which nowadays runs well into six figures is no light responsibility; the more so because it is a spare time activity which is not merely unpaid but is quite likely to find the company director somewhat out of pocket.

The Trust has, indeed, been singularly fortunate in attracting as Council members, officers and chairmen of committees men and women of great competence and dedication, some of them – at least in ornithological circles – household names. The weight of responsibility they have carried, and the countless hours they have devoted in the interests of the Trust, are an inspiration and an ideal. For above all the Trust is an organisation of amateurs – of people who carry out their tasks for the love of it. What happens in administration could if necessary happen in research.

In a world with a developed sense of values, to be an amateur is to have added distinction. David Lack, one of the most distinguished professional ornithologists this country has produced, was quite explicit as to his views. He wrote in an address to BTO Regional Representatives in 1956:

> Research is merely a term for finding out something, or to put it more accurately, something previously unknown. It may be something very simple, for instance that the Rock Pipit is a regular passage migrant at the local sewage farm, or that the Yellowhammer tends to lay smaller clutches in the autumn than in the summer, or it may be the propounding of an elaborate theory based on 20 years' observations and masses of statistics and tables. In any event, it is a delightful pastime, one of the most delightful of all pastimes. Further, this pleasure is within reach of all ornithologists, being easier technically, though harder morally, than most people think. Do not suppose that it is something which should nowadays be left to the professional, for in this field the amateur has as many advantages as the professional, though they are different advantages.

And at the conclusion of the same paper he reflected:

> Why should we take this trouble?
> Dr Tinbergen's view is that 'a rational explanation may make people understand in a way, but cannot make them share the joy'. We bird-watchers feel that the steel-and-concrete environment we are creating all over the world satisfies only part of our habitat demands. But just being in our ancestral habitat does not entirely satisfy us; sight-seeing soon bores us; we want to do something. And I strongly feel that our bird study is sublimated hunting. All aspects of hunting: habitat selection, stalking out quarry, trying to outwit it, and finally experiencing intense satisfaction in getting what we want.

Both of them – Dr Lack and Dr Tinbergen – were expressing views which they had come to after much thought, views which commanded widespread acceptance. Unless we humans have changed, in step with our changing world, the views they expressed so many years ago are applicable today. They are a message of encouragement to every bird-watcher with a sense of curiosity. And in so far as they are commonly held, then the Trust can truly say, with Robert Browning, 'grow old along with me, the best is yet to be.'

3: The Trust in action

He rises early, for he must
count Corncrakes for the British Trust;
or hear if *Cuculus canorus*
sings first in the auroral chorus . . .

* * *

The Heron murmurs pessimistically:
'Can I, oh can I, be statistically
significant, or can I not?'
and th' unbridled Guillemot,
bewildered by so many 'ifs',
is seen to hurl himself from cliffs.

M. F. M. MEIKLEJOHN

A review

RONALD HICKLING

The number of field enquiries carried out by members of the Trust over fifty years is great and the variety bewildering. If we are to review them systematically they have to be categorised in some way. A convenient method is to divide them according to the manner in which they are managed, considering them under three headings.

The ringing scheme is one category in itself, and many consider it the most important project conducted by the Trust. It has been in the care of the Trust since 1937, when Harry Witherby handed over to us the responsibility for his *British Birds* ringing scheme as 'the best means of securing the future of the scheme'. It is concerned in part with practical management – the issue of rings and sale of equipment, recording details of ringing in its central register, investigating reports of birds ringed abroad, training new ringers, issuing permits and licences, and other mundane matters – but its ultimate function is scientific. Duties are carried out by a small staff (themselves all ringers), and controlled by a Trust committee consisting mainly of ringers, but on which the Nature Conservancy Council and Trustees of the British Museum (Natural History) are represented also. In addition, the ringers hold an annual meeting at their conference at which many matters of policy and practice are discussed. Thus the raising of standards of ringing and handling, which goes on steadily year by year, has been carried out by ringers themselves. Training, of trainees and the more experienced, is incessant. Finance is provided in three ways: by the Trust out of its general income, by the Nature Conservancy Council under contract, and by ringers themselves through annual permit fees and the sale of equipment and rings. The Trust's central computer now makes possible much more efficient use of data, and allows the Trust to play a greater part in the European ringing network ('Euring'). The next development, which has indeed already begun, is the acquisition by ringing groups and observatories of their individual mini-computers.

The scientific value which has accrued from ringing, based on research and analysis both by Trust staff and academic and individual researchers, has over the years been mainly from additions to our knowledge of movement and migration. This is discussed in Chapter Five. Careful examination of birds in the hand has resulted in an accumulation of information on weights and measurements, length of life, effects of weather, and other aspects of the biology of the bird. Information under this head is presented in the Appendix. The study of moult has been a feature of ringing for some years, for only from the live bird in the hand can any significant new advance be made in our understanding of this important element in the bird's life. The success of all these scientific advances, however, will always depend on the excitement of trapping birds for ringing, and the thrill of handling the living bird.

The second category of enquiry comprises those schemes which are long-term or of a complex character, requiring organisation, data collection and analysis by full-time staff of efforts in the field by members. The Common Birds Census, for example, is a running programme designed to monitor the populations of our common birds and through them the changes in the environment; the Breeding Atlas collected the observations of many thousands of fieldworkers; and the Estuaries Enquiry was mounted in response to a need for vital information on those threatened and fragile ecosystems. These projects are discussed in detail later in this chapter.

The third category contains enquiries which are extremely varied in character, but whose common feature is that they arise from the particular interest of an individual member, who makes a proposal to the Trust and then organises, analyses and writes up the results of an enquiry which depends on members' support. That support is in turn dependent on the extent to which the organiser can fire enthusiasm, and unpredictably on the nature of the enquiry. These we have come to regard as 'traditional' Trust projects, and they are the envy of a number of countries. In our fifty years well over one hundred and fifty such schemes have been carried out and the results published. Some are single 'one-off' enquiries, some are repeated at intervals (often ten-year intervals), and one, the Heronry Census, has been repeated year after year throughout the Trust's life. Except for a short period when the Heronry census was organised by an assistant secretary it has been amateur-led throughout; sometimes it has been only a sample census, in other years a complete national survey. Its significance as an indicator of population stability, and as a measure of the ability of a population to recover after a harsh winter, was first shown by David Lack in his book *The Natural Regulation of Animal Numbers* (1954) (Fig. 1).

For the reşt the range is immense: from the Peregrine in its remote fastnesses to the Black Redstart of inner cities, from milk bottle opening by tits to the behaviour of Short-eared Owls in a vole plague, from the disappearing Wryneck to the proliferation of winter gulls, from the history of the Pied Flycatcher to the effects on Buzzards of myxomatosis in rabbits. Many of us persist in regarding this type of enquiry as the most enduring of Trust activities.

Nevertheless, most will now concede that the kind of research institute we have become – with long-term enquiries managed and organised by skilled staff, fieldwork carried out by amateur naturalists, analysis and interpretation the province of professional scientists, yet with the scientific policy still controlled by Officers and Council elected by the amateur membership – is an endeavour of the highest quality and importance. Fieldworkers have shown themselves willing to play this subordinate role – and I write this just having returned, wet and cold, from a CBC field session on an inclement April morning.

But the change, a 'quiet revolution', did not come about by accident. The Trust had decided, in its early days, that organisation of complex long-term projects was beyond its competence; it believed that limited and achievable objectives offered the best chance of the Trust advancing, little by little, our knowledge of birds. The weaknesses of this view were well demonstrated in a study of the breeding distribution of thirty species, carried out by C. A. Norris in 1952. This enquiry required observers to evaluate the breeding status of the selected species on the basis of 25 km squares. It was ambitious –

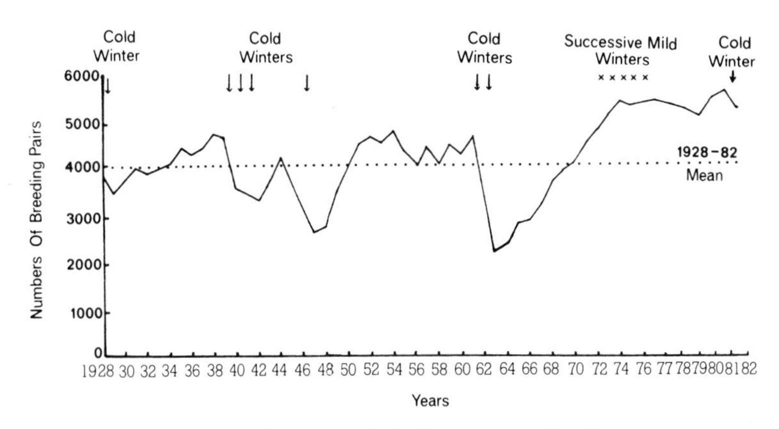

Fig 1 Heron population levels in England and Wales, 1928–1982.

and a complete success. The major weakness of a far-reaching enquiry organised by a spare-time ornithologist was also exposed: it took eight years before the results were published. But it pointed the way forward. Pressures from outside bodies such as the Nature Conservancy emphasised the need.

During the years around 1960 much discussion – informal and formal – went on of ways to raise the standard of the Trust's involvement in bigger schemes. The leaders in these dialogues – far-sighted and bold – were the late Dick Homes and Stanley Cramp. At last an *ad hoc* Research Committee was set up to investigate these matters. The committee met only once, but it was a meeting of the greatest significance. It had before it a paper by Kenneth Williamson and Robert Spencer which analysed some remarkable bird movements – mainly of Goldfinches, Linnets and Robins – and showed how such phenomena could be interpreted by co-ordinating results from separate enquiries conducted by the Trust. This set the tone of the meeting. Stanley Cramp undertook to produce a plan for future research. It was an astonishing document for an amateur organisation, and included proposals which have not yet been fully implemented. Such a programme clearly called for control by a first-class scientist. Here was the dilemma. Where was the money to come from?

It came unexpectedly. It seemed that Max Nicholson, then Director-General of the Nature Conservancy, had been thinking on similar lines. He insisted that, as part of the comprehensive contract then being negotiated between the Conservancy and the Trust, a top-quality Director of Research should be appointed, to be funded under the contract. Dr David Snow, due to return to this country from an important research post in the Galapagos, was appointed, and the path forward was set.

The new pattern of research, which some feared might inhibit amateur fieldworkers, continued to attract support. The growing numbers of Trust members, and the increasing involvement of members in long-term projects, bear witness to this. But it involved difficulties; members had to be prepared to raise their standards in the field. In the words of R. D. Laing in another context, '. . . the method is simple. But oh, that it were as easy as it is simple!' The remainder of this chapter will examine this part of the Trust's work. But first let us take a light-hearted look at Trust-type fieldwork, in verses which the author has given us permission to quote:

When I was young, long years ago,
I upped and joined the B.T.O.
I climbed the hills, and strode the heather,
Regardless of the wind and weather.
I sat in hides and gazed at nests,
Counting the little feathered pests.
I surveyed roosts, I took up ringing,
I rose at dawn to hear them singing.
I stayed out late, got wet and chilled.
With watching birds my days were filled.

But now that I am old and grey
I think I've found a better way –
I don't get wet, I don't walk far;
I do my watching from a car.
I sip my coffee, munch my bun,
Have little toil and lots of fun.
I trickle on from gate to gate,
And then I simply sit and wait
'Til birds, and yet more birds, I see,
I don't hunt *them*; they come to *me*.

LADY R. G. TAYLOR

The Common Birds Census

S. M. TAYLOR

The CBC's modest start in 1961 gave no hint of the riches to come: twelve species were nominated for censusing, and only 28 returns were received. The next year all farmland species were included and the response more than doubled. There were a few woodland samples also, and nine plots had too few visits to be useful – standards were high from the start. The exceptionally severe winter of 1962/63 helped the infant project in two ways: it provided a wide range of population changes, and it generated interest. Many species were scarce in the spring of 1963, and the census results were eagerly awaited. The forty-nine farmland and seven woodland plots censused in both years showed that Green Woodpecker, Wren and Mistle Thrush had all suffered losses of 75% to 80%, while Pied Wagtails were down by two-thirds, and Moorhen, Lapwing, Stock Dove and Song Thrush all lost between a half and two-thirds of their 1962 numbers. On the other hand, some species – Chaffinch and Carrion Crow, for example – were hardly affected. The woodland and farmland figures agreed almost exactly for Wren and Song Thrush.

The data were scrutinised closely. The findings appeared to be typical of farmland in general, because the proportional changes were remarkably consistent throughout, and the species densities (pairs per 100 ha) were very similar on the re-censused plots and on the forty-five newly recruited in 1963. Not much was known about the abilities of different species to withstand prolonged cold, but confirmation was found in data from the previous hard winter, in 1946/47. After this, Ticehurst and Hartley (1948) had collected many observers' assessments of local changes in numbers, each species being placed in one of five categories from 'extermination' to 'increase'. Williamson and Homes (1964) allotted these categories values from −3 to +1 respectively, and worked out the average value for each species. These correlated extremely well with the 1962–63 CBC changes; only one species – Bullfinch – showed a significant disagreement.

In 1964 woodland censusing started in earnest, and the mapping method was introduced for all habitats. With it came the requirement for observers to submit *habitat maps*, showing the nature of boundaries, field use, position of trees, standing and running water, etc. These were intended to help the headquarters analysts interpret the species maps carrying the census results, but they were to prove most valuable tools for other purposes too.

With twenty years of farmland and eighteen years of woodland censuses to review, this account must be selective; but it will aim to show the kinds of use that can be made of CBC data, and the kinds of testing to which the scheme has been submitted, both in the field and in the office. As at the beginning, the primary interest has continued to be in the year-to-year changes revealed – as we shall see, these were to hold some surprises and to pose some difficult questions – but attention was soon focused on the relationships between birds and their habitats. In 1965 and 1966, the first investigation was made into the importance of different features on farmland; statistical methods were used to relate the numbers of Whitethroats, Dunnocks and Chaffinches to such habitat characteristics as length of hedge and presence of hedgerow trees – measured, with a good deal of tedium, from 65 habitat maps. Morgan and O'Connor (1980) used the same data in connection with Yellowhammers.

The recovery of Wrens after the hard winter gave a chance to study, not the importance of features within a given habitat, but the selection of the habitat type itself. Williamson (1969) found that they first recolonised woods and streamsides, then orchards and gardens, and then hedgerows. Other studies of this sort, for other birds recovering after a disaster, remain to be made. Another early project, in 1965, concerned the whereabouts of registrations within the habitat: exactly where, on a given area, were breeding Blackbirds or Dunnocks noted, in relation to hedges, trees, etc?. This work was inconclusive, largely because the technical tools to handle it were not available, but the carefully-measured data were used later in other work. In more recent investigations, the approximate sizes of territories have been measured from the species maps, and used in complex studies of the factors controlling population densities. Given several years' censuses on the same plot, the 'quality' of a breeding territory can be assessed – sites that are always used are presumably more desirable than sites used only in some years. O'Connor (1979, 1980a) found that Yellowhammer territories measured from the maps became smaller as population levels rose, and that inferior territories were taken up later in the season than superior ones.

With a long series of censuses on the same area, it is possible to form a good idea of the typical bird communities and the parts of the habitat they are using. For example, Benson and Williamson (1972) used eight years' censuses on a Suffolk farm, and Robson and Williamson (1972) ten years' work on a Westmorland farm, forming an interesting contrast. Bull, Mead and Williamson (1976) analysed censuses made on a Norfolk farm for several years before and after a drastic hedge-removing operation, and were able to assess its effects directly.

Weather effects

With a lengthening run of index data, covering different weather patterns, other types of investigation become feasible: the following unpublished study is an example. It concerns relations between annual changes in the CBC index and weather effects as measured by the published monthly sunshine, rainfall and average temperature for the years 1962 to 1977. Most of the weather variables turned out to be irrelevant, but for several species there was a strong positive link between index changes and November temperature, sometimes

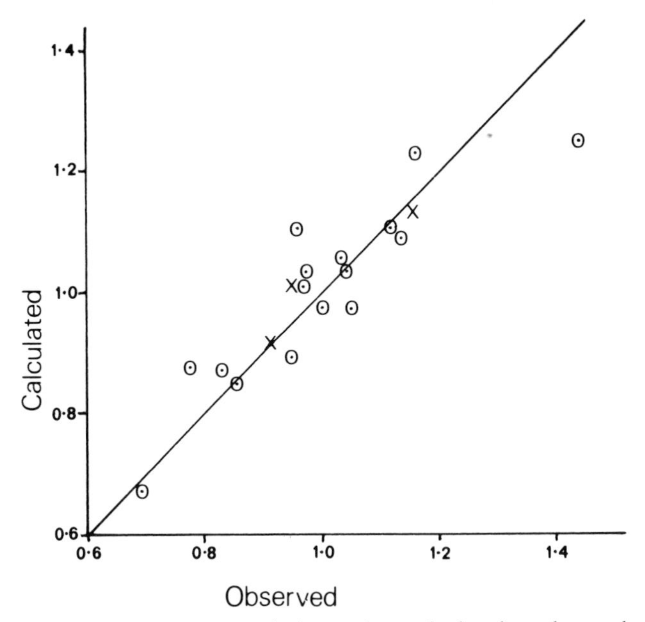

Fig 2 Linnet: year to year population ratios, calculated *vs* observed. Calculated value = 0·105 TN + 0·067 TF − 0·012 where TN and TF are the England and Wales mean temperatures, °C, for the intervening November and February ($R^2 = 0{\cdot}81$).

Circles: 1962–63 to 1977–78, used to derive equation.
Crosses: 1978–9 to 1980–81.

with other variables as secondary ones. Thus changes in the Linnet index were significantly correlated with November temperature and (less strongly) with February temperature, perhaps implying that a fine autumn allows birds to face the winter in good condition, while a fine February allows survivors to avoid its last sting. Possessed of an equation for predicting changes in the Linnet index, I waited with interest for more CBC data and for the long-delayed Monthly Weather Reports. The three points marked with crosses in Fig. 2 show that the wait was worthwhile.

In his comprehensive study of the processes that control British Great Tit populations, which relied heavily on CBC data throughout, O'Connor (1980b) found a similar equation for that species.

The nature of the CBC index, and some examples

The CBC index is designed to follow the fortunes of individual species in one of two general habitat types: 'farmland' and 'woodland' (the latter includes some parkland and scrub). The percentage change from one year to the next is found using the figures for all plots on which a species occurs and which were censused in both years. The result is expressed in terms of an index having a base value of 100 in 1966. A species that doubled in numbers from 1966 to 1967 would have an index of 200 in the latter year, while a fall of 10% in the next season would make the 1968 index value 180, and so on. This method of construction means that *absolute values* must not be compared between one species and another, though *relative changes* may. If one species index rises from 200 to 400 and another from 30 to 60, both populations have doubled; but the first is not necessarily more abundant than the second. For example, an index value of 100 on farmland means, very roughly, a breeding density of 40 territories per 100 ha for Blackbird, ten for Song Thrush, fourteen for Blue Tit, seven for Great Tit and 25 for Chaffinch (these figures are estimated from the 1981 results). The datum year was taken as 1966 because it was the first in which the losses of 1962/63 appeared to have been made good. The index datum value of 100 had no special virtue except convenience, though it has proved to be a reasonable norm for some species.

Figure 3 shows typical index values, on a logarithmic scale so that equal proportional changes correspond to equal vertical distances. Except for the most severe winters, some species have maintained very steady levels. From 1964, Blackbird and Yellowhammer have varied by less than 20%, Skylark and Chaffinch by under 30%, Robin, Willow Warbler, Dunnock, Starling and Tree Sparrow by under 40% and Great Tit, Blue Tit, Mistle Thrush and Song Thrush by under 50%. Some species have increased at a moderate but steady rate throughout: Carrion Crows nearly tripled, and the migrant Turtle Dove doubled, between 1962 and 1981.

The Stock Dove index has shown a massive and continuing increase. In a 1981 study, using all the Trust's data on this species, O'Connor and Mead concluded that since 1930 it has gone through three phases: roughly stable numbers from 1930 to 1950, a severe population crash and reduced breeding success in the 1950s on agricultural land (but not in deciduous woods, suburbia or coastal areas), and an explosive recovery since 1960; it is this last which the CBC has monitored.

The farmland index for Wren is typical of the CBC data for the smaller resident birds, which sustain very heavy losses in hard winters but recover quickly, since with reduced competition for the best habitats many of their numerous progeny can survive. The 1978/79 winter halved the breeding population of Long-tailed Tits and reduced Wrens and Goldcrests by two-fifths; but the last two almost completely recovered in one season, and even the single-brooded Long-tailed Tit made up its rather greater loss in two. In their study of the effects of the 1978/79 winter, using both CBC and ringing data, Cawthorne and Marchant (1980) gave more details of its effect on Wrens in particular.

Some of the summer migrants have shown considerable changes, too. Between 1962 and about 1968, Blackcaps increased six-fold, Chiffchaffs quadrupled and Sedge, Willow and Garden Warbler numbers doubled. By analogy with Stock Dove, one speculates as to whether they were recovering

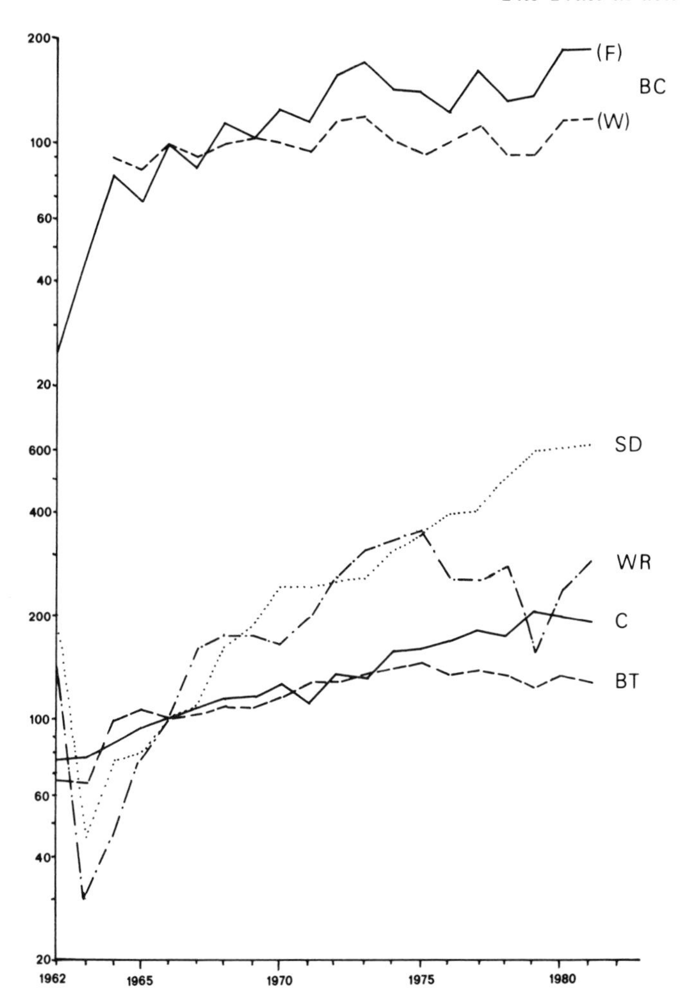

Fig 3 Some typical CBC indices (F: farmland; W: woodland): Blue Tit – F; Carrion Crow – F; Stock Dove – all; Wren – F; Blackcap – F & W.

from some pre-CBC disaster. (Over the same period, the numbers of Swallows, Whitethroats, Spotted Flycatchers and Redstarts were more or less constant.) In 1969 Sedge and Garden Warblers and Redstarts entered a long period of decline, and only the last has made any show of recovery; undoubtedly these changes were linked with the Whitethroat 'crash' discussed next. But why, over the same period, have Blackcaps increased by a further 50% and Willow Warblers remained at a stable level, while Chiffchaffs declined steadily from 1972 to 1976 (halving their index) and then climbed half-way back?

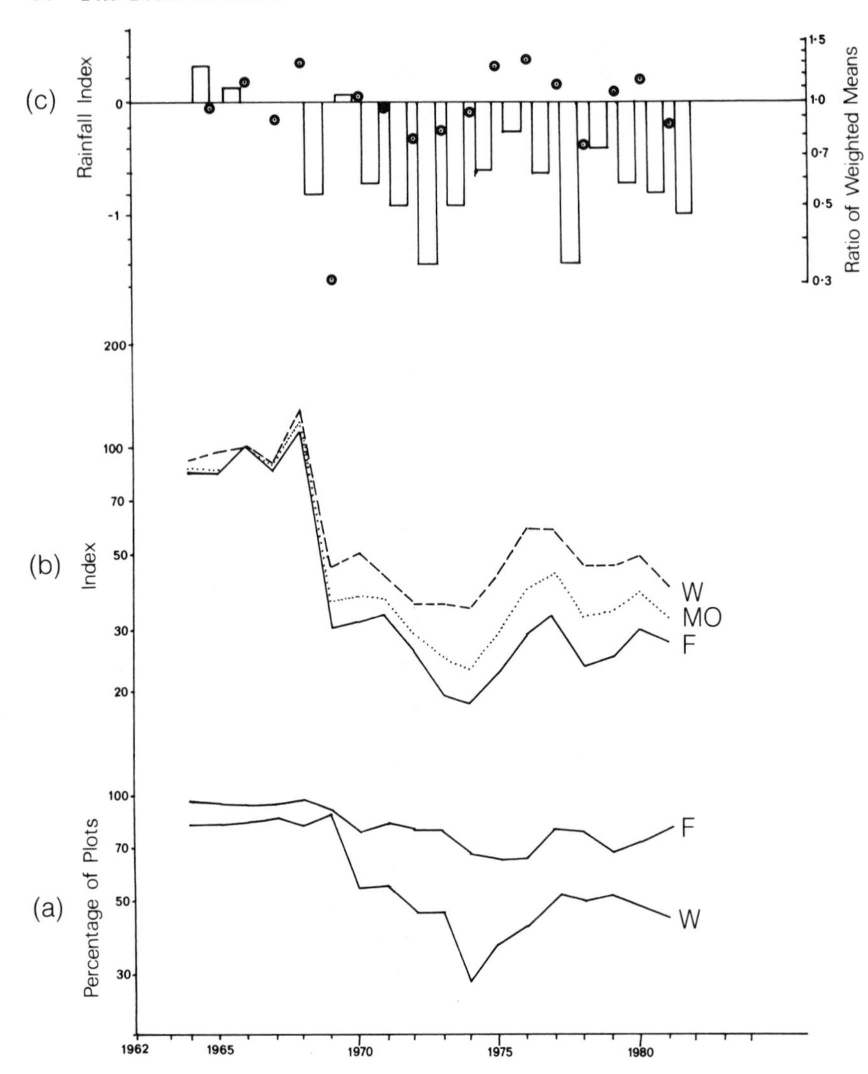

Fig 4 Whitethroat
(a) Percentage of plots on which Whitethroats bred (F-farmland, W-woodland).
(b) CBC indices for farmland, woodland and weighted mean (MO).
(c) Bars: Lamb's rainfall index for Sahel region – deviation from norm, in standard deviation units; circles: ratio of CBC weighted mean index to value in previous year.

The Whitethroat decline

In 1969 the Whitethroat indices fell markedly (Fig. 4); since then the farmland index has averaged only 28%, and the woodland index 44%, of the previous values. Winstanley, Spencer and Williamson (1974) concluded that the decline was caused by the drought that started in 1968 in the Sahel region of Africa, where the birds winter. Here the main rainfall, from April to July, controls the extent of the vegetation and insect life in the ensuing winter; major losses then will reduce the following year's European breeding stock. The human consequences of the drought made headline news for several years; it still persists, a fact not widely known, and the Whitethroat population, like the human one, has adjusted its level to what can be maintained on the reduced food supply. Lamb (1982) published an index of rainfall for the Sahel from 1941 to 1981, based on the readings of a large grid of rain gauges. This shows (see Fig. 4) that there were substantial variations during the period covered by the CBC, both before and during the drought. If rainfall is controlling Whitethroat numbers, these variations should be detectable in the CBC index. To measure the population changes it is convenient to take the proportional change from year to year in a Whitethroat index calculated as a mean of the farmland and woodland indices (weighted according to the numbers of sample plots, which varied much more on woodland than on farmland). There is a strong correlation between the rainfall variations and the population index changes over the ensuing winters, even omitting the major drop between 1962–63. Marchant (1982) showed similar correlations between the CBC index values for Whitethroat, Sedge Warbler and Redstart and the flows of the Rivers Sénégal and Niger; but using the index values and not year-to-year ratios means that, at least for Whitethroat, much of the statistical significance comes from the large fall in both population and rainfall in 1962–63.

The Whitethroat data illustrate another use of the CBC returns to learn more about habitat preference. Figure 4 shows that the proportion of all plots on which Whitethroats were present fell more rapidly and further in woodland than on farmland: when competition was greatly reduced, some of the diverse habitats grouped under 'woodland' were quickly abandoned. On farmland, with a relatively larger fall in breeding pairs, there was much less tendency to forsake plots altogether – either because 'farmland' comes nearer to the birds' ideal or because it contains a less diverse range of habitats. (Incidentally, the sharp fall in occupancy came a year after the sharp fall in numbers; presumably the birds breeding in 1969 returned to familiar areas.) By more detailed studies of this sort, information about habitat preferences can be found: here again the habitat maps are invaluable.

Habitat changes

The habitat maps also have great value in their own right as records of areas of countryside on known dates. Plots can be re-mapped long after they cease to be censused, so the maps have a long-term usefulness. To show their potential in habitat monitoring we summarise a study by Dr R. J. O'Connor into the rate of loss of hedgerows. He used a sample of 61 farmland plots, including counties from Kent to Cornwall and Hampshire to Yorkshire, and altogether was able to make 150 comparisons between one year and the next, within the period 1962 to 1976. The annual average hedgerow loss increased fairly steadily from near zero in 1962 to about 3 m/ha/yr in the last few years, and the overall average annual rate was 1·5 m/ha, or about a quarter of a mile per square mile. The maximum county figure was an average of 8 m/ha/yr for the three Yorkshire farm plots in the sample.

Validation of the CBC and its techniques

When three years' farmland data were available, Taylor (1965) showed that the changes measured on farmland were consistent throughout the data, and were not affected by increasing experience of observers. These tests were extended to 1965 and 1966 by Bailey (1967), in the same paper which defined the index in terms of 1966 as datum year, and they have been done regularly ever since. When setting up the woodland index (Bailey 1968) he applied similar tests, with satisfactory results.

It has always been realised that the CBC measures changes more precisely than absolute densities. No observer is likely to register all territory-holding males, or the same proportion of them for all species; and there are bound to be differences between observers. Attempts have been made to check on the absolute figures by nest-finding, by intensive studies, and by having different observers make many visits each (Snow 1965, Bell *et al.* 1973), but these applied only to particular plots and were not entirely successful for different reasons. We have had to be content with indirect evidence. Thus, in 1969 it was demonstrated to senior scientists of the Nature Conservancy and the Natural Environment Research Council that in a given year there was no important difference between densities found by observers with different levels of experience, so that observer effects were not likely to be large. Also, the various studies in which density figures have been used – those mentioned above, and many others – have given results that would not have been possible if the densities were seriously at fault.

In 1976 P. Goriup, an M.Sc. student in Conservation Studies at University College, London, showed that the annual loss and recruitment of plots had not noticeably distorted the nature of the farmland index – a topic of perennial concern. So as to cover a range of body size, habitat type and population changes, and to include both residents and migrants, he chose Blue Tit, Wren, Whitethroat, Blackcap, Skylark and Blackbird. For these he constructed population indices from the counts on 21 farmland plots censused annually from 1964 to 1973, and showed that the results were not significantly different from the general CBC index values.

Encouraging though all this was there remained a feeling that direct validation was to be preferred, if only a means could be found. The chance came when in 1976 the NERC and the NCC, then jointly funding the CBC, requested a rigorous test of all its aspects. A site was chosen within the Aston Rowant National Nature Reserve on the Chiltern Hills, and arrangements were made for four observers to make separate and independent CBCs there in 1977 and to repeat them in 1978. Each was to be based on ten visits spaced from early April to mid-July, so that in all there were forty visits in each year. The site, on Beacon Hill, comprised nearly 29 ha (69 acres) and was much more complex than most CBC plots. It included rough grass paddocks, short-grazed open grassland, open scrub with few trees, dense scrub with many trees, clumps of trees and mature closed woodland, and had a dense bird population rich in species. There was no human disturbance, apart from the noise of traffic on the M40 motorway 500 m from one boundary. All in all, it provided a stern task both for field workers and for analysts. The observers differed in their experience of CBC work (from none at all to eleven years) and in their previous knowledge of the site. The field results were converted to species maps at BTO headquarters, and three independent analyses were then made by three members of the Populations Section. Two were experienced analysts (one of them was also one of the field workers) and the third was a newly trained recruit. Maps were analysed in random order of species, and in ignorance of observer identity.

A comprehensive study of the results led to important conclusions. First, from every point of view there was very close agreement among the analysts. Second, the four observers produced significantly different numbers of registrations for many species, and these led to different assessments of the numbers of territories in use. Third, the observers remained consistent in their performance from year to year, so that the four independent estimates of annual change were in good agreement. (This is the fundamental requirement for the index method of monitoring.) More detailed studies showed the effects of weather on the census results, both as the season advanced and in departures from the seasonal pattern. For many species there were more registrations on warm than on cold days, but comparatively few were affected by changes in wind speed (O'Connor and Hicks 1980).

The CBC technique has been much used to assess the bird communities of remote and little-studied habitats, an expedition of census workers making ten or so censuses in the course of a fortnight (e.g. Williamson 1969). The Aston Rowant data were used to examine the effects of the timing of such expeditions, by combining all four observers' results and splitting the series of 40 visits into six periods (O'Connor 1980b). For early or late breeding species there were obviously some effects, but overall the pattern of community structure from the 'expeditions' agreed well with that from the full data.

The Waterways Bird Survey

S. M. TAYLOR

The WBS was started as a national scheme in 1974 in response to pressure from Trust members who were concerned for the well-being of the wildlife along rivers and streams. The concept was that of a linear CBC, along a length of waterway instead of over an area; each 'plot' was to comprise a 4 km or more length of waterway, with its immediate surroundings. The technique otherwise resembled that of the CBC, and the object was to provide an index that would monitor the populations of specialised birds like Mute Swan, Moorhen, Kingfisher and Dipper, and others like Reed and Sedge Warblers and Yellow Wagtail that might not find suitable habitat in the surrounding landscape. For the first few years the scheme was experimental, but it proved its usefulness and became an 'official' monitoring tool alongside the CBC proper.

An index of population levels is produced from counts on those stretches censused in successive years, as for the CBC. The base year, with all species indices set at 100, was 1974. Marchant and Hyde (1979) reviewed the data for the first five years and subsequent reports have appeared annually in *Bird Study*. The number of plots available for year-to-year comparisons has varied from 45 to 54, and many species are found on only some of these, so in most cases only broad trends are apparent so far. Nevertheless, Marchant and Hyde (1980) were able to discuss some interesting regional differences and to show that the breeding density (pairs per km) of Mute Swan, Mallard, Moorhen, Coot, Common Sandpiper and Kingfisher decreased with increasing river gradient, while for Pied and Grey Wagtails density increased with increasing altitude. For Whitethroat the trends have closely followed those of farmland and woodland, as might be expected if the major controlling influence is climate in its wintering area. For a few species, such as Snipe, it has been possible to produce an annual index by combining the waterways and farmland data, though neither by itself is sufficient.

Already the WBS has been able to show directly the effects of some river management activities (Chapter Seven); in future it will be possible to predict the likely effects of proposed management schemes. Two steps to this end were a considerable expansion of the scheme in 1981 and the introduction in 1982 of a standardised method of habitat description. Successive 500 m stretches of the waterway and its banks are given codes according to a simple scheme: this will facilitate comparisons between one 'plot' and another as well as allowing investigations of the characteristics of preferred territories within a given area. The detailed understanding that will accrue is likely to be all the more necessary since regional waterways authorities have reduced the amount of environmental monitoring they perform. The WBS may well be the only means of detecting early effects of pollution in some cases.

The Nest Record Scheme

P. G. DAVIS

This long-term project, known initially as the Hatching and Fledging Inquiry, was devised in 1939 by James Fisher and Sir Julian Huxley to 'establish vital statistics', and with subsidiary objectives that would 'include the collection of information on the dates of the various stages, and on incubation and fledging periods'.

The details of over 600 nests submitted in the first year seemed promising, but the effects of World War II soon became apparent and by 1942 the intake had fallen to 184 cards from a mere 13 contributors. However, the organisers did not lose heart and the following year numbers began to increase steadily, from 500 in 1943 to over 1,000 in 1948, and to over 2,500 by 1949. The present intake is about 22,000 cards annually.

In 1947, when James Fisher was still organiser, the collection of cards was transferred to the Edward Grey Institute at Oxford, so that John Gibb could extract data for a proposed new edition of Witherby's *Handbook of British Birds*. Gibb gradually took over the running of the scheme, and in 1949 he was appointed organiser. Under his guidance progress was rapid. He devised a new standard nest record card, a modified form of which is still in use today, and in 1952 he added a new card to be used for colonial nesting species.

Gibb left Oxford in 1952 and the card collection returned to the BTO office where J. F. Burton, who had recently been appointed Assistant Secretary to the Trust, discovered that one of his duties was to take over the running of the scheme. This he did until 1959; and in March 1960 Henry Mayer-Gross became the first full-time organiser. The importance of the Nest Record Scheme had been recognised by the Nature Conservancy, which increased its grant to the Trust to enable this appointment to be made; both the Trust and ornithology are indebted to the Conservancy (and its successor, the Nature Conservancy Council) for this support, especially in those early years. Clearly, the appointment of a full-time organiser revitalised the scheme, for in 1960 the card intake rose to 11,000; by 1962 it had reached 15,100.

As early as 1943 it was felt that enough cards had accumulated to attempt a first analysis. David Lack and E. A. Armstrong, working on Robin and Wren respectively, both consulted the data, and James Fisher began an analysis for the Blackbird, extracting his material from the 330 cards which were then available. When, in 1955, M. T. Myres and D. W. Snow completed further analyses for this species the number of cards at their disposal had risen to 6,000. The first published analysis was for the Song Thrush in 1949 (by Miss E. T. Silva), and this has been followed by a steady stream of publications right up to the present time. It is almost impossible to imagine that a serious worker nowadays would attempt to study the breeding biology of any species without first consulting the relevant BTO nest record cards.

These early analyses raised the question of whether the percentage success figures obtained, by analysing only those cards on which the outcome of the nest was recorded, might be biased through exclusion of the many nests which were not followed through. J. A. Nelder in Britain and H. Mayfield in the USA devised somewhat similar methods of dealing with this problem, involving the probability of nests surviving from day to day, which now permit the inclusion in analyses of nests whose ultimate fate was not recorded. Soon, when the Trust's computer has digested the 42 years' intake which is awaiting its attention, it should be possible to analyse each year's cards at the end of the year, so that season-to-season comparisons will become much more readily obtainable. Computer analysis of the cards will undoubtedly open up a whole range of exciting possibilities: contributions are received from all parts of the country so that regional comparisons will be possible; some species are more successful in certain habitats than in others; while weather during the breeding season, a very variable factor in Britain, must surely affect productivity. Much of this information is available from the cards but its manual extraction, even for a single species, is a slow and laborious process.

In March 1970 Henry Mayer-Gross produced *B.T.O. Guide* no. 12, entitled 'The Nest Record Scheme', which explained in greater detail the instructions and requirements which appear on the cards. This publication also offered much good advice to would-be nest finders. At that time it might have seemed that the original aims of the scheme had been achieved; clutch size and the variations which occur both early and late in the season had been established. From existing cards he had been able to indicate the length of the breeding season for each species – the huge intake of cards since 1970 would do little to change these charts – and incubation and fledging periods were well documented. The scheme's initial ambitions appeared to have been fulfilled; but as in any worthwhile enquiry of this nature the early investigations had exposed a host of related problems which have yet to be solved.

As far back as 1950 Dr Elizabeth Lack had produced a paper showing the gradual decline in clutch size for the Wood Warbler as the season advanced, but no explanation for this was offered. The tailing-off at the end of the season (when food is becoming less plentiful) is easy to understand, but why there should be a period of only a few days when clutches of seven predominate, followed immediately by an even larger number of clutches of six, is more difficult. It may be that the larger clutches are from females which have bred in a previous year; these can return to a territory with which they are already familiar and breeding can proceed without delay. Younger birds, breeding for the first time, have first to secure a territory and since they are less experienced it seems reasonable to suppose that their broods might be rather smaller. Both Wood and Willow Warblers find much of their food in the tree canopy, often (since their territories overlap) using the same trees; but the peak period for clutches of seven in the case of the Willow Warbler is at least a fortnight earlier than that of its near relative, so a decline in the availability of food as a reason for the reduced clutch size can be discounted.

This difference in the production capabilities of old and young birds may be more frequent than is suspected but there is, at present, no supporting evidence from nest record cards largely because, in the majority of cases, second year and older birds are indistinguishable except by minute examination in the hand (and not always even then). In the case of the Blackbird, one of the few species where such a distinction can be made in the field, David Snow found that the clutch size of second year females was significantly smaller than that for older birds but (as David Lack had found when working with the Robin) there were far too many territories within the study area for him to follow the fortunes of individual birds; hence it was impossible to say whether younger birds produced fewer broods in their first season.

There are considerable differences, too, in the production capabilities of different, though frequently closely related, species. Some of these are apparent from the charts in Mayer-Gross's *Guide*. These charts show the length of the breeding season from the first egg date (on a nest record card) to the last record of a young bird still in the nest; hence they take into account exceptional seasonal variations, and repeat nests where an earlier clutch or brood has been lost. Two single-brooded species, Marsh Warbler and Nightingale, have the shortest breeding seasons, of nine and eleven weeks respectively; neither could possibly produce two successful broods in that time. Many small migrants are known to be double-brooded; but how frequently this occurs, and what proportion of the population is involved, are still unsolved mysteries. Examples are the Whitethroat, 16 weeks, Redstart and Whinchat both 13 weeks, and Pied and Spotted Flycatchers at 14 and 15 weeks respectively. The Stonechat is a partial migrant, abandoning many inland sites during the winter, but territories are usually re-occupied in late February and early March and in this way a season of 21 weeks (time enough for three broods) is achieved. The only true migrants potentially capable of rearing three broods in a season are Swallow and House Martin; they do so by extending the breeding season until well into September or even early October, a season of 22 weeks.

Logically, if a species is to maintain itself, the number of young surviving each year should be sufficient to balance adult deaths. From the examples quoted it would appear that there must be a wide variation in survival rates both in and immediately after leaving the nest, if these species are to achieve stability.

In 1974 Robert Morgan, who had taken over the organisation of the scheme from Henry Mayer-Gross in 1971, initiated a monitoring scheme for a selected list of species, designed to ensure that there would be a sufficient number of case histories where the performance of the pair was recorded from the beginning of the season to the end; it had long been apparent that later broods were seriously under-recorded. In a few cases, where the density of the species in the study area makes detailed investigation difficult, a full-scale investigation using colour-ringed birds may be necessary; but for less numerous species, where contributors have recorded their own Spotted Flycatcher nesting on their garden wall for example, an analysis of these cards should be equally satisfactory.

We began by setting out the original aims of the scheme – to discover the basic facts – and the scheme can fairly claim to have achieved its earlier objectives. Now the emphasis is changing, and the use of a computer will enable cards to be examined quickly; almost certainly this will mean that the Nest Record Scheme is about to assume an important rôle as a barometer of the failure or success of each breeding season. The Common Birds Census can demonstrate fluctuations in breeding populations of the various species from year to year; it will be the duty of the Nest Record Scheme to comment on how these populations fared during the summer, and the mysteries surrounding some of the fluctuations may become a little clearer.

Distribution maps and bird atlases

I. J. FERGUSON-LEES

The Atlas of Breeding Birds in Britain and Ireland, based on fieldwork by over 10,000 observers during 1968–72 and published in 1976, is now an established part of the ornithological literature with a firm place on our bookshelves. At the time it represented the largest co-operative survey carried out by naturalists anywhere in the world. It was jointly organised by the BTO and the Irish Wildbird Conservancy, with funding also from the Leverhulme Trust and the Irish Department of Lands. Every one of the 3,862 10-km squares of the National Grids in Britain and Ireland was visited during the five years and the resulting distribution maps for each of the 229 breeding species reached a degree of precision not previously approached.

Even the simplest bird maps are comparatively new. Until the late 1940s they had been produced only in local surveys or in studies of individual species. Distributions were described in often lengthy paragraphs listing the counties concerned or defining the edges of the range with localities from which the bird had been recorded: this left the reader with the problem of trying to visualise the whole. Probably the pioneer bird maps for Britain and Ireland were those compiled by W. B. Alexander for James Fisher's *Bird Recognition*, the first volume of which appeared in 1947: these were based on the published literature, on a vice-county system. Vice-counties, used more by botanists than ornithologists, also provided the first attempts at shading-in areas of comparable size where a species had been found. In this system, the larger counties are divided up into two or more smaller areas and the result is a patchwork of 152 units (roughly equivalent therefore in area, but not shape, to 50-km squares). There followed *Birds of the Soviet Union* (1951–54), P. A. D. Hollom's maps in *A Field Guide to the Birds of Britain and Europe* (1954), and K. H. Voous's *Atlas of European Birds* (1960), all covering huge areas on an inevitably minute scale. Much more comprehensive observation and recording in the 1960s made possible more complete versions of both British and European maps of breeding distribution in various books, though these relied largely on the method of joining known localities on the limits of ranges and were able to take little account of gaps or isolated pockets; they were also often based on subjective assessments.

But the first steps had already been taken towards establishing the grid technique. In 1960 C. A. Norris published a paper in *Bird Study*, in which were plotted the British and Irish ranges of 30 species surveyed in 1952 after a pilot scheme in the West Midlands two years earlier; it used 25-km squares as the plotting unit. The use of grids was not new; various authors here and abroad had attempted to plot plants and individual species of birds in this way over the previous 75 years, but it was the first attempt at such a widespread objective survey. Then in 1962 the Botanical Society of the British Isles published its *Atlas of the British Flora*, which mapped plant distributions on the basis of presence or absence within each 10-km square of the National Grid. It was this that finally stimulated the launching of *The Atlas of Breeding Birds in Britain and Ireland*, although not until there had been a great deal of discussion over more than two years about the feasibility and value of such a large project.

The fieldwork for the Breeding Atlas led to a number of individual counties undertaking similar surveys on finer grids to give a more detailed picture of distribution in their smaller areas: the grid used was generally the 2-km square, or 'tetrad', but at least one local society worked on a 1-km unit. (Some idea of the effort involved comes from the realisation that, because one is dealing in squares, there are twenty-five 2-km squares in each 10-km square, or around 385,000 1-km squares in Britain and Ireland as a whole.) In a wider direction it also led, following equally successful projects in France and Denmark, to the formation of a European Ornithological Atlas Committee, at an international conference held in Buckinghamshire in December 1971 under the joint auspices of the BTO and Vogelwarte Radolfzell of Germany. The aim of the EOAC was to foster further projects, leading eventually to mapping on a European scale. As a result, atlases of breeding distribution, plotted by 5-km, 10-km or 50-km squares, or similar units, have now been produced for a total of nine European countries. More particularly, the aim is that during 1985–88 every European country will take part in a 'European Atlas of Breeding Birds' (to include European Russia) on at least a 50-km grid.

So far, surveys of distribution have tended to concentrate on breeding. Whether on a British or a European scale, maps in bird books have often included some form of shading to indicate regions where the species is present on passage or in winter; but the background literature, for winter in particular, is much less detailed and, of course, birds move about when they are not nesting. Nevertheless, one or two ambitious schemes are in progress in, for example, the Grampian region of Scotland and the Netherlands, for plotting distribution throughout the year. The BTO is now in the midst of a Winter Atlas project, again in conjunction with the Irish Wildbird Conservancy: following a pilot study in 1980/81, a programme of fieldwork over three winters was launched in November 1981. Even with the Breeding Atlas as an example, the lead-up involved just as much discussion and just as many doubts about the practicability of covering the whole of these islands; yet in the first of the three winters about 70% of all the 10-km squares received a visit of at least one hour, and a still larger proportion had been further explored by the end of the second.

In fact, the Winter Atlas will take us into a new phase of dot-distribution recording. All previous bird atlases of this kind had worked on a 'presence or absence' basis, using different sizes of dots only to reflect different degrees of proof of breeding; there had been no attempt at assessing or indicating relative abundance in different parts of the area covered, though to some extent (because it is easier to prove nesting where a species is common) this had been reflected in the prevalence of larger or smaller dots. The Winter Atlas, however, is collecting details of numbers actually seen and now that the BTO has advanced into the computer age it will be possible to show, still by the use of different-sized dots, the squares with larger or smaller concentrations. Where appropriate, with two or more maps, it will also be possible to compare different winters or different parts of the same winter. Thus, a heavy snowfall in January, resulting in widespread movements of birds to the south-west, will be reflected in a build-up in southern Ireland or a general drop in numbers through mortality or crossing to the Continent.

Although the founders of the BTO probably never envisaged its involvement in extensive mapping, we have come a long way in the 50 years, particularly in the last 30. Many observers find a seemingly insatiable fascination in atlas fieldwork, which appears to fulfil all that is best in competitiveness and 'collecting' while at the same time providing a fitting tool for co-operative study and the amassing of distributional data; but the rising costs of organisation, stationery and publication must put a limit on the frequency and development of such surveys. Yet the European Atlas hopes to include some assessment of abundance and certainly the next Breeding Atlas in which the BTO is involved will do so. How refined this aspect will become in future we do not know, but obviously computers make storage and analysis far easier and raise the possibility of more regular updating. Already we have a Breeding Atlas as a baseline and soon will have a Winter Atlas as well. Dare we contemplate Spring and Autumn Passage too? If so, how shall we decide to 'freeze' such transitory pictures on to maps?

Birds of Estuaries Enquiry

A. J. PRATER

The length of coastline of Britain has been estimated at 4,390 km in England and Wales, 3,860 km in mainland Scotland and 6,250 km around Scottish islands, giving a total of 14,500 km. In Britain there are 133 estuaries and bays with 1 km^2 or more of intertidal flats; and there are approximately 2,600 km^2 of mud and sand flats in these and smaller estuaries, plus an undetermined area along beaches and rocky coasts. The area of saltmarsh in Britain was estimated to be 448 km^2 during the late 1960s.

Like many of the surveys organised by the BTO, the Birds of Estuaries Enquiry was born out of a practical conservation need. Small-scale loss of mudflats and saltmarshes by reclamation has been with us for many hundreds of years, but modern technology made very large schemes potentially feasible.

After barrage schemes had been suggested for the Solway and Morecambe Bay during the mid-1960s, it was realised that estuarine birds, particularly waders, could be threatened by habitat loss. The wader research initiated under the Morecambe Bay Barrage Feasibility Study was the first extensive, professionally co-ordinated, census study on this group of birds in Britain. However, it was apparent immediately that knowledge from elsewhere was fragmentary. In 1969, Gareth Thomas of the Royal Society for the Protection of Birds searched through the available literature for wader census data and highlighted its inadequacies. In the meantime, in 1968, Dr W. R. P. Bourne had put forward a proposal to the Trust's Populations and Surveys Committee that a survey of estuary birds, particularly waders, was desirable. After some discussion, it was agreed that it was not only desirable but also practical and that a joint BTO/RSPB project should be started. Initial contacts during the first half of 1969 enabled almost half of the major estuaries to be counted during the 1969/70 pilot year. The organisation of the pilot survey was undertaken by David Glue of the BTO and Dr P. J. K. Burton of the International Waterfowl Research Bureau's Wader Research Group.

It was soon apparent that the survey could produce the information required and the Nature Conservancy – now separated into the Nature Conservancy Council (NCC) and the Institute of Terrestrial Ecology (ITE) –

agreed to fund a five-year project. The aims of the Birds of Estuaries Enquiry were threefold. Primarily it was to document the species and numbers of birds using each of Britain's estuaries. These data could be combined to give overall totals, so providing a conservation assessment of each and a comparison between them. Thus, should a development be suggested, it would be possible to assess, in general terms, its impact at a local, national or international level.

Secondly, annual counts could monitor bird population levels and keep a check of natural or man-induced changes. The third aim, which to some extent would be a by-product of any regular comprehensive count, was to document seasonal population fluctuations which could be combined with ringing studies to help describe the migration and local movements of birds. This was achieved through the Wader Study Group by including some of the wealth of information obtained by the specialist wader ringing groups around the country. The counts were designed to assess estuary bird numbers, but it was realised that quite large numbers of some species were found on rocky or sandy coastlines; some data were collected from these habitats as part of the Estuaries Enquiry, but much remains to be learnt.

The writer was appointed as National Organiser in June 1970. The Birds of Estuaries Enquiry was organised and administered from the BTO but maintained a close relationship with the RSPB, through wardens and regional officers counting or organising counts, through undertaking the printing costs of the annual reports and through invaluable advice. In February 1969 an Advisory Committee was set up, under the chairmanship of the Deputy Director Conservation of the RSPB; its membership was drawn from a wide range of informed parties and its assistance has been extremely valuable throughout. It was responsible to the BTO's Populations and Surveys Committee.

It was soon realised that because waders move rapidly between estuaries all around the country, it would be desirable to co-ordinate counts in Britain and Ireland. Consequently, during January 1971, A. J. Prater and A. Grieve (RSPB) counted waders on some Irish estuaries; at the same time the Irish Wildbird Conservancy launched their Wetlands Enquiry with the aim of documenting waterfowl on both coastal and inland sites. Close liaison has been maintained since with their organisers, who were C. D. Hutchinson (1971–76), L. Stapleton (1976–78) and P. Smiddy (1978–79); results of their counts have been published recently (Hutchinson 1979). The Wildfowl Trust became a co-sponsor of the Birds of Estuaries Enquiry in 1972 and has continued, through G. L. Atkinson-Willes, M. A. Ogilvie and D. Salmon, to write the section on wildfowl in the annual report. Following the change in structure of the Nature Conservancy, the Estuaries Enquiry continued to be financed by both NCC and NERC through the agency of ITE until 1977; subsequently, all of the funding came from the NCC. The funding was reduced to two man months between 1978 and 1982. During this period the survey was organised firstly by P. A. Hyde and latterly by J. H. Marchant. From autumn 1982 a new, three-year, full-time post was established, this time with joint funding from the NCC, RSPB and BTO. The present survey organiser is M. E. Moser, who reinstated year-round coverage and is, himself, conducting detailed survey work on the Solway Firth.

1981 saw the publication of *Estuary Birds of Britain and Ireland*, written by A. J. Prater, with contributions from Dr R. J. O'Connor and C. D. Hutchinson and much help from other BTO staff members. This book summarised the ecology of estuary birds, their migrations and populations, the threats they face, and considered all regular species in detail. It followed *The Atlas of Breeding Birds in Britain and Ireland* as the second in a series describing the work and results of major BTO surveys.

During the period 1969–1976, the main part of the Estuaries Enquiry, about 1,000 observers took part, covering over 200 British and Irish estuaries. The willingness of birdwatchers to turn out month after month over a six-year period, whatever the weather, was the prime reason for the success of this project – as it is for all BTO surveys. However, in order to keep the system working, the national organiser also depended on two intermediate tiers of organisers. There was an organiser for each estuary who co-ordinated observers, at least where the estuary was large, to make sure all counted synchronously and all were available for each count; these local organisers knew their own estuaries well and could ensure all areas were visited and, if someone had to drop out, were a focus enabling a standby counter to be found quickly. The results from each estuary were submitted to the BTO via a county organiser, who also maintained liaison with county bird societies.

The results of these counts have transformed our ability to protect the limited estuary habitats. From a position of fragmentary knowledge in the late 1960s, where all that could be demonstrated was that some (many) birds occurred, we have reached a position of being able to show with some certainty the true status of each estuary at both national and international levels. Of course there are several aspects where further detailed research or survey work is required, but from the very extensive counts much has been achieved. The Estuaries Enquiry, allied with other related surveys, has now produced what is probably a more comprehensive set of data on birds than is available for any other habitat in Britain.

Right from the very beginning of the Enquiry in 1970, there has been a tremendous demand for the information gathered. It has been used by the NCC, ITE, RSPB, Wildfowl Trust and by many local or county societies and organisations for many reasons. Sometimes it is to augment detailed scientific research programmes, but usually it is to indicate the importance of an estuary or even an area within an estuary. In most cases the BTO's national organiser makes a statement of the scientific case either in writing or in person at a public inquiry or similar.

During the last twelve years, data have been used to assess the importance of virtually every large and most small estuaries in Britain. The roll call of estuaries where major developments have threatened serves to highlight the need for the data: Morecambe Bay, Wash, Dee, Solway, Ribble, Severn, Thames, Firth of Forth, Moray Firth, Strangford Lough, Burry Inlet and many, many more. An example of how development has affected one estuary, the Tees, is shown in Fig. 5.

The ability of the Estuaries Enquiry to obtain regular and up-to-date information is vital in conservation activities in Britain and Northern Ireland. The injection of further funding for the next three years is indicative of the invaluable rôle that this survey plays, and it is hoped that it will have a secure future for very many years to come.

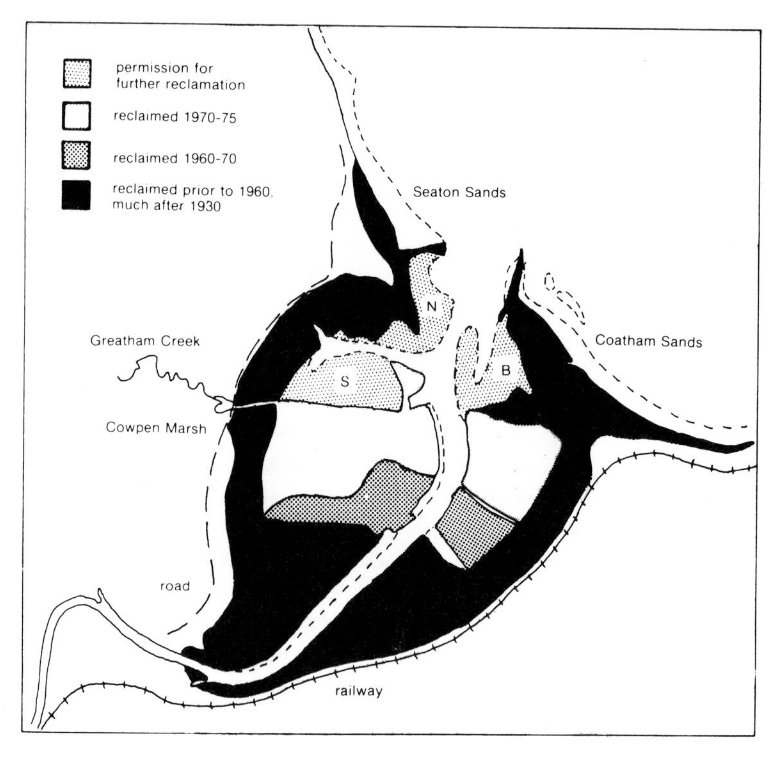

Fig 5 Estuary of the Tees, and areas recently reclaimed. From Prater (1981).

The Garden Bird Feeding Survey

P. AND E. WILLSON

We first heard of the Garden Bird Feeding Survey in spring 1970, although it was not so called at the time. David Glue, who had the responsibility of organising the survey, outlined its purpose as he sat drinking coffee and watching Blue Tits feeding in our garden. He explained that there was no national monitoring scheme for garden bird populations in winter, and after the exceptionally hard one experienced during 1962/63, when the BBC had repeatedly asked people to put out food for starving birds, the information produced about the effects of such activities was largely guesswork. The Populations and Surveys Committee felt that, with increasing urbanisation and loss of rural habitat, gardens would become increasingly important. Such a survey could provide useful information on a national scale, and should also prove popular with members unable to participate in more energetic activities of the Trust. It had been agreed to launch a pilot study beginning in the autumn of 1970, and we agreed willingly to help.

Information about the pilot study appeared in *BTO News* in June 1970 and volunteers were invited to take part. Almost four hundred Trust members expressed a wish to participate, with several hundred further offers of help as a result of articles in the daily press and many bird club bulletins. The pilot study was designed to test recording methods, and the number of participants was limited to two hundred, with as wide a geographical spread as possible. The late Norman Pullen became the pilot study organiser.

The first winter was relatively mild, with plenty of natural food available for birds. After the initial period, from October 1970 to the end of that year, a preliminary report was submitted to the Populations and Surveys Committee. It stated that the pilot study had convinced both the organiser and Trust staff that the Survey could go a long way towards fulfilling its four-fold aims:

to determine what birds took food artificially presented to them by householders, and when, what foods were being provided, and which were consumed most readily. The report noted that a total of fifty-one species had taken food or water at 123 feeding stations.

For the second winter, 1971/72, because of the growing interest in the survey (now confirmed as a continuing enquiry) participants were extended to 400 – providing a formidable task for an amateur organiser. Analysis of the 400 returns was divided between three sets of people; we had been persuaded to become one of them. Norman Pullen, however, then felt he could no longer organise the GBFS alone. After visiting him and profiting from his sound advice we found ourselves writing letters, addressing envelopes, licking stamps and finding space in our home for forms and site cards. We had become 'Willsons the GBFS'.

In 1972/73 the number of participants was reduced to the former level of 200, a more manageable number, and has been held at around this level ever since. The natural fall-out is always replaced from the queue of people waiting to join in. However, many of the original participants still remain, including sites 001, 003 and 007. After thirteen years the Survey is continuing as vigorously as ever. To us, numbers have become names, and names have become friends. Much of the routine work has now been taken over by the Beech Grove computer, but the letters and comments we receive have become more personal and more interesting.

The methodology of the Survey is to record accurately each winter (October to March) the numbers of birds of each species seen feeding or drinking at any one time on food or water artificially presented within a defined area on a weekly basis. Observers are asked to supply details and a diagram of the feeding area and of the number of ground, raised and hanging units. There are rural and suburban/urban sites, and results from these are analysed separately. Each year the 'top ten' species feed at over 90% of the sites, with Blackbird, Robin and Blue Tit showing 99% to 100% in most winters. These are the 'bread and butter' species. The 'sugar and spice' is provided by records of such birds as Merlin, Kingfisher, Dipper and Firecrest. Every winter so far has produced yet another new species coming for food or water, and the total has now reached one hundred and twenty.

As the Survey has continued over the years, so new information has been gleaned. For example, it became obvious that birds of prey were cashing-in on areas where small birds were encouraged to feed; during the 1981/82 winter Sparrowhawks appeared at 20% of feeding sites, Kestrels at 13%, Little Owls 3%, Tawny Owls 2% and a Merlin at one site in Scotland. The year before a Barn Owl and a Goshawk were seen attempting to take prey. Some observers are worried by the attention of raptors, while others welcome it. From the Isle of Skye: 'Recently a Golden Eagle flew fairly low overhead. What a scoop that would have been had it liked the look of a Starling or two.' And from North Devon: 'I have not been able to tempt a Buzzard into the

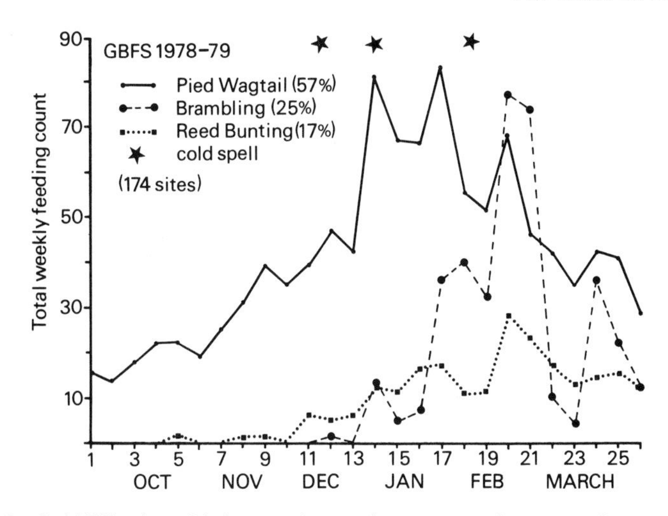

Fig 6 Cold Weather. Birds react in varying ways to the onset of cold weather as demonstrated during the series of intense cold periods in mid-winter 1978/79. Insect eaters like Pied Wagtail turn quickly to artificially provided foods. Many seed eaters, including Brambling, usually appear only when the natural crop is exhausted, departing early for their breeding grounds. Others such as Reed Bunting may remain faithful to a particular garden, once located, and stay until spring arrives.

garden, although last summer one sat on a tree staring for an hour and a half at my daughter sun-bathing. I'm not sure whether he was just disapproving or sizing up the chances of carrying her off.'

As the result of the careful observations by regular observers we now have a list of twenty-six species of birds which have been recorded taking food from hanging containers. These include such unlikely ones as Dunnock, Blackcap, Rook, Reed Bunting and Feral Pigeon.

In any winter study the weather plays an important part and it is especially true of this survey. In a mild winter, with few cold spells and plenty of seeds and berries on trees and bushes, birds do not need to resort to artificial foods, although the tit family will almost always come to peanuts. But it is during periods of sharp frost and lying snow that GBFS people become excited. Then such birds as Mistle Thrush are recorded feeding in gardens more frequently and in greater numbers. Fieldfares and Redwings appear, especially in the post-Christmas period when usually the coldest weather is experienced. Reed Bunting and Brambling are seen in gardens where they have never been seen before; 'little brown jobs' like Meadow Pipit and Skylark come in from the fields to feed; gardens where there is a stream or wet area occasionally attract such birds as Snipe and Water Rail. Even 'escapes' appear: Budgerigar, Ring-necked Parakeet, Lady Amherst's Pheasant and Californian Quail have all been recorded searching for food.

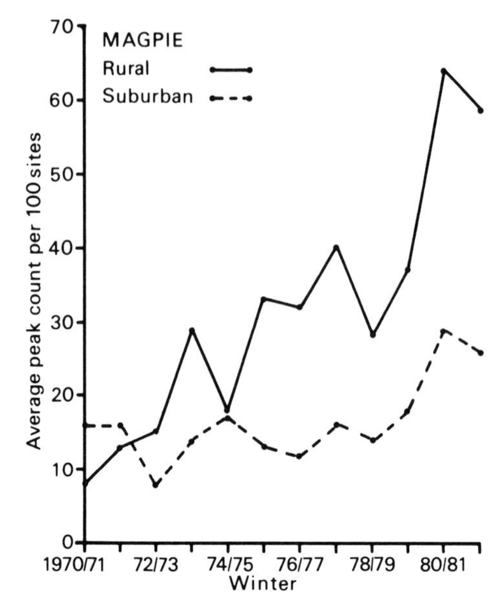

Fig 7 Magpie indices. The corvids are proving to be a very adaptable family, most members turning increasingly to garden foods. The Magpie has shown the greatest advances, chiefly in rural areas, though it is now a widespread early morning visitor to many bird tables in towns and cities, demonstrating its versatile feeding behaviour and catholic tastes – virtually no food is left untouched.

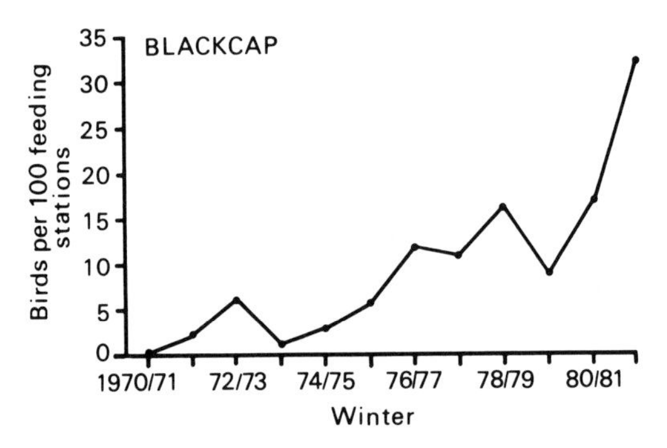

Fig 8 Blackcap indices. There has been a spectacular increase in the number of Blackcaps wintering in Britain and Ireland in the last twenty years, most birds turning to birdtable food stuffs, especially during the post-Christmas months. Bread, fat, dried fruit, apples and peanuts are the preferred items. Evidence from ringing suggests that these birds are of Continental origin where breeding populations are known to have flourished in several countries.

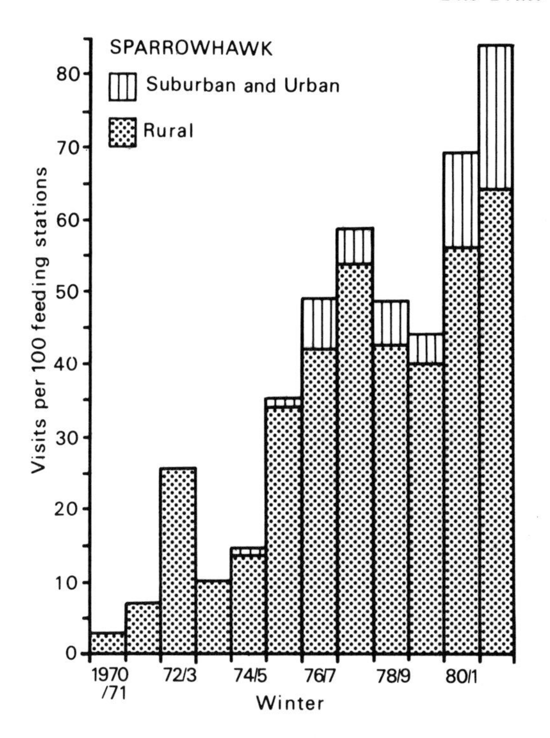

Fig 9 Sparrowhawk fortunes. The withdrawal of organochlorine chemical pesticides in the last twenty years has led to a recovery in the breeding performance and population level of Sparrowhawks in Britain. Since the mid 1970s especially, instances of Sparrowhawks appearing in feeding areas to chase and kill small birds have become more frequent, mainly in rural gardens, but even at suburban sites in recent years.

And of course they get it. Not only peanuts and '*swoop*' and sunflower seeds, but anything else they might fancy. From Surrey we heard: 'Great Spotted Woodpecker found pork crackling on ground, held it in claws and ate from it, then picked it up, hopped to the open garage door and climbed up to the edge to facilitate take-off.' Also from Surrey: 'The over-wintering Blackcap fed exclusively on Christmas cake.' Northern Ireland also has Blackcaps of catholic taste, that were 'even seen to feed from the dog's dish on a mixture of dog meal and meat'. More typically from Omagh: 'It will be seen that my birds are indeed Irish; they are mad about potatoes.' From the Isle of Skye came the comment: 'I am interested in the various foods provided by some observers but no one has mentioned haggis. They don't get much, as we like it too much ourselves.' Apart from good food, GBFS birds get protection too. Perhaps it would be better not to mention from where this came: 'I am going to strangle the ginger Tom from next door but seven.'

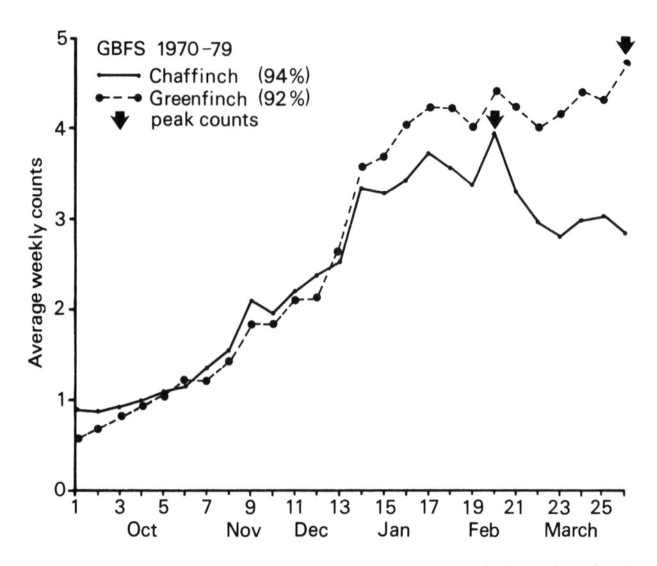

Fig 10 Finch feeding patterns. The maximum use of birdtable foods during the course of a winter varies greatly from species to species. A few, like the Wren, steadily decline in attendance, probably reflecting natural mortality. Other species, such as Magpie and Black-headed Gull, peak during the coldest mid-winter months. The majority, however, build up in numbers as temperatures drop and natural foods in the hedgerow and woodland dwindle, augmented by birds from the Continent. Birds like Chaffinch and Greenfinch rely most on garden foods in February, March and even into April.

Not only do cold winters have an adverse effect on bird populations, but excessively hot and dry summers too. After the drought of 1976 the BBC consulted the GBFS, as so many people had written to their Natural History Unit at Bristol because they were concerned that so few tits were coming to bird tables and nut bags. We carried out a mini-survey with a small sample of observers. Tit numbers were indeed down. This may have been because there was so much natural food available that autumn, or it might have been due to a poor breeding season. The experience of some ringers, who had reported that they had ringed fewer first-year birds than usual, supports this view. The CBC also confirmed that the number of breeding birds was low.

And who are the GBFS observers? Equal numbers of men and women, young and old, members of the BTO, non-members (who often become members), occasionally school groups, people who do nest record cards and CBCs, ringers (who often send us ringing information), a few disabled people who find this excellent therapy, people from all over England, Scotland, Wales and Northern Ireland. These are people who look forward to winter! In addition to recording forms, a separate sheet is provided for comments on weather conditions or anything extraordinary. These are very informative, the detailed observations never fail to amaze us, and it is this which makes the organisation of such a survey so rewarding. Since the GBFS started 782 sites have been watched and recorded.

Obviously people like to know the results of the work they do, and each year when sending out the forms for a new season a letter is included giving some general comments on the previous winter's results. Also enclosed is a Winter Master Sheet containing more detailed information, and on the reverse of this are given interesting and often humorous comments selected from letters and forms which we have received. Thus all observers who take part are kept in touch.

Should birds be fed in winter? The answer to that question is another one: how could it be prevented? It is probably the oldest and closest of man's relationships with birds, and the Trust is surely wise to make use of information which can be gleaned from this pastime. The importance of gardens as bird habitat in winter is indisputable. For example, on one bitterly cold day last year we set forth to do a stint for the Winter Atlas; as we left there were twenty-two Blue Tits feeding at our bird table, but in five hours walking through woods and fields our total count was five!

However, perhaps one of the most important aspects of any voluntary activity is that it should be enjoyable. Comments received from many who take part in this survey prove it to be so and may be summed up in one from Avon: 'This period has been the most exciting and interesting in my garden's history because of the Garden Bird Feeding Survey. Long may it continue.'

Register of Ornithological Sites

RONALD HICKLING

This project – which in its early days we often referred to as an 'Ornithological Domesday Book' – was born in that period of mingled euphoria and frustration following the end of the fieldwork for the Breeding Atlas. Euphoria because as the final cards for the Atlas came in (and we knew that well over 10,000 observers had taken part) they were accompanied by such expressions of enthusiasm that we realised we had a huge work-force eager to take part in further schemes of a like nature. Clearly there was an urgent need to make use of this before enthusiasm waned for loss of direction. The frustration came because of our inability to find a single scheme which would satisfy the varied interests and skills which the Atlas had been able to use. We realised that several schemes would have to be devised to use all this potential for the benefit of ornithology; yet inevitably they would have less impact than the single all-embracing project which the Atlas had proved to be. One proposal – yet another brain-child from the fertile mind of Dr W. R. P. Bourne – was to compile a gazetteer of the most important bird sites in Britain. It was argued that in carrying out their Atlas fieldwork observers would have returned often to those places where they could confidently expect to see most birds – their 'best' sites. Such a list would provide a ready selection of those places most in need of protection and conservation in a changing countryside. Moreover, since most of this information was already recorded in field notebooks (or at worst in memories), it should be relatively easy to collect. But there was a need for speed – before pencil notes faded or memories dimmed.

The Populations and Surveys Committee therefore set up a Working Group consisting of Dr Bourne, I. J. Ferguson-Lees, Dr J. J. M. Flegg and Dr R. K. Murton under the chairmanship of R. A. O. Hickling; it first met on 27 September 1972 and the Register of Ornithological Habitats came into being. Its name changed somewhat over the next few months; we finally settled on A Register of Ornithological Sites as a more accurate and suitably modest title.

The basic concept worked out at the first meeting served the Register very well right through to its completion, although a number of refinements were made during the course of the enquiry. The aim, as stated in the Working Party's original minute, was:

> . . . to provide a register (in published gazetteer, card index, and punch-card/tape forms) of all sites in Britain (and, it was hoped, in Ireland) of ornithological value. 'Value' could only be broadly defined, but as an example it was anticipated that the Register could be used (a) to pinpoint the single Barn Owl nest site in a parish (local scale); (b) to select the most species-diverse woodlands in a county (regional scale); or (c) to defend the largest wetland area in Wales (national scale). 'Value' would be initially assessed by the observer in the square: ultimate categorisation of the site would follow consultation between the national organiser and/or county recorder or his equivalent. The published gazetteer would be subject to the same strict safeguards for rare species (and additionally for 'tender' sites) that had been applied to the Atlas records.

In the event the Register proved adequate to meet the criteria under (b) and (c), but not sophisticated enough to deal with the highly detailed requirements of (a).

The proposal met with the instant approval of the Royal Society for the Protection of Birds as it could provide information on a scale not previously available which would greatly assist them in devising conservation strategies. The Society, by a generous gesture, provided finance to support the first six months of the venture. This enabled the Trust to appoint a national organiser, R. J. Fuller, and to initiate a pilot survey.

The first task of the organiser was to devise a recording card. This entailed some hard and fundamental thinking about the purposes and methods of the survey. It will be realised that this was a new concept in Trust enquiries, and much experience had to be gathered pragmatically along the way. The standardised recording card for each site eventually adopted called for a simple description of the habitat, including the use of a habitat code described in detail on an instruction sheet, with a sketch map and a description of the ornithological interest of the site. The back of the form required each species present to be classified into four categories: passage, breeding, summering/non-breeding and wintering. (An example is shown on page 217 of R. J. Fuller's *Bird Habitats in Britain*, 1982.) The form, the devising of which had so concentrated the minds of organiser and Working Group, also called for precision on the part of observers. It ceased to be a mere 'notebook' exercise, and sent the recorders out into the field. One effect was to reduce the number of sites originally listed, in an initial burst of enthusiasm, from 5,500 to just over 4,000 carefully considered examples.

After the conclusion of the RSPB contract the Trust carried the financial burden itself for some time. A contract was then negotiated with the Nature Conservancy Council which would enable the fieldwork to be completed and the results to be documented and written up. The NCC's interest was as practical as had been that of the RSPB; the information was to be used. The final Register would, in appropriate sections, be lodged with the Regional Offices of the NCC, a copy would be held by RSPB, and the master copy (which it was hoped would be updated regularly) would be retained at Tring. It was also intended that information would always be available to bona fide enquirers, such as planners, local authorities, nationalised undertakings and conservation bodies. The practical importance of the Register was soon demonstrated: throughout the course of the enquiry the organiser was called upon to supply information and advice, notwithstanding the incompleteness of the Register.

It has already been stressed that the value of a site would be a subjective opinion of the observer. Clearly this would prove an unreliable basis if the final Register was to be used for any kind of site analysis or grading. In his book, *Bird Habitats in Britain*, Rob Fuller discussed the problem thus:

> Not unexpectedly, birdwatchers and naturalists have come to value some species and bird communities more than others. Such evaluations are central and constant themes in nature conservation. In order to decide which aspects of wildlife and the countryside are most worthy of special conservation measures, value judgements are essential. At the most basic level the prairie farmlands of East Anglia are considered intrinsically less interesting than the vast fens from which they have derived. At another level, value judgements are used to compare the relative worth of different woods, heathlands, flood meadows and so on.

As a result of long discussion with scientific officers of the NCC, the organiser proposed to the Working Group (which agreed) that sites should be placed into one of five categories:

international importance	A(1)
national importance	A
regional importance	B
county importance	C
local importance	D

Complicated standards, involving varied criteria and cut-off points, were worked out and adopted as a framework for site evaluation of all documented sites.

Finally, the NCC agreed that the practical conservation value of the whole project would be enhanced if the final report to them was published in book form, available also to the public. Such a book, it was estimated, would take two years to prepare, and the contract had already run its course. The NCC agreed to provide finance for a further year, if the Trust would itself finance the second year; this was approved by Trust Council and Rob Fuller was commissioned to write it. As he worked on it the concept grew. No comprehensive review of bird habitats in Britain had ever been attempted, and the information in the Register provided a basis upon which such an in-depth study could be made. The title eventually chosen, *Bird Habitats in Britain*, indicates the scope of the treatment.

Fig 11 Sites of regional importance. From Fuller (1982).

The publication of this book has enhanced considerably the reputation of the Trust, but it is not believed that work in this field should stop there. The Working Group made its final report to Council in the following terms:

> The Sites Register was conceived as a continuing tool of conservation and the results achieved must be regarded as Phase 1 of this scheme. The efforts of BTO members and staff, and the expenditure of money from the RSPB, NCC, and our own resources, will only be justified by the future usefulness of the Register. It is the view of the Working Group therefore that the scheme should be treated as an ongoing project, providing information and advice to conservation and planning bodies, and receiving a constant updating and amplification of original data.

4: Our changing avifauna

Robert Spencer

> I well remember the (black-headed) gulls' first appearance as a London bird in the severe winter of 1880–81. Finding themselves well treated, they returned each year thereafter and everyone knows how tame they are.
>
> G. E. LODGE

Most people do not really notice birds unless they become birdwatchers. On the basis of published membership figures we may guess that there are at least half a million committed birdwatchers in Britain, and possibly many more. We may guess, too, that only a minority of that number have been watching birds for more than fifteen years. If we were to double the time span, we could be confident that a very small proportion of today's birdwatchers have clear recollections or notes about birds going back as far as thirty years.

This short-lived contact which most of us have with birds has an important influence on the way we think about them. Any changes in bird numbers or ranges usually occur rather slowly, so that although we are sometimes aware of annual variations of the kind 'there aren't so many House Martins on my house this year', we tend not to notice longer-term trends. In short, most of us assume that the bird distributions and numbers which we observe are pretty much what they were in our father's day, and claims that, for example, Cuckoos were much more abundant in the years before World War II are shrugged off as subjective, and probably with little foundation.

Yet if we take the trouble to search the literature we find that the ranges of many species are much more plastic than we suppose, and their populations much more given to fluctuation. The present-day birdwatcher, accustomed to Black-headed Gulls as a familiar part of almost every urban winter landscape, assumes that it was always so and reads with amazement the above statement by Lodge, the eminent bird artist. The change since then has been truly remarkable, the *London Bird Report* for a century later recording up to 25,000 Black-headed Gulls congregating on a single reservoir. In reality we should think of changes in bird numbers and distribution as the normal rather than the exceptional, of many birds as being fairly delicately adjusted to their environment and capable of reacting quite rapidly in response to changes in that environment.

Change, then, is the theme of this chapter; change in all its different manifestations. Changes in numbers are of crucial importance. Given that a species becomes scarce, the surviving population is likely to concentrate in those areas which it finds most attractive – the optimal habitat – and this may involve a contraction of range. Conversely, if – for whatever reason – a species continues to thrive, it must sooner or later outgrow the space available for it within its normal area of distribution, and expansion of range results. If the increase in numbers originates abroad then colonisation of Britain may result, as happened with the Little Ringed Plover and the Collared Dove; but the converse is also true, and British Lesser Redpolls have recently colonised adjacent parts of the Continent. Some species appear to be expanding their ranges in Britain and on the Continent, quite independently but presumably in response to similar environmental trends. This is the situation with several of the woodpeckers.

The link between changes in numbers and changes in range seems clear enough, but we must probe more deeply by seeking to understanding what causes the changes in numbers. Here we shall enter a realm where speculation is more commonplace than hard fact, but most people would agree that changes in the environment often lead to population changes and that, whilst some habitat changes can occur naturally (for example, through climatic deterioration) many are the direct outcome of man's activities. We shall find, too, that for some species, man's changing attitude to it alters its fortunes. Lodge, in the quotation which prefaces this chapter, stresses that the gulls found themselves 'well treated' and this must have eased their occupation of the capital city. They were fortunate, for bizarre though it now seems, some duck shooting continued in the London parks until the early 1930s, and thus just into the era dealt with in this book. With consideration of changing attitudes to birds such as these, we touch upon a theme which is dealt with elsewhere in the book. Nor is the overlap confined to a single chapter, for when we come to consider that most sacred of cows, the British and Irish List, we shall find that it in turn is influenced by the changing skills and interests of birdwatchers. T. A. Coward, the ornithological giant whose writings guided the pre-Witherby *Handbook* generation of birdwatchers, wrote: 'I find pipits in the field almost hopeless, and not much better in the hand'. Times really have changed! Yet this is not an isolated example. That inveterate explorer of the by-ways of ornithological literature, Richard Fitter, noted in his *London's Birds* that 'W. H. Hudson . . . as late as 1906, made the astonishing admission that "in its winter plumage it is almost impossible to tell" the black-headed gull from the common gull.' The fortunes of birds and man are interlinked: man the hunter, man the forester, man the farmer, man the industrialist – even man the birdwatcher. We must now look more closely at some of these changes in fortune, selecting where possible examples which are representative of the various trends we have identified.

SPECIES WHICH HAVE DECLINED DURING THE PERIOD 1933–1983

The Wryneck and the Corncrake spring readily to mind when one thinks of species which have suffered a prolonged decline in the last fifty years. They are but two names in a growing list. The Red-backed Shrike, for example, has contracted its range remarkably since the 1939–1945 war, during which time the breeding population has fallen to a tiny fraction of its former level. The Nightjar is still to be found over large areas of the country, yet many traditional haunts lie deserted and the breeding population is now greatly reduced. Unlike the Red-backed Shrike, which has retreated towards the south-eastern corner of England, the present-day strongholds of the Nightjar are to be found in the west and south of the country, the species being nowhere more abundant than on the Dorset heaths. It is mainly in the south-west, also, that the remnant populations of the Cirl Bunting and the Woodlark are to be found. In Britain the Cirl Bunting was always a bird with a western bias, but as recently as 1938 could be described as 'widely distributed' as far north as the north coast of Wales (Sharrock 1976). By 1980 Sitters (1982) found that the population in the key county of Devon was probably reduced to fewer than 100 pairs, with no more than 24–40 pairs in the remaining eleven counties which harboured the species.

The Woodlark has had a very chequered career as a breeding species in Britain and Ireland. In the first half of the nineteenth century it was reported to be well distributed throughout England, as far north as north Cumberland in the west (Macpherson 1892), and it was said to breed in Ireland. A decline set in and even within the main breeding range in the southern half of England the species decreased, the lowest point possibly being reached in the late 1880s. Soon after 1920 (1923 has been suggested as a key year) the species began to increase in many counties, both in south-eastern England and westwards to Somerset and Brecon. The increase continued until about 1951, then after a short period of stability, a decline set in. The last nests were reported in Yorkshire in 1958, in Lincolnshire 1959, in Bedford 1956, and in Essex 1961. The Suffolk coast population, estimated in 1956 at 20 pairs, was reduced to two by 1962. The recording area of the London Natural History Society carried 45 pairs in 1950, but by 1964 none at all could be located. Several authors, notably Harrison (1961), have speculated about the causes of the second decline. Woodlarks appear to be relatively tolerant of disturbance, but probably suffer from habitat loss. Summer temperatures may be implicated, for the mean annual temperature at Kew increased steadily from 1920–1950, coinciding with the period of expansion, and then started to decline. The current trend is difficult to determine. Sharrock (1976) put the 1965 population at 'only about 100 occupied territories' and that for the Atlas fieldwork years at between 200 and 450 pairs. Yet a survey organised by the Hampshire Ornithological Society in 1981 located 116 pairs or singing males in that one county. In contrast, the *Devon Bird Report* for 1980 suggested a population of about 20, which is no more than there were in 1967.

Another species which appears to be retreating to the south-east is the Stone-Curlew. It is, however, an unobtrusive bird by day, easily overlooked, and intensive nocturnal fieldwork in recent years, whilst confirming contraction of range, indicates that there still are healthy populations in its main breeding strongholds.

The species so far listed are all retreating southwards. Others are either retreating towards the north or at least suffering marked reductions in the southernmost parts of their ranges. This is the case with the Peregrine, which was lost from virtually all southern eyries during the pesticide era, and generally speaking has not returned to the south coast of England. It is also the case with the southern race of the Guillemot (*albionis*), which still breeds in most of its traditional south coast sites but in greatly reduced numbers. Cramp *et al.* (1974) quoted for Lundy Island a 1939 population estimate of 19,000 pairs, but only 1,674 during the Operation Seafarer survey of 1969–70. It has been suggested that chronic oiling in the English Channel has played an important rôle in reducing the southern colonies, but this is speculation. Cramp *et al.* reported that the numbers had increased, 'sometimes markedly', at various Scottish colonies, and the east coast waters of Scotland are certainly not immune from oiling.

Of all the species which have retreated northwards, the most dramatic is the Corncrake. More than most birds it has a special claim to feature in this chapter and in this volume, for it was the subject of one of the earliest comprehensive surveys carried out by the Trust, and of a repeat survey in the years 1978–79. C. A. Norris, who organised the first survey on behalf of the Trust, was able to draw upon 1,180 questionnaires and 800 letters for 1938, and a further 650 questionnaires and 600 letters for 1939. Then World War II intervened and so it was not until 1945 that the preliminary results were published, and two years afterwards (Norris 1947) that the interpretation followed.

Norris's historical research presented a fascinating picture. For example, in 1834 the species was 'far from being scarce in the neighbourhood of Hampton Court'; while the previous year Selby, writing of the banks of the River Trent below Newark, reported: 'I have, in the course of an hour, killed eight or ten in a single field.' A decline was noticed as early as 1850 in Essex and 1875 in Middlesex, while in Dorset in 1914 the Corncrake was described as 'a vanishing species'. By the time of the first enquiry Norris found that to the south and east of a line drawn from Middlesbrough to Swansea the species was 'still found in isolated instances in most counties'. North of that line there was 'local distribution of varying intensity, but considerable decreases'. Only in the north-west of Ireland, the extreme west and north of Scotland and in the Outer Isles was the species numerous, with little or no change of status.

In seeking a cause for the decline Norris examined in turn predation, human interference, disease, overhead wires, the growing use of artificial fertilisers, mortality on migration and climatic change, but could find no convincing evidence. He did, however, settle on changes in farming practice as being implicated. The mowing machine (before which scythes were used) was invented in 1814 and, after a small initial impact, gradually became popular so that by 1852 the machines were described as 'great favourites with Middlesex farmers'. The decline of the Corncrake marched closely with the rise of the mowing machine. In contrast to the use of a scythe, mowing machines moved quickly, often in a spiral pattern, so that the Corncrakes would be trapped in the ever-decreasing stand of grass in the centre of the field. Furthermore, speedy, early mowing opened the way to a second crop of hay, which also reduced the time available to Corncrakes to fledge their young or to lead them away to safety. Only in the extreme north and west, where hand mowing prevailed, was the status of the Corncrake unchanged. Norris also noted that the decline of the Corncrake was not confined to Britain and Ireland, but had occurred in several countries in northern and western Europe.

In 1978 the Irish Wildbird Conservancy organised a survey of the Corncrake in Ireland and this prompted the Trust, in conjunction with the Scottish Ornithologist's Club, to carry out similar work in Britain. The two reports (O'Meara 1979, Cadbury 1980) make depressing reading. Cadbury reported that of 730–750 calling birds, all but twelve were in Scotland. O'Meara reported the species to occur in the breeding season mainly west of a line from Belfast to Cork; the greater numbers were in Galway, Mayo and Donegal 'but nowhere could they be said to be numerous'. Both authors have drawn attention to the present importance to the species of small fields, and Cadbury emphasises that 61% of all records were from fields of grass cut for hay or silage. Since silage cutting is generally earlier than mowing for hay, the

Corncrake is even more jeopardised by modern farming practices. 'The future of the Corncrake, even in its present strongholds in western Europe, appears bleak' comments Cadbury, and one must agree. There must be adverse factors not yet discovered, for O'Meara reported: 'No correlation was found between silage making and decline in numbers and it is noted that the birds are now absent from areas where there is no such activity and little mechanisation.'

Reference has already been made to the loss of the Peregrine from its southern English eyries – a loss which coincided with the introduction of various farm chemicals (see Ratcliffe 1980 for an authoritative account), but other species were affected. The Sparrowhawk, for example, virtually disappeared from the south-eastern third of England so that, from being regarded as a pest species, it was given the special protection of listing on Schedule 1 of the Protection of Birds Acts. A similar fate befell the Barn Owl, and the Stock Dove became a scarce bird in many districts. These are all declines for which there is a known timetable, a generally – though perhaps not universally – agreed cause and, in recent years, a return towards the position as it was in the early post-war years. The improvement has been least in the Barn Owl and there is no room for complacency.

There are other species which have, or are believed to have, declined seriously in numbers, some fairly recently but others over a longer time scale. Ringing evidence has been interpreted as showing that the Wheatear population may have been declining since as long ago as the early 1950s (Spencer and Hudson 1979). A similar type of analysis of ringing figures (Spencer and Hudson 1978) offered some confirmation of the claim that Cuckoos are not so common as they were before World War II: that they may, in fact, have been declining since the late 1930s.

Of course, the Trust's Common Birds Census has revealed changes in the post-1961 fortunes of various species, the most profound ones being those of summer migrants which winter within the African Sahel zone. Different aspects of these are treated at some length in Chapters Three and Five, to which readers are referred.

COLONISATION OF BRITAIN FROM THE SOUTH

The year 1954 saw the publication of one of the most influential British bird books this century: *A Field Guide to the Birds of Britain and Europe*, by Peterson, Hollom and Mountfort. Until that event no readily available book gave details of a species which is today taken for granted by everyone – the Collared Dove. Fitter and Richardson (1952) came nearest to doing so in their *Pocket Guide*, where the 'Collared Dove or Domesticated Turtle-Dove' *Streptopelia risoria* is described and depicted, with a comment that: 'One such species (*S. decaocto*) has spread rapidly NW over Europe in recent years, and is now breeding in parts of Germany; if the spread continues at the present rate it may be expected to colonise the British Isles before long.' Prophetic words! So swiftly was the invasion forthcoming, so rapid the deployment from a bridgehead in East Anglia, and on such a scale, that even ten years later a new-comer to birdwatching could be forgiven for assuming that here was a founder-member of the British avifauna. In those ten years, as Hudson (1965) showed, the British and Irish population increased from four birds to a minimum of 18,855, aided by continued immigration. Dramatic though the spread was, and without parallel, it occasioned no real surprise, for in 1953 James Fisher had published a paper documenting the explosive way in which the Collared Dove (a bird of Asiatic origin) had burst out of a European footing in the southern Balkans at the beginning of the twentieth century, to race north-westward to the North Sea at Schleswig by 1949 and The Netherlands in 1948–49. Today no one knows how large the population is. In *The Atlas of Breeding Birds in Britain and Ireland* Sharrock estimated the 1972 population at 30,000–40,000. Since then, although the species has been demoted from the special legal protection of Schedule 1 to a place on Schedule 2, part II – the pest list – it cannot be open to doubt that on farmland the Collared Dove is more abundant than ever. Hudson believes that in urban areas the numbers may have stabilised or even declined slightly.

As a coloniser from the south-east, the Collared Dove is without rival if judged in terms of numbers, but it is far from unique. For examples, Black Redstart and Little Ringed Plover both preceded it: Cetti's Warbler, Firecrest, Serin and Mediterranean Gull have followed in its wake, while other species such as Fan-tailed Warbler are just across the Channel, ideally placed for a further leap forward should the conditions be propitious. We must look more closely at their fortunes.

Of those listed, the Black Redstart is by many years the senior species as a British bird, the first record dating back to 1829. Despite an isolated case of breeding in Durham in 1845 it remained a very scarce passage migrant for several decades. By 1871 a change had occurred, for Newton (revising Yarrell's *History of British Birds*) was able to describe it as a regular winter visitor to south-west England and the Isle of Wight, less regular along the coast eastwards to Norfolk, and a straggler inland as far north as Liverpool. *A Practical Handbook of British Birds*, published in 1920, regarded the Black Redstart as a regular passage migrant in autumn and spring along the south and east coasts as far north as Yorkshire, and in the Northern Isles, as well as being a winterer in southern England.

All these events precede the era of the Trust, and are but a prologue, for it is important to see developments in Britain in their European setting. Voous (1960) describes the species as having considerably extended its breeding range in Europe since the middle of the nineteenth century, probably to follow human cultivation and towns. He adds that it appeared in the plains of north Germany and Jutland in the second half of the last century and colonised the Danish Islands from 1890. The French *Atlas des Oiseaux*

Nicheurs de France (1976) describes the species as appearing in the Marne about 1880, in Anjou about 1950, and in the interior of Normandy as recently as 1958. It was recorded in 86% of all French atlas squares, compared with 73% for the Common Redstart. The eastern provinces of the Netherlands were occupied from about 1852, and by the time of the *Atlas van de Nederlandse Broedvogels* (1979) it was to be found in 63% of all squares (76% for the Common Redstart).

Thus, when the Black Redstart commenced breeding more or less regularly on the English south coast, from 1923 onwards, it was not an isolated event but part of a general drive northwards. There was no dramatic explosion of numbers, such as was to occur with the Collared Dove, and it was not until the second decade of the Trust that the species could be regarded as firmly established. The story of how the Black Redstart found the bomb sites of war-time London much to its liking is well known, but with peace and rebuilding there was a slow decline to a low point in 1962, when there were only 11 known breeding pairs. Since then it has demonstrated a willingness to adopt a wide variety of micro-habitats. Thus Morgan and Glue (1981) found that by 1977 Black Redstarts were holding territories on a considerable variety of industrial buildings including gas works, docks and warehouses, railway sheds and power stations. There was evidence, too, that it had finally broken out of the confines of south-east England, with records of pairs and territory-holding males in seventeen counties, and from as far north as Lancashire and Yorkshire. Even so, the annual numbers of pairs and territorial males combined seldom exceed 100, compared with a Dutch population estimated at 3–4,000 pairs. Perhaps the more appropriate comparison is with Denmark, colonised last century and a breeding population put by Dybbro (1976) in the Danish Atlas at no more than 200 pairs.

There are some interesting parallels between the history of the Firecrest as a British bird and that of the Black Redstart. The species have similar distribution in Europe and both occurred in Britain first as vagrants, then as passage migrants and later as winter visitors. There is even a 19th-century alleged breeding record (1863 in Windsor Park) to match the 1854 record of the Black Redstart breeding in Durham. Where these two species do differ is in the degree of conspicuousness, for whereas the male Black Redstart can attract attention by singing from the top of a tall building, the Firecrest is small and often hard to see as it flits about in the tree tops. Furthermore, in both appearance and song it is easily passed over as just another Goldcrest.

The Witherby *Handbook* describes the Firecrest as a 'fairly frequent visitor from October to April along the coast from Cornwall to Kent'. The species was also said to occur fairly frequently on the east coast as far north as Norfolk. A turning point in Britain occurred between autumn 1952 and spring 1953, when there were sufficient records to merit publication of a special analysis (Redman and Hooke 1954). These events fit into a clear European pattern, with north Germany colonised since 1900, first breeding in the Netherlands in 1928 (it now occurs there in 22% of all Atlas squares) and first breeding in Denmark in 1961. This last was the year in which four Firecrests, three of them singing males, were first discovered in the New Forest. Who knows whether or not they had been overlooked in previous years? It would be easily done. It was not until the following year that breeding was proved. Thereafter there was an annual presence of singing males, the numbers increasing slowly to about a dozen, with an isolated peak of 27 in 1969.

The recent fortunes of the New Forest population are not so well documented, but in 1972 there was a new focus of attention. Leo Batten, then a member of the BTO staff, returned from a spring holiday in the Mediterranean where Firecrests had been a part of the daily pattern of his life, and resumed a Common Birds Census in a wood in Buckinghamshire. Almost immediately he heard the by then familiar song of the Firecrest, and in the course of the season's fieldwork was able to locate four singing males – amongst many more Goldcrests. For four consecutive seasons the numbers increased, to a high point of 46 in 1976 and then, as in the New Forest, they fell back. More localities have since been discovered, and it would appear that the species is fairly securely established as a British breeding bird. Today, also, it occurs much more widely in Britain as a passage and a wintering bird, at which season it has even been known to visit gardens in Northern Ireland. The first Irish record was in Co. Cork on 7 December 1943 yet today the species is considered to be of almost annual occurrence in the country.

Next in sequence in the colonisation of Britain was the Serin, found breeding in Dorset in 1967, the first occurrence having been in Hampshire in 1852. Among the land birds, few species have so remarkable a record of spread. Said to have been on the move for two hundred years, in the last 90 it has spread from the Mediterranean lands to the north-east Baltic and beyond, adapting as it advances, so that the northerly populations are fully migratory. Olsson (1971) summarised the situation vividly in four sentences:

> The steady advance of the Serin from country to country defies adequate explanation other than that of genetic change in migratory habits. Climatic factors have been suggested, but if this were so surely many other species would have behaved in the same way. Furthermore the climatic range today of the Serin extends from mild humid maritime conditions in the west to Continental weather in the east, from the summer heat of North Africa and Asia Minor to the cold of Sweden and Finland. Equally, it seems impossible to show that sufficiently extensive and uniform habitat changes have taken place to the benefit of the Serin.

Set against so splendid a history of advance on the Continent, it must be admitted that the Serin's performance in Britain has failed to live up to expectations, although it is becoming of more regular occurrence as a migrant – November being the principal month, followed by May, October and April in descending order of records. The Witherby *Handbook* knew of over thirty records for England, two for Scotland and two for Ireland, whereas Sharrock and Sharrock (1976) were able to show 136 records for the fifteen years 1958–1972. Even so, the foothold appears to be tenuous: breeding not yet annual. Since the Danish population is also tiny, whilst the Dutch Atlas was able to report 350–400 pairs, it may be that climates which are both mild and of maritime humidity do not really suit this attractive little finch.

Of the four species of passerine colonisers we are considering here the most recent – Cetti's Warbler – shows every sign of being the most thrusting and successful. It, too, reached Britain in the process of a concerted drive northward through western Europe. At the start of this century it was confined, in France, to the Mediterranean coast and the Pyrénées-Atlantique. The expansion came in two waves. A first surge took Cetti's Warbler into the northern half of the Loire basin by 1927, where it virtually halted for twenty-five years. The second push north began in the 1960s, and in two waves: one up the southern coast of Brittany and the other north-east (inland) towards Paris. The English Channel was reached at several points by 1971.

As with the Collared Dove, the expansion of range by Cetti's Warbler characteristically takes place in a succession of relatively big leaps, the intervening areas being occupied only later. Thus, the first British record was at Tichfield Haven in Hampshire in March 1961, and two were recorded the following year; but 1963, the year of the Little Ice Age in western Europe, brought all expansion to a halt and it was 1967 before the next bird was recorded. By 1971 there were at least two pairs at Stodmarsh in Kent – a place which may be thought of as Cetti's Warbler's beach-head for the invasion of Britain. By 1973 there were at least 16 males, in two counties. Two years later the figures were 76 males and 3 counties, while by 1977 the score was 148 males and 9 counties and the following year 175 males and 12 counties. The frosts and snows of 1978/79 and of 1981/82 knocked the species back a little, yet in less than a decade it had occupied much of southern England and built up numbers larger than the Black Redstart had managed to achieve in a span of over fifty years.

This brief review of species which have moved into Britain from the south began with a non-passerine – the Collared Dove – and will end with another. As a British breeding bird the Little Ringed Plover belongs very much to our review period, yet the recent convert to birdwatching might well suppose it to be of long standing. Yet the Witherby *Handbook* lists no more than 16 records, the earliest being of two in Sussex before 1850; but it also records the unprecedented breeding of a pair at Tring Reservoir in 1938. It was in fact an isolated occurrence, there being no recorded repetition until 1944, when three pairs bred, but in Middlesex. The Little Ringed Plover's ability to cope with disturbance and to nest in busy areas has perhaps given it a special place in our affections: so much so that more than once an enquirer has asked of the BTO 'I suppose that you moved to Tring because of the Little Ringed Plovers?'

Sixteen authenticated records in about 90 years would hardly seem a promising basis for colonisation but, as with the other species noted here, it is necessary to look at the European scene as a whole. Once again a picture emerges of a steady and continuing push northwards. Even in France, where atlas work established that the Little Ringed Plover occurs in a quarter of all squares, it was nevertheless said to be still advancing, as for example into southern Brittany in 1954. In the Netherlands, according to Kist (1956), it bred only sporadically before 1925 but regularly since then, being locally rather common. By the time of the Dutch atlas fieldwork in 1973–75 the population was put at somewhere between 800 and 1,300 pairs. Thus, what happened in Britain from 1938 onwards was a reflection of western Europe as a whole, the colonisation by the Little Ringed Plover being steady rather than dramatic. Fortunately the species found, in the person of E. R. Parrinder, a veritable Boswell of a biographer, and the spread was documented in a series of papers between 1952 and 1975, of which that published in 1964 is perhaps the most helpful in depicting the build-up. Over the years it became difficult, if not impracticable, to collect all the information systematically, but the table which follows illustrates the trends more clearly and concisely than would be possible by mere description.

Spread of Little Ringed Plover in Britain

Year	*No. of pairs*	*No. of counties*	*New counties involved*
1938	1	1	Hertford
1944	3	2	Middlesex
1945	2	1	—
1946	4	2	Berkshire
1947	12–15	5	Essex, Kent, Yorkshire
1948	24	8	Suffolk
1949	27	8	Sussex, Buckingham
1950	29	10	Surrey, Lincoln, Derby
1951	38	10	Bedford
1952	(39)	13	Hampshire, Cambridge, Huntingdon, Stafford
1953	54	16	Gloucester, Northampton
1956	70	—	Oxford, Cheshire, Leicester, Nottingham
1959	98	—	Warwick
1962	157	—	Norfolk, Durham
1967	230	—	Lancashire
1973	477	—	Northumberland, Wiltshire, Worcester, Westmorland, NE Wales, 'Scotland'

Until 1962 the annual rate of increase was about 15%, falling later to a little over 10%. There has been no recent census, but it seems reasonable to project a present population of about 1,000 pairs.

Two factors, in particular, seem to have facilitated the spread of the Little Ringed Plover. Firstly, as already mentioned, it is remarkably tolerant of man's close presence and will re-lay if it loses a clutch. Secondly, it occupies an ecological niche which is not effectively filled by any other species. The 1973 survey located 187 pairs in sand and gravel pits, 27 on waste ground adjoining industrial plant, 20 on areas associated with mining (a northern feature, this), 15 at reservoirs, including those under construction, and 12 in minor categories. Only four pairs were found on river shingle and three on lake edges. The sites chosen were overwhelmingly artificial, and there can be no doubt that the spread of the species was particulary helped by the great post-war boom in building and the associated demand for vast quantities of sand and ballast. So often man's interests seem to run counter to those of birds: here is one of the exceptions.

During the period under review the Avocet and Savi's Warbler spread from the Continent to breed in Britain and appear now to be safely established. As former residents of England they do not really qualify as colonisers, and so their recent histories need not appear here.

COLONISATION OF BRITAIN FROM THE NORTH AND EAST

We have seen that colonisation of Britain from the south has been undertaken by rather few species, but that the numbers of birds involved were to be counted in tens, if not in hundreds or thousands. There have been many more attempted colonisations from the north or east, but generally speaking many fewer birds of each species have been involved and for few of them can one feel that they are now securely established members of our avifauna. If one accepts the presence of nest and eggs as criteria (i.e. attempted but not necessarily successful breeding) then at least fourteen northern species have attempted to establish themselves in Britain – chiefly in Scotland – in the fifty years of our review. In three cases the first known attempt pre-dates our period, but because the attempt continues it seems sensible to record the known starting point. Below, then, in tabular form is the list.

The list invites several qualifying comments. For example, the named regions suggest that colonisation has been overwhelmingly from the north rather than the east, the sole exception being the Little Gull. It is important

	County/country	*First year*	*Maximum possible pairs in best year to date*
Green Sandpiper	Westmorland	1917	1
Brambling	Sutherland	1920	4
Redwing	Sutherland	1925	53
Temmincks' Stint	Scotland	1934	6
Turnstone	Outer Hebrides	1938	1
Wood Sandpiper	Sutherland	1959	12
Fieldfare	Orkney	1967	12
Snowy Owl	Shetland	1967	1
Bluethroat	Inverness	1968	1
Goldeneye	Scotland	1970	37
Shorelark	Scotland	1973	2
Little Gull	Cambridge/Norfolk	1975	2
Lapland Bunting	Scotland	1977	16
Purple Sandpiper	Scotland	1978	1

to bear in mind that the localities named are for the first known breeding, and as we shall see later, some subsequent attempts have been in localities suggestive of an easterly origin. It should also be stressed that no species is listed in the table unless there has been at least one attempt subsequent to the first and under this rule the Great Northern Diver, for example, has been excluded. Five species are in the minimum possible category of no more than one breeding attempt in a year, and these can be disposed of first, in the order of listing. A Green Sandpiper chick was found in Inverness in May 1959 (Clafton 1959). The first Turnstone record is listed on the basis of a clutch of eggs (Hale 1980), and has not yet been accorded official recognition for the April date would be exceptionally early; however, there was probable breeding in Sutherland in 1976, when a downy chick was found but unfortunately not identified specifically. Of the Snowy Owls it may be said that although there was only one pair (or one male with two females) the site was used for nine consecutive years; but the old male concerned disappeared, although the site has continued to be occupied by females, with unfertilised eggs being laid in at least one year. The Bluethroat record is in some ways the most controversial in that it concerned a female flushed from a clutch of eggs; no male was ever observed. However, in 1980 a male of the Red-spotted form was singing in Inverness in suitable breeding habitat, while in 1979 a male, probably of the White-spotted form, held territory for six spring weeks in Nottinghamshire. Finally, there is the Purple Sandpiper, found breeding in the same locality in three consecutive years. In short, there is in all five cases evidence to suggest that the attempted breeding reflected part of a genuine extension of range, however gradual, as distinct from an isolated and atypical breeding attempt, such as that of the Bee-eaters in Sussex in 1955 (Barham *et al.* 1956) or the Moustached Warbler in Cambridge in 1946 (Hinde and Thom 1947).

Of the remaining species in the table, some will doubtless be limited in any possible future expansion by the availability of suitable terrain which is not too disturbed in the breeding season. Others, at least potentially, could become quite common British breeding birds, and it is to four of these – Redwing, Fieldfare, Bluethroat and Goldeneye – that we must return for a closer examination.

The first breeding of the Redwing in 1925 signalled no dramatic change. Subsequently breeding was far from annual, occurring, so far as is known, in only 17 out of 41 of the years up to 1966 and involving fewer than thirty cases. The years from 1966 onwards brought about a marked development. These were the years of active fieldwork for the breeding season Atlas which meant both that more observers than usual were active and that many little-known localities were explored in the process. Some of the recorded increase can perhaps be atributed to this extra effort, but there is little doubt that there was also a genuine increase in the number of birds breeding. In the Redwing we have a species with two well-marked races, the Icelandic (which comes as a winter visitor mainly to Ireland and the western half of Britain) and the Continental. Of what stock are the birds which are breeding in Britain? A pair which bred on Fair Isle in 1935 were judged to be of the Icelandic race, and since most of the breeding localities in Scotland lie within the winter quarters of those birds they might be thought the most likely colonisers. Kenneth Williamson, who was as skilled as any man at separating the two races in the hand and in the field, argued (1975) on theoretical grounds in favour of their being of Continental origin. For so long as the records were all from northern and western Scotland it remained possible that some, or many, of the breeding birds were Icelandic *coburni*, but that could hardly be true of a small community first found breeding in Kent in 1975. These birds seem certain to have been of Continental origin (a few pairs breed as near to Britain as Denmark) and so to belong to the category of colonisers from the east or the north-east.

Rather similar considerations apply to the Fieldfare. Although only one race is concerned, there are two populations which could equally well have supplied the colonisers: those breeding to the north of the Baltic (in Fenno-Scandia) and those of north-central Europe. It is this more southerly population which has been expanding steadily throughout our period, with breeding in Switzerland in 1923, France 1953, Austria 1964 and Belgium 1966. Regular breeding in the Netherlands began in the early 1970s, and colonies of 2–12 pairs now form in south Limburg. Thus, although the first few breeding records were from Scotland, and presumably involved birds from Scandinavia, later records from such counties as Derbyshire (1974), Kent (1978), Suffolk (1978) and Surrey (1979) must almost certainly represent a continuation by southern stock of the westward push across north-central Europe.

With the Bluethroat we find, again, a situation where there are two populations (races). The Red-spotted, Scandinavian, form may eventually succeed in colonising Scotland, although it should be added that there have been significantly fewer occurrences of the subspecies at bird observatories in the last two decades and it may well be a victim of the Sahelian droughts, referred to earlier. The White-spotted or southern race, on the other hand, breeds as near to Britain as the Netherlands. A nester in areas of reeds and sallows, it has benefited considerably (if temporarily) from the reclamation of the IJsselmeer, being fairly common in the Flevoland polders. This phase must gradually end as the polders are brought more fully into cultivation. When that happens it may be that some of the displaced birds will find congenial surroundings just across the North Sea, in East Anglia.

The Goldeneye's history as a breeding bird in Britain is quite different. No marked spread of population on the Continent is known to be involved and apart from a 1932 record in Cheshire, so atypical (in a rabbit burrow) as to seem improbable but for the fact of proper authentication, nothing happened until 1970 when a pair with young was found in Inverness. Since then the over-wintering birds have lingered longer on certain favoured lakes while the provision of nest boxes seems to have encouraged breeding. The report of the Rare Breeding Birds Panel for 1980 reports that in one county alone eggs were laid in 26 nests, 25 of them in nest boxes. With 165 young hatched in 1980 and 286 in 1981 there would appear to be the basis for a thriving British population in the not too distant future. Indeed, because Redwing, Fieldfare, Bluethroat and Goldeneye could all find suitable – even ideal – breeding sites in a number of counties they could become so well established as not to merit special attention in any possible centenary account of the changing status of our avifauna.

Before leaving the subject of colonisation from the north and east we must look briefly at some species which, like Savi's Warbler in the south, represent a renewed presence. Foremost in the list, in terms of publicity if not in actual numbers, must be the Osprey. Here was a species whose extermination in Britain was deliberate – in the sense that the collectors need not have taken eggs and specimens: it was a matter of greed. And what was lost by human concupiscence has also involved much deliberate assistance from man for the restoration (Brown and Waterston 1962). Kenneth Williamson (1975) proposed an underlying climatological reason why the Osprey should have returned to Scotland, but would it have succeeded, at all or so quickly, had it not been for the protective efforts of the RSPB and a vast army of volunteer wardens who have served over the years?

The Ruff and the Black-tailed Godwit are two more species which have recolonised Britain in our era, the godwit after an absence of about 100 years. So far as is known the last historical case of Ruff breeding in Britain was at

Cley in 1922, after which there was no record until 1963. In the early stages it seems likely that drainage rather than persecution started the decline. Later, undoubtedly, shooting, netting and the taking of eggs hastened the decline of both species. The actual return to Britain has obviously been unaided, but protective measures and strict secrecy have been necessary to afford the breeding birds maximum security. The Black-tailed Godwit, like the Redwing, has both an Icelandic and a Continental race. It is thought likely that the northerly breeding records – there are a few localities from Cumbria northwards – are from Icelandic stock, whilst those breeding in south-east England probably originated in the Netherlands. So far as is known there have been many fewer breeding attempts by the Ruff, at many fewer localities, yet there are grounds for believing that the population is slowly increasing. It is of interest that in both these species breeding has followed, or been associated with, a steady build-up in the numbers overwintering (Prater 1981) and that in the case of the godwit the increased overwintering seems also to be related to the increase in the Icelandic population. It should be added that with the build-up of the Avocet breeding population has come a steadily increasing population wintering in the south-west of England.

At least three other species appear to have recolonised Britain from the north in recent years (Murray 1979), in two cases the events being so unexpected – even improbable – as to be particularly gratifying. Earlier in this chapter reference was made to the drastic decline in numbers of the Red-backed Shrike and the Wryneck, of their retreat to the south-eastern corner of England and of the risk of their extinction. In 1965 two pairs of Wrynecks were found in Inverness in circumstances suggestive of nesting. Since that date the centre of interest has switched from south-east England to the north, with Wryneck pairs being located in a number of Scottish counties and breeding occasionally proved. For the Red-backed Shrike the position was so bad that by 1973 Bibby felt justified in entitling a paper 'The Red-backed Shrike: a vanishing British species'. Yet four years later, 1977, the Rare Breeding Birds Panel were able to report 'a very much better year than expected for this species'. Apart from Lincolnshire and Nottinghamshire there were records from four unnamed Scottish counties and nine other reports of single birds between late May–July in the Highlands 'which brings new hope'.

Since it is inconceivable that populations which are in drastic decline in southern England could suddenly start to colonise parts of Scotland some 500 miles from their natal area, it has to be assumed that this colonisation of Scotland by the Red-backed Shrike and Wryneck is from Scandinavia, from a healthy stock which is in some way unaffected by those factors, environmental or innate, which have led to the species' declines in southern England. It remains to be seen whether they have a long-term future in Scotland. The Reed Warbler, nesting in Scotland since 1973, may or may not conform to this pattern. With breeding occurring as far north as Orkney, a Scandinavian origin seems likely, yet it is also true that there has been recent northward expansion of the English population, with regular breeding now occurring almost to the Scottish border.

In recent years other species have been observed in Scotland during the breeding season, including Hobby, Red Kite, Nuthatch and Lesser Spotted Woodpecker. All could have been of English or Welsh origin, but they too could have been from Scandinavia or elsewhere in the north-west of the Continent. It is too soon to tell whether they were forerunners or vagrants.

CHANGES OF RANGE WITHIN BRITAIN AND IRELAND

> In April and May . . . the writer was prompted by Dr Robert Carrick to make a census of breeding Starlings within an area in south Cardiganshire which covered nearly 80 square miles. The area included a variety of habitats and two large villages with populations of over 1,000, but, in spite of a thorough search, not one Starling was seen. The local inhabitants had never heard of Starlings breeding in the vicinity and regarded their arrival as a sign of impending snow. Indeed 'aderyn-yr-eira' which is a common Welsh name for the species, means 'snow-bird'.

Few would guess, on reading the above extract from a paper by J. L. Davies (1949), that the year in question was 1947. Particularly of our common breeding species, we assume stability and it comes as a surprise to read in the same paper:

> The species has never become widespread since its arrival in the region as a breeder in the first half of the last century and, in spite of probable minor fluctuations in numbers, has still not colonised large parts of the region which seem eminently suited to such colonisation.

A subsequent short paper (Lloyd 1950) provided evidence that Starlings might have been slightly commoner in the late 1920s, but did nothing to alter the impression of a species very much less ubiquitous than the Atlas shows it to be today. That certain species, such as the Fulmar, have increased enormously in numbers and distribution in the last fifty years is well known. Many fewer people are aware that some common species have become much less, others much more, common during that same period of time. For example, most birdwatchers today would agree that the Blackbird outnumbers the Song Thrush, locally by 5:1 or more. It did not always do so. At the beginning of the century the Song Thrush was the commoner species and probably still was when the Trust was formed, although only just so. The relative abundance of these two species at a local level is discussed in *Birds of the London Area since 1900*, but ringing figures indicate that similar changes occurred nationally. At one time more Song Thrushes than Blackbirds were ringed each year, but gradually the numbers of Blackbirds came nearer to matching those of Song Thrushes. It is difficult to name a change-over year, but it can be said that it was sometime during the 1939–1945 war (when ringing was at a minimum), for since then the numbers of Blackbirds ringed

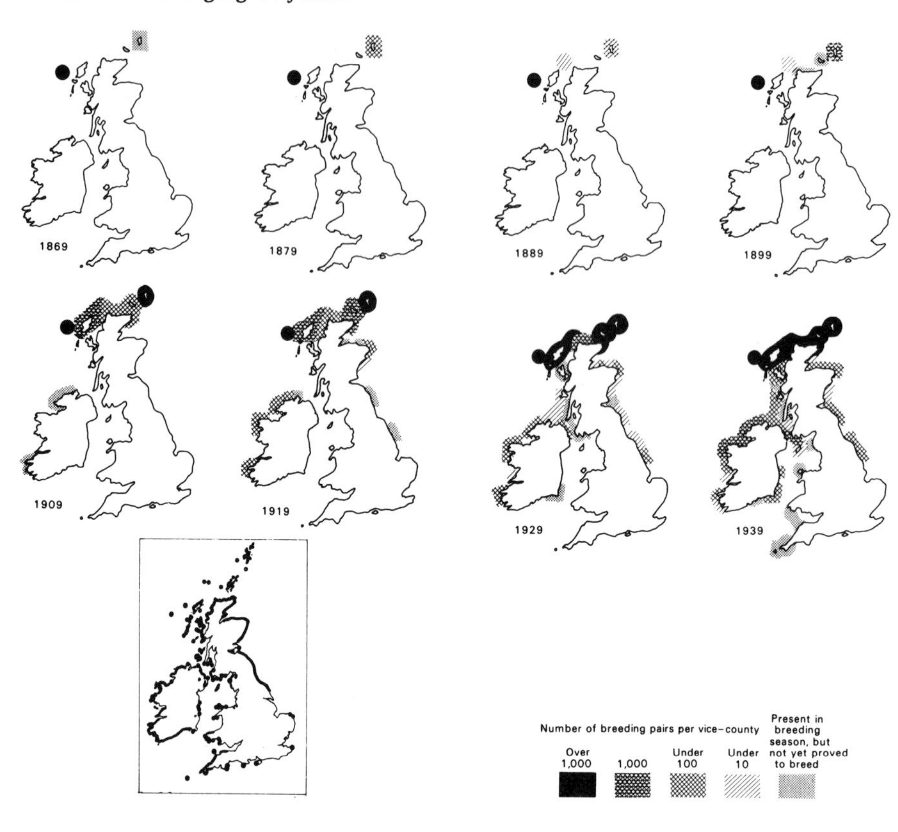

Fig 12 The spread of Fulmar in recent years. The small inset map indicates the breeding range, but not numbers, in 1972, from John Parslow's *Breeding Birds of Britain and Ireland*. From Fisher and Flegg (1974).

have always exceeded the numbers of Song Thrushes. It seems possible that there have been many such changes which have gone unrecognised and undocumented, yet many have been recorded and it is to some of these that we must now turn.

Reference has already been made to the Fulmar and its remarkable expansion of range. It is a species which might so easily have become the emblem of the BTO in place of the Gannet for, apart from an enquiry organised by J. A. Harvie-Brown in 1911, all the surveys since then (beginning in 1934) have been Trust enquiries, many of them under the dedicated direction of James Fisher. In some ways it could be said that the individual reports, packed with detail, make rather dull reading. They are rather like single frames in a ciné-film: each one is vital, but the picture only becomes animated when the film moves. Thus rather than poring over the details one turns to the sequences of maps which James Fisher prepared for his influential Pelican book *Watching Birds*, first published in 1941, or to the map, tables and summaries to be found in *The Seabirds of Britain and Ireland* (Fig. 12).

There are so many similarities between the fortunes of the Kittiwake and those of the Fulmar that we need not go into any detail. Suffice to say that it has gone some way towards circling our coasts as a breeding species, even to the extent of attempting to breed on dunes in Norfolk and (more successfully) on the pier pavilion at Lowestoft. The one significant difference between them is that, while the Fulmar has established numerous new colonies, much of the Kittiwake increase has been absorbed into the expansion of existing colonies. Indeed, the Kittiwake must have been increasing at about 50% per decade for at least half a century, before the truth dawned in 1959 – a sobering thought.

Several species of duck have extended their ranges or increased markedly in abundance during our review period. For example the figures provided by Parslow (1973) and Sharrock (1976) encourage the guess that the population of Tufted Ducks must certainly have doubled and perhaps trebled in fifty years. In doing so it must surely have been aided by the great development of sand and gravel pits, and of reservoirs, as discussed by Myrfyn Owen in Chapter Seven.

Two species which seem particularly to have thrived in the face of sustained persecution, first in Scotland and now in northern England, are the Red-breasted Merganser and the Goosander. The spread of the Goosander has been more dramatic and more thoroughly documented, so it will be followed here. Historically, it is another coloniser from the north, the first breeding record, in Scotland, dating back only to 1858 at the earliest, and possibly not until 1871 (Meek and Little 1977). By the end of the nineteenth century Goosanders were probably breeding over most of northern Scotland, but the advance southwards was slow. Dumfries, in the west, recorded first breeding in 1926. To the east, although there was nesting in Selkirkshire as early as 1930 the first proved breeding in the adjacent border county of Roxburghshire was not until 1967. Goosanders crossed the border southwards to summer in Northumberland as early as the late 1920s, but the first proof of breeding there was not until 1941. Thereafter the progress was steady and persistent. In Northumberland, Meek and Little estimated 90 pairs by 1973 and 130–150 pairs two years later. In the west, the first definite breeding in Cumberland was not until 1951. Ten years later the Pennine rivers of the county had been occupied, while by 1977 the breeding population was somewhere between 20 and 100 pairs. The expansion did not halt in Cumberland. In 1975 Meek and Little recorded 15 pairs in Westmorland and north Lancashire. Elsewhere a single pair were found nesting in Donegal in 1969 but the species had not increased its hold on Ireland by

1975. More important numerically was the position in Wales. Probably in 1968, and certainly by 1970 there was breeding in Powys (Montgomery). The first breeding for Radnor (also Powys) was in 1972, and in Gwent 1976, just possibly a year earlier. Thus, by 1977, Lovegrove (1978) was able to report a minimum Welsh breeding population of ten pairs and added that the species was already being persecuted on game fishing rivers such as the Wye and Severn.

The Red-breasted Merganser has followed a somewhat similar course. The first breeding in England was at Ravenglass (Cumberland) in 1950, after which the whole county was quickly occupied. Then followed Anglesey, the adjacent mainland of North Wales and South Wales. The reader is referred to Parslow (1973) and Sharrock (1976) for the details.

If persecution of the sawbills by fishing interests has been sustained and increasing, it is possible that, at least for a while, the Buzzard experienced a respite. Moore (1957) mapped its distribution in 1800, 1865, 1900 and 1954 (Fig. 13). Throughout the nineteenth century the pressure of the gin and gun drove the species ever westwards. In the twentieth century, and probably at an accelerating rate during the two world wars (when many of the large estates could not be keepered), this fine raptor was able to spread back eastwards, in some places re-occupying areas from which it had been driven before 1865. Regrettably, it is clear that game interests are once again persecuting this species, there being both direct and indirect evidence for the truth of this claim. Working on Speyside, and using a retriever dog which had been specially trained to search for poisoned baits, Picozzi and Weir (1976) established the cause of death of 47 Buzzards found within 20 km of their study area: 54% had been poisoned and a further 15% shot or trapped. The figures from ringing recoveries can be interpreted as indicating that the proportions probably apply to much of Britain.

Another raptor to make a come-back in Britain and Ireland is the Hen Harrier. It, alas, was extirpated in England during the nineteenth century so that by 1900 the survivors were confined to Orkney, the Outer Hebrides and to Ireland. In Orkney, where it was not persecuted, the species prospered and was later able to advance southwards again so that by about 1939 40–50 pairs had colonised the northern Scottish mainland. The timing was felicitous for, because of the distractions of war, they were not persecuted and hence able to spread rapidly. By 1960 Hen Harriers were well established in south-west Scotland and ten years later they occurred as breeding birds over most of Scotland and in parts of England and Wales. The spread was inadvertently assisted by man, for the many young plantations associated with the vast expansion of forestry provided them with ideal breeding sites where they have been largely free from disturbance. With much more tree planting scheduled to take place before the end of the century, and much rotational clear-felling and replanting, the future of the Hen Harrier seems relatively secure.

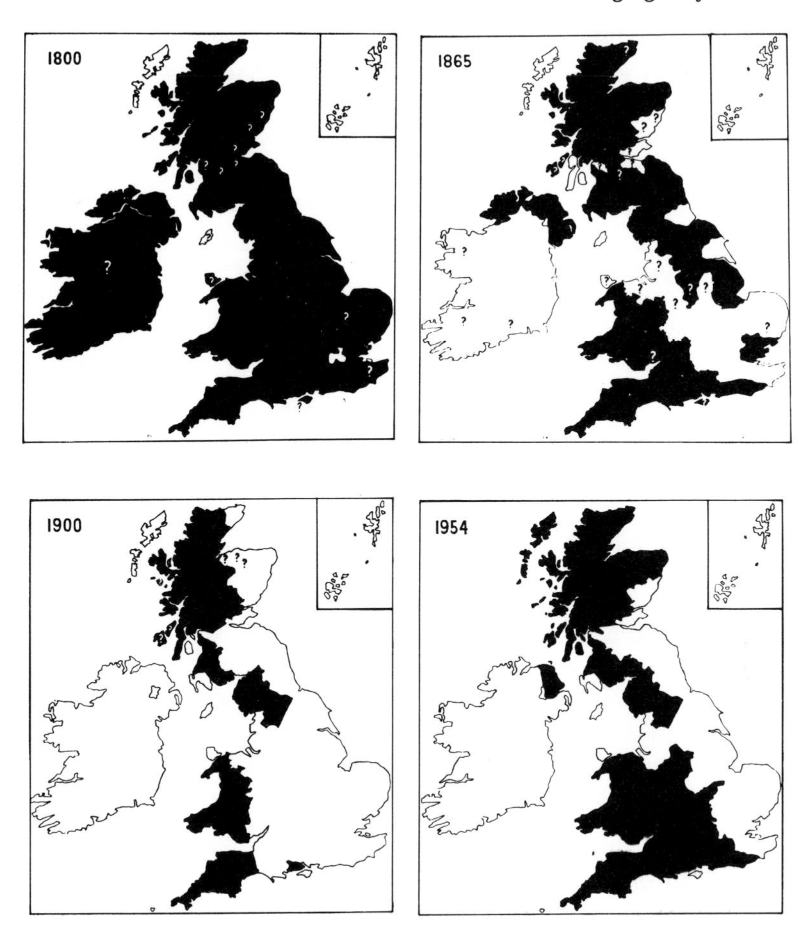

Fig 13 Changing distribution of the Buzzard. From Moore (1975).

Optimism of a more cautious kind was expressed by E. M. Nicholson (1957) when writing of another bird of prey which 'now appears to have a fair prospect of recovery under vigilant protection'. It was the Marsh Harrier, whose desperate plight earlier in the century was described by Nicholson: 'The level rose to 1 again by *ca*. 1908 and there was one brood reared in 1915, but in 1918 no nesting was even attempted in Norfolk, which was throughout this period the only British breeding-area of the species.' Happily, aided by protective measures the Marsh Harrier did make a come-back, with four pairs breeding annually in Norfolk from 1927–1936. Suffolk was re-colonised just before or during the 1939–45 war, with further nesting taking place in several other counties, and by 1958 the breeding population stood at 17–20 pairs, of which 12–14 were in East Anglia. There followed a swift decline, with no more than six pairs, as a maximum, from 1963–1966, and only two or three by 1970. In 1973 the Rare Breeding Birds Panel began to publish an annual summary and from then on these reports give the national picture, though bigamy in the species still makes stock-taking by pairs a little difficult, as the table reveals:

	Sites occupied	*Potential breeding population*	*Young reared*
1973	4	4M, 6F	16
1974	4	5M, 6F	10
1975	7	7M, 9F	18
1976	11	14 pairs	25
1977	13	16–17 pairs	44
1978	12	15M, 16F	34
1979	18	24M, 26F	39
1980	32	18–26 pairs	40

Thus the history of the Marsh Harrier in Britain this century is of a decline to the point of extinction, recovery to a peak in 1958, swift decline again to a dangerously low level at the start of the 1970s, and finally a rapid build-up. Persecution first brought the species to the point of extinction. Various explanations have been offered for the decline in the 1960s, including disturbance by coypu, and shortage of food due to the decline of the rabbit. Whatever the cause, the recovery has been astonishing and one must wonder whether the new breeding stock is entirely self-supporting, or whether there has been immigration.

The nearest likely source of immigrants is the Netherlands, and in that country there have been remarkable civil engineering developments since 1939 in the draining of the IJsselmeer and the creation of three vast polders (Anon 1959), as follows:

Polder name	*Approximate area (acres)*	*Year dry*	*Treatment comment*
Noord-oost Polder	120,000	1942	Neglected until 1945 because of war.
Oost Flevoland	133,000	1957	90,000 acres seeded with phragmites, mainly in 1958. Still 10 km^2 of reedbed in 1966.
Zuid Flevoland	100,000	1968	About 10,000 acres still intractably wet in 1981 and declared a reserve.

The phragmites is used in the reclamation process to prevent the growth of weeds, to hasten the drying process by transpiration, and to provide humus. Ornithologically it has produced a succession of magnificent breeding sites for wetland birds, including the Marsh Harrier. Some idea of the size of Harrier breeding populations in the Netherlands can be found by looking at the numbers ringed, although bias is always possible if there is special effort. Also there are bound to be annual fluctuations, and so a clearer picture of trends is obtained by taking the average of each five-year period from 1945 to 1979 (see below).

Even if there proved to be an upward trend and, potentially, an 'exportable' surplus in the Netherlands it would not establish a link with Britain. Now, due west of the Dutch breeding grounds (or the same flying range from Africa for returning harriers) lies the British breeding stronghold of East Anglia; transposition to the western shores of the North Sea could bring Dutch birds into that region. Five-year averages of the numbers of Marsh Harriers listed in the *Essex Bird Reports* (acknowledging the impossibility of eliminating duplication) provide a possible indicator of passage into East Anglia and afford comparison with the Dutch figures, as follows:

	Average annual ringing in Netherlands	*Average annual sightings in Essex*
1945–49	17·8	?
1950–54	31·6	5
1955–59	30·8	8
1960–64	20·4	4·8
1965–69	16·6	7
1970–74	58·8	11·4
1975–79	404	19

There is statistically significant positive correlation between the two sets of figures. This could indicate that the build-up of birds in Britain has been speeded by emigrés from The Netherlands. Alternatively, since the 1960s decline as described for Britain exactly matches the situation in the Netherlands, a common factor may have influenced both populations. It is difficult to escape the suspicion that here is another manifestation of pesticide damage to wild birds.

Bird ringers learn from experience that woodpeckers are usually very sedentary, so that movements of more than a few miles are exceptional. This might be a poor basis for range expansion yet both here and on the Continent there have been some very marked changes of range, both before and during our period of review. Baxter and Rintoul (1953) describe the Green Woodpecker as an uncommon visitor to Scotland and give fewer than 50 records. Earlier writers on Cumberland, e.g. Macpherson and Duckworth (1886), knew the Green Woodpecker as 'an exceedingly rare casual visitant', while to the south Mitchell (1885) reported only two districts in Lancashire where breeding was known to occur. Some time around about 1940 the Green

Woodpecker began to push north, but perhaps on a modest scale for in 1946 the journal *British Birds* published a short note (page 344) about an 'unmistakeable view of a Green Woodpecker' at Eaglesfield, Dumfries-shire. By 1976 the Atlas text was able to record an advance of over 200 km in 20 years, and the species continues to consolidate its position, though it may be feared that the setback caused by the cold winter of 1981/82 will take several years to make good.

The history of the Great Spotted Woodpecker is even more chequered. The Witherby *Handbook* describes it as: 'Formerly rare Cumberland and Westmorland: now generally distributed and increasing.' Of Scotland, the *Handbook* text reads: 'Became extinct about the middle of the 19th century, but since 1887, when bred in Berwick, has gradually increased and spread . . .' Baxter and Rintoul report (on the authority of Harvie-Brown) that the Great Spotted Woodpecker formerly bred as far north as Sutherland but became extinct between 1851 and 1861. Theories as to the reason for the loss proliferated but none of them was satisfactory. Harvie-Brown thought that the great increases in the numbers of squirrels and Starlings were contributory causes; other writers speculated that the decline was caused by the burning and destruction of old timber. Whatever the cause of the decline, an increase started about 1940, being no less dramatic than that of the Green Woodpecker. Inevitably, later writers sought a common cause. Oakes (1949), reviewing the position in Lancashire, came to the conclusion that tree felling *outside* his faunal area had deprived the birds of their habitats and thus led to an influx into his county. Unfortunately, this explanation inspires no more confidence than do felling and squirrels (two seemingly incompatible tendencies) as causes of the decline in Scotland.

It may be that some unsuspected and widespread factor is working to the benefit of woodpeckers, for the Syrian Woodpecker has long been moving north-westwards from south-eastern Europe – roughly in the track of the Collared Dove (Yeatman 1971); while the Grey-headed Woodpecker is spreading steadily westwards, with the first breeding record in Belgium being established during the course of fieldwork for that country's Atlas. Perhaps most remarkable of all has been the very rapid advance northwards and westwards through France of the Black Woodpecker, with breeding records from two of the Channel departments by 1979 (Cuisin 1980). The author concludes that 'in France (as elsewhere) Black Woodpeckers are modifying their habits and habitat'. If he is right, and if the trend continues, the first accepted British record of this fine bird may be imminent.

So many passerine species have extended their range within Britain in the last fifty years as to necessitate rigorous selection if this section is not to be overburdened. Although its range extensions have been relatively modest compared with those of some species, the Pied Flycatcher was the subject of a very thorough survey by Trust members, under the enthusiastic direction of Bruce Campbell, and this alone gives it a special claim. Moreover, there have been such coming and goings, such extensions and contractions of a range which is itself hard to relate to the European scene, that it merits selection.

Long before our day it was the subject of disagreement. Is there perhaps a note of something more than mere parochialism in the following claim by the authors of *Birds of Cumberland* (Macpherson and Duckworth 1886): '. . . while we learn from Mr F. S. Mitchell (B. of Lancashire p51), that the Pied Flycatcher is more scarce than formerly in Lancashire, we point, in reply, to its extension of breeding grounds in Cumberland, as showing that this species is working its way steadily northwards.' Bruce Campbell's careful documentation (1954) showed that a distinctive feature of this flycatcher's history in the 19th century was the number of disconnected breeding records in lowland Britain – in Hampshire, Kent, Surrey, Middlesex, Berkshire, Buckinghamshire, Norfolk, Bedfordshire, Lincolnshire, Rutland, Nottinghamshire and Oxfordshire. Such events happened irregularly, in the occasional big years, but they virtually ceased to occur after 1900. Thus the first 40 years of this century were 'a period of recession in terms of country records', but there were signs of increase in the west. The portents were not misleading. Bruce Campbell published a map of Pied Flycatcher breeding distribution in the years 1948–52. The fieldwork for *The Atlas of Breeding Birds in Britain and Ireland* occupied the years 1968–1972: exactly twenty years later. Even after making allowance for a much bigger labour force for the later survey, it is clear that there had been fairly marked changes during the twenty years.

The reasons for the increase are still somewhat obscure. Bruce Campbell, after considering various possibilities, settled on afforestation as the underlying cause, pointing out that the resurgence in the early 1940s coincided with the northward march of the woodpeckers. Voous (1960) says that the species established itself in central Europe only from the beginning of the 20th century, settling in parks, gardens and pine forests planted by man. Is this true of Britain? Perhaps not. The afforestation in Britain has been predominantly of conifers, which our Pied Flycatchers generally eschew. It is in the broadleaved woodlands, especially in oak, that they flourish. The one thing which can be said is that nest box schemes proliferate year by year and that generally speaking a high proportion of the boxes are occupied by Pied Flycatchers. It may simply be that the provision of numerous suitable nesting sites is leading to the production of a surplus population which is available to colonise new areas.

Our next species, the Bearded Tit, has experienced remarkable changes in fortune over the last 150 years. Records suggest that at one time it was relatively abundant in wetland localities in the eastern half of England from Lincolnshire southwards, but continual drainage in the 19th century threatened its strongholds, while its attractive appearance meant that it could be sold as a cage bird at 5/– a pair (Axell 1966). It needed only the added onslaught of collectors to reduce it to a dangerously low level before the end of the century. From 1895 it was protected by law, and the work of the Norfolk Naturalists' Trust led to the re-establishment of small but healthy populations in Norfolk and later in Suffolk. The Bearded Tit is particularly vulnerable to severe winter weather, and possibly more so to deep snow than to hard frost. Thus the hard winter of 1939/40 must have had a harmful effect; but because of war-time circumstances, with many coastal areas out of bounds, no census was possible before another severe winter (in 1946/47) hit the species again. For 1947 Axell put the survivors at 2–4 pairs. These hung on, and the population crept back to an estimated 50 pairs in 1952, but then the great east coast floods of January 1953 destroyed many breeding sites so that the population was almost halved. This time there seems to have been a rapid recovery, with an estimated 60 pairs in 1954, 108 pairs in 1957 and nearly 300 by 1962.

These growing numbers did not remain bottled up in East Anglia. In a series of autumn eruptions parties of Bearded Tits radiated outwards to establish colonies at suitable sites along the south coast, and by the time of the Atlas the species was thriving as far to the south-west as Radipole in Dorset, and, later, to the northwest at Leighton Moss in Lancashire. Now, once again, it is necessary to consider to what extent these rapid increases in numbers and range might have been influenced by events in nearby Holland, where the development of vast reed beds has already been described in considering the fortunes of the Marsh Harrier. Bird ringers in the Netherlands and in Britain soon found that they were catching increased numbers of the species. Thus in 1964 a total of 326 were ringed in the Netherlands, one of them subsequently being recovered in Britain. The following year no fewer than six were recovered in Britain. By 1973 the Bearded Tit population in the IJsselmeer polders was, in the words of Buker *et al.* 'many tens to perhaps some hundreds of thousands'. Of 1,668 Bearded Tits ringed in Britain that year seven were subsequently recovered on the Continent. Colonies were established as far north as Lake Tåkern in central Sweden where, by 1974, the numbers were estimated to be several thousand. Thus, again, what happened in Britain was part of a wider pattern of events in western Europe. Doubtless, severe winters will from time to time take a toll, and perhaps some of the more northerly populations will be wiped out. On the other hand, many of the colonies now established in Britain are in areas with winter climates less severe than that of East Anglia, so that there seems little likelihood of the species once more being confined to a few east-coast reed beds.

The final species to be mentioned in this section is the Redpoll. It was never localised in its distribution in the manner of the Bearded Tit but was, in Parslow's (1973) words, 'scarce or absent in parts of Midlands and southern half of England'. Thus in Suffolk in 1932 it was said to be less rare than was generally believed, while in Essex Clegg (1929) described it as 'still an uncommon breeder'. Nearly forty years later, Hudson and Pyman (1968) reported it 'scarce in summer but may be increasing'. Yet such was the explosive nature of the population growth when it came that the *Essex Bird Report* for 1975 describes the Redpoll as: 'Now a common breeder in an increasingly wide range of habitats'. It is convenient to highlight events in Essex in the interests of simplicity. That they reflect a general trend in southern England is to be seen in the population index figures for the Common Birds Census. Taking 1966 as 'normal' (i.e. index = 100), then by 1970 the figure was 224 and by 1975, after a succession of unusually mild winters, 360. A peak of 416 was reached in 1977 before the first cold winter for some time reduced the index figure to a mere 285. There has been, in fact, an exportable surplus, with populations of the British race becoming established in nearby Denmark and the Netherlands. In the latter country 2–9 pairs were breeding by 1961. In the period 1967–72 the Dutch breeding pairs numbered 230–375, whilst during the following quinquennium those totals had increased from 428 to 617.

It is generally considered that expanded afforestation has played a significant rôle in promoting the Redpoll's increase (Newton 1972), but fairly swift decreases can also occur. These appear to be associated with the failure of seed crops, especially of birch, and this factor almost certainly accounted for part of the decline after 1977.

CHANGES IN PATTERNS OF BEHAVIOUR

No review of bird changes in Britain during the past fifty years can afford to overlook some of the more striking changes which have taken place in the behaviour of birds. There is, for example, the process of urbanisation in birds; nowhere more marked and nowhere more thoroughly documented than in London, though it is occurring elsewhere. Cramp (1949) identified three factors which together determine whether a species can thrive in a town: food supply, suitable nest sites, and adaptability to human presence. Food supply, it must be said, is much influenced by man's activities. Air pollution is held to have been an important factor in driving certain species away from London, and certainly Cramp (1975) was able to show that subsequent to the passing of the Clean Air Act in 1956 there had been an increase in the number of species and the numbers of individual birds breeding in inner London. The cleansing of the River Thames had similar beneficial effects, as recorded by Grant *et al.* (1974). In this case it was not breeding but wintering birds which were involved. As an example, the figures for Redshank on the Thames between London and Tilbury in six successive winters from 1967/68 onwards (maximum counts) were 50, 100, 200, 958, 434 and 799 respectively.

Quite apart from the improved conditions arising from reduced pollution, birds have learned to exploit new feeding opportunities. Fitter (1949) mentions a Jay which was seen to enter a litter basket in Greenwich Park and emerge with a piece of bread; the practice, worthy of special note then, is now commonplace. The *London Bird Report* for 1957 records a Jay in Kilburn which was seen to pull up peanuts threaded on a string. Examples of versatility and adaptability could be multiplied almost indefinitely.

Cramp's second requirement for successful occupation of cities is a degree of flexibility or versatility over the selection of nest sites, and he mentions by way of example a 'clear tendency for both blackbird and song thrush in the parks to build at a greater height than normally'. Examples of more radical change abound in the publications of the London Natural History Society. Of Jays (which have been particularly successful adaptors during 50 years) it is recorded that two pairs nested in holes in trees in 1951, whilst the report for 1965 includes the entry 'Old Brompton Road, a pair with three or four young in nest on ventilator at No. 222 in June.'

Cramp's third and perhaps most crucial requirement is the ability in birds 'to adapt themselves to the presence of human beings, to stand the noise and disturbance, especially at nesting time, without becoming too confiding for their own safety'. The list of species which have been able to make this adjustment, notably during our review period, is impressive. In addition to the Jay, already referred to, the Magpie has become increasingly an urban bird, and in Manchester occurs at a higher density than in the adjacent rural areas (Tatner 1982). Kestrels have adapted well, and thrived too, if the numbers of pairs attempting to breed is of any guidance. In the area of the London Natural History Society, Montier (1968) obtained figures for the five years 1963–1967. In the first year he lists 10 definite, one probable and 16 possible pairs, making a total of 27; by 1967 the numbers located for each of these categories had risen to 98, 13 and 31 respectively, with the grand total at 142. The urban Tawny Owls, usually adapted to a diet in which birds rather than rodents predominate, have thrived in many cities, probably being less affected by the agricultural pesticides which so markedly damaged rural populations. Nor is this business of learning to co-exist in close proximity with man confined to the birds in our towns and cities. For most of our era the Great Spotted Woodpecker has been growing in boldness so that today it is a regular, and occasionally tyrannical, visitor to bird tables.

In all these examples which we have been considering it is arguable that a slowly growing tolerance of man preceded and facilitated the exploitation of urban habitats, this in turn leading to a net gain in the overall population. There are other species in which it seems possible that population pressure in the country as a whole has hastened the penetration of urban, suburban and other industrial areas. In some birds the two processes may well have occurred simultaneously, this seeming likely in the case of gulls. The Lesser Black-backed Gull has, in fact, undergone a further behavioural change chiefly during our fifty years. Formerly a total migrant, wintering along the coasts of Iberia and north-west Africa, in the 1920s a few adults started to winter in Britain, especially in Morecambe Bay. A special BTO enquiry carried out in the winters of 1949/50 and 1950/51 established a growth in overwintering numbers (Barnes 1952), a trend which still continues.

The whole subject of gulls wintering inland was taken up by Hickling, in three major BTO enquiries held at ten-year intervals, beginning in 1953. The scale – one might say the enormity – of the increase can be demonstrated in just two figures. In the roosts censused, the 1953 total of gulls was 333,000; twenty years later the total had grown to 923,000 (Hickling 1977). Moreover, a breakdown by species showed that all species were increasing, the large gulls at an even faster rate than the small ones:

	1953	*1963*	*1973*
Black-headed Gull	247,320	282,650	584,026
Common Gull	48,899	115,550	142,420
Herring Gull	35,383	46,600	114,981
Lesser Black-backed Gull	165	5,990	17,714
Great Black-backed Gull	2,532	4,925	13,688

These figures, it must be stressed, are for England and Wales alone and are for the inland roosts only, so that the total growth in numbers must have been considerably higher.

Behind such a rapid build-up in numbers there must lie improved food sources, and the growth of municipal refuse dumps has been identified as of key importance for the larger gulls. The mechanisation of farming, with more frequent tilling of the soil may be another factor: in most months of the year it is now possible to see gulls following the plough. Problems have followed in the wake of this big build-up in numbers (see Chapter Seven). Gulls, with Starlings, represent a major bird-strike threat at airfields. They represent a threat to human health in that they spend their days feeding on refuse tips and then roost at night on drinking-water reservoirs. Indeed, the availability of more and more reservoirs, offering safe roosting sites, has been suggested as an important factor in the increased numbers. Small wonder that there is more than one government-financed research programme into the pattern of gull activity! Nor is roosting on water the only way in which gulls represent a health hazard: Herring and Lesser Black-backed Gulls have taken to the rooftops as safe breeding sites and show every sign of being there to stay. In 1977 Monaghan and Coulson reported the results of a Trust-aided investigation carried out the previous year, making comparisons with an earlier survey in 1969. They found that some 3,000 pairs of Herring Gulls were by that time nesting on buildings, mainly in coastal towns. More important was the annual rate of increase in the habit: only 6% in south-east England, but in north-east England and south-east Scotland an alarming 29%.

In contrast to the noise and dirt of the large gulls we turn, in closing this section, to two passerines which have shown marked changes of behaviour in the last twenty or so years as well as becoming more common. The first is the Reed Bunting. In 1964 Kent published a paper showing that, despite the traditional breeding-season separation of the Yellowhammer and Reed Bunting into dry and wet ecological niches respectively, a survey carried out in Nottinghamshire in 1963 revealed a substantial proportion of Reed Buntings breeding in what might be regarded as typical Yellowhammer habitats; he postulated that this change might have come about by some change in the Reed Bunting's 'psychological' need for water. Whatever the cause, publication of the paper encouraged others to look, and it soon became apparent that adoption of dry habitats by Reed Buntings was widespread. In the 1960s and early 1970s, when the fieldwork was being carried out, the CBC index for the Reed Bunting was climbing whilst that for the Yellowhammer was not, and there was some possibility that high numbers alone were obliging young Reed Buntings, needing to establish territories, to seek elsewhere than in wetlands. This hypothesis finds some support from a further change in Reed Bunting behaviour: in the late 1960s Reed Buntings started to visit gardens in winter. At first they started to come in February and March, when natural food supplies might be expected to be running low; in later years the first birds would arrive with the first frosts, as early as November. At the peak, it was possible to see 20 or more Reed Buntings at once in gardens favoured for feeding, and they adapted quickly to the presence of humans in the vicinity, often continuing to feed after sparrows and finches had taken off in alarm. Reports of garden feeding came from many parts of the country, ranging from the south of England to Newcastle-upon-Tyne; although no formal enquiry was organised, it seems fairly certain that the practice of garden feeding was, and remains, widespread.

The final species to be dealt with in this section is the Siskin, a bird which increased enormously its numbers and breeding range in Britain during the post-war years. Like the Redpoll, it spread south to breed in counties where it had previously been only an uncommon winter visitor, but more than that (and more important in this particular context) it took to visiting gardens. The sequence of events was later investigated by Spencer and Gush (1973), who were able to trace the apparent start of the habit to Surrey in 1963. By 1971 the practice of visiting gardens had spread to nineteen counties, ranging from Sussex in the south to Aberdeen in the north, and westwards as far as Devon. As with Reed Buntings, Siskins tended to visit gardens late in the winter season (often March) when natural food supplies might be running low, and in gardens which they particularly took to they tended to linger into April or even May. If they returned in subsequent years, the tendency was for it to be progressively earlier.

Common to nearly all the gardens frequented by Siskins was the availability of red plastic bags filled with peanuts, and this fact invites speculation. In the wild, Siskins in winter feed very much on the seeds which they extract from alder cones, and a red nut bag could be thought of as an outsize cone – being of approximately the same shape. As such, it could represent a supra-normal stimulus, Siskins being in some sense pre-adapted to it. It can be shown experimentally that when green and red nut bags are hung out on the same tree it is the red ones which are found first. This observation opens up the possibility that Siskins learn quickly the importance of red plastic bags and then fly about the country looking for them – a process which Lukas Tinbergen termed having 'a specific search image' (see Gibb 1962). Certainly, some such explanation is needed to account for the speed with which the garden-feeding habit spread about the country.

CHANGES TO THE BRITISH LIST

Check-lists, it must be said, are part ornithology and part sociology. It is helpful for there to be an official list of birds for each country, and the *important* birds on such lists are those which breed or occur regularly on passage. Yet it is the vagrants which for many birdwatchers form the most *interesting* part of all such lists. The use of the word sociology may be justified on two grounds. Firstly, scientific ideas regarding taxonomy change from time to time. When the BTO was born ornithology was still struggling to free itself from the powerful influences of museum taxonomy. Thus, unlike the present-day *Handbook of the Birds of the Western Palearctic*, the Witherby *Handbook* was based on the race rather than the species, there being, for example, quite separate entries for 'The British Song-Thrush', 'The Hebridean Song-Thrush' and 'The Continental Song-Thrush'. Today, we lump rather than split, and if two species hitherto thought to be quite distinct are described by the experts (in the light of the latest research) as conspecific, then the list can actually decrease. On the other hand, we have accorded full species status to the Scottish Crossbill, Pink-footed Goose and Isabelline Shrike, all of which were formerly regarded as races.

It can decrease for another reason: hoax. There was in British ornithology the equivalent of the Piltdown scandal in anthropology, in which a succession of false records were published. Skins were usually available: it was not that the identification could be doubted, it was the provenance of those skins. The exposure of the fraud was undertaken by E. M. Nicholson, I. J. Ferguson-Lees and J. A. Nelder (1962) in a splendid piece of ornithological detection. The starting point was simple improbability: of the 219 occasional and irregular visitors to Britain listed in the Witherby *Handbook* 'no fewer than 28 – just over one-eighth – owed their inclusion solely to occurrences reported between 1903–1919 from a small area in east Sussex and west Kent, within roughly a twenty-mile radius of Hastings'. They became known as the 'Hastings rarities', and as a result of the publication of this paper 17 species and a dozen subspecies were removed from the British list. It had to be done, for a false science is no science at all. Yet it can also be added that 11 of those deleted species have now been restored, having been recorded again in circumstances which leave no room for doubt.

There is another justification for describing the British list as part sociological. Lists must, at least in part, reflect the skills, interests and enterprise of the observer force of the country. A truly remarkable number of species has been added to the list – it is correctly the British and Irish list – in the period under review, as the following table of decadal totals reveals:

1901–1910 = 20	1951–1960 = 29
1911–1920 = 5	1961–1970 = 27
1921–1930 = 5	1971–1980 = 20
1931–1940 = 4	1981– = (5)
1941–1950 = 5	

Of course there are genuine ornithological reasons why some of the additions to the list should have occurred when they did (see the complete list at the end of this section) and not sooner. The Collared Dove (1956), Cetti's Warbler (1961), Fan-tailed Warbler (1962), Penduline Tit (1966) and Trumpeter Finch (1971) are all species which are extending their ranges in the direction of Britain. American species, for the most part, cannot indulge in a creeping colonisation of Britain, so when more and more New World species are located in Britain or Ireland we must look for a different explanation. Kenneth Williamson suggested that the shift southwards in the position of the storm tracks across the Atlantic would tend to concentrate present-day American vagrants in the south-western sector from southern Ireland to Brittany, rather than in the under-watched northwest coast of Scotland. Equally important must be the human factor. For example, in 1956 the British Ornithologists' Union reported that it had come to the conclusion 'that the possibility of so-called "assisted passage" should not necessarily deny to a bird the right of admittance to the British List (see *Ibis* 98: 156–7)'. This meant that the small New World passerines which had hitherto been banned from consideration on the ground that they could not fly the Atlantic without a lift could now be accepted – retrospectively if necessary – provided that the full authenticating data were still available.

Part of the remarkable spurt in the post-war years must be due to the growth of the bird observatories network, for only Skokholm and the Isle of May were operational before the war. Apart from such factors one may also mention improved optical equipment, improved field guides and the fact that there is today much more international travel. Species met with overseas are more readily recognised when they turn up in Britain. Perhaps, too, there is such a thing as fashion or cult. Thirty years ago gulls were gulls: rather boring because one had to take pains to look carefully in order to identify them, and definitely not worth the trouble. The attitude has changed.

Nowadays it is appreciated that in amongst a flock of Black-headed Gulls may be a species superficially similar but from the New World. In all probability these American visitants (as the old bird books would term them) have been coming since the earliest days of ornithology. And when attitudes change there is an automatic feed-back mechanism (one hesitates to describe it as a vicious circle), for the more that people look so the more they are apt to find, whilst the more that is found the more people are prepared to look.

Additions to the list (other than naturalised species such as the Ruddy Duck) must nowadays all be rarities at the time of their arrival, and attitudes to rarities vary. Some high-minded ornithologists, not all of them professional, are apt to dismiss them as meaningless. For many, they are the highlight of each year's birdwatching; in that growing fraternity awarded the ungracious name of 'twitchers' they are the whole reason for birdwatching, worth travelling anywhere and at any time to see. Between the extremes there is, as always, a middle road. In two invaluable summaries and analyses (Sharrock 1974, Sharrock and Sharrock 1976) the authors demonstrated that whilst isolated records of scarce or rare birds may seem meaningless, when they are collected and collated at a national level, patterns – unsuspected patterns – start to emerge.

Today we are able to detect the almost simultaneous arrival on coasts from Norfolk to Fair Isle of, for example, Pallas's Warblers, as happened in October 1982. Here is a species which breed nowhere nearer to Britain than about 85°E, or roughly on the longitude of Calcutta. We know little enough about the route taken by these waifs before they reach Britain, a journey of some 6,000–7,000 km, and can only speculate why they should turn up in such numbers and regularity when their winter quarters lie in south-east Asia (Rabøl 1969). Only the long-term collection of records, carefully and laboriously vetted and assembled by that institution of our times, the *British Birds* Rarities Committee, can provide future migration researchers with the raw material on which to base their studies and test their hypotheses. Let us not make the mistake of dismissing the interest of rare birds as lying solely in the problems of their identity.

More than once in this chapter mention has been made of major changes in our bird fauna which escaped detection for several years. Despite the existence of the BTO, a countrywide network of county and local societies, and the growing chain of RSPB members groups, significant increases and decreases could still occur undetected unless we watch out for them. The world of birds is a world of change, of advance and retreat, of adaptation and decline. This guarantees a future in which birdwatchers of all persuasions will always find their challenges.

Acknowledgements Some of the research on which this chapter is based was carried out in preparation for London University Extra-Mural classes at Morley College, which I shared with Adrian Cawthorne. I am most grateful to him for a stimulating partnership. Dr Jan Wattel of the Free University of Amsterdam drew my attention to the interesting paper by Kist and kindly translated its contents. Dr Tim Sharrock, who has done as much as any man in recent years to collect, collate and interpret bird records and would have been the ideal author of this chapter, read my draft text and saved me from some errors as, later, did my long-time friend and colleague Bob Hudson. To all of them I express my gratitude, whilst stressing that responsibility for errors as yet undetected, for the choice of what to include and what to omit (the scope is enormous), and for interpretation of facts, lies solely with me.

Finally, I hope it will not be thought out of place in a volume such as this if I pay tribute to three friends, the late Dick Cornwallis, the late Ken Williamson and the editor of this volume, Ron Hickling, for in their great company I cut such ornithological wisdom teeth as I possess. They were a constant source of enthusiasm and inspiration and if I could believe that in this chapter I had caught something of their infectious attitude to birds and bird research I should indeed be gratified.

NEW BIRDS TO BRITAIN AND IRELAND

1901 (none).
1902 *Allen's Gallinule* (Jan) off Norfolk. *Arctic Warbler* (Sept) Orkney. *Rock Bunting* (Oct) Sussex.
1903 *Bairds Sandpiper* (Sept) Norfolk. *Red-flanked Bluetail* (Sept) Lincs.
1904 *Citril Finch* (Jan) Norfolk.
1905 *Slate-coloured Junco* (May) Clare. *Sandhill Crane* (Sept) Cork. *Yellow-breasted Bunting* (Sept) Norfolk. *Dusky Thrush* (Oct) Notts.
1906 *Red-rumped Swallow* (June) Fair Isle. *Greater Yellow Legs* (Sept) Scilly.
1907 (none).
1908 *Pallas's Grasshopper Warbler* (Sept) Dublin. *Belted Kingfisher* (Nov) Cornwall. *Brünnich's Guillemot* (Dec) Lothian.
1909 *White-throated Sparrow* (May) Outer Hebrides. *Black-winged Pratincole* (Aug) Yorks. *Pied Wheatear* (Oct) Isle of May. *Lanceolated Warbler* (Nov) Lincs.
1910 *Blyth's Reed Warbler* (Sept) Fair Isle.
1911 *Thrush Nightingale* (May) Fair Isle. *Pine Bunting* (Oct) Fair Isle. *Madeiran Petrel* (Nov) Hants.
1912 *Black Wheatear* (Sept) Fair Isle.
1913 *Dusky Warbler* (Oct) Orkney.
1914–1920 (none).
1921 *Blue-cheeked Bee-eater* (July) Scilly.
1922 (none).
1923 *Laughing Gull* (July) Sussex.
1924 (none).
1925 *Pechora Pipit* (Sept) Fair Isle. *Paddyfield Warbler* (Oct) Fair Isle.
1926 (none).
1927 *Common Nighthawk* (Sept) Scilly.
1928–1930 (none).
1931 *Pallid Harrier* (May) Fair Isle. *Bridled Tern* (Nov) Kent.
1932–1935 (none).
1936 *Booted Warbler* (Sept) Fair Isle. *Black and White Warbler* (Oct) Shetland.
1937–1945 (none).
1946 *Moustached Warbler* (Aug) Cambridge.
1947 *Collared Flycatcher* (May) Shetland.
1948 *Olive-backed Pipit* (Apr) Skokholm. *Bonelli's Warbler* (Aug) Skokholm.
1949 (none).
1950 *Isabelline Shrike* (Sept) Isle of May.
1951 *Terek Sandpiper* (May) Sussex. *Olivaceous Warbler* (Sept) Skokholm. *Red-eyed Vireo* (Oct) Wexford.
1952 (none).
1953 *Magnificent Frigatebird* (July) Inner Hebrides. *Semipalmated Sandpiper* (July) Norfolk. *Gray-cheeked Thrush* (Oct) Fair Isle.
1954 *Black Duck* (Feb) Kilkenny. *Royal Tern* (March) Dublin. *Stilt Sandpiper* (Aug) Spurn. *Wilson's Phalarope* (Oct) Fife. *Citrine Wagtail* (Sept) Fair Isle. *Baikal Teal* (Sept) Fair Isle. *Siberian Thrush* (Oct) Isle of May. *Common Yellowthroat* (Nov) Lundy.
1955 *Yellow-rumped Warbler* (Jan) Devon. *Ring-necked Duck* (March) Glos. *Sardinian Warbler* (May) Lundy. *Thick-billed Warbler* (Oct) Fair Isle.
1956 *Lesser short-toed Lark* (Jan) Kerry. *Olive-backed Thrush* (May) Mayo. *Western Sandpiper* (May) Fair Isle. *Collared Dove* (July) Norfolk.
1957 *Summer Tanager* (Sept) Bardsey. *Rose-breasted Grosbeak* (Nov) Antrim.
1958 *Northern Waterthrush* (Sept) Scilly. *Northern Oriole* (Oct) Lundy. *American Purple Gallinule* (Nov) Scilly.

1959 *Song Sparrow* (Apr) Fair Isle.
1960 *Slender-billed Gull* (June) Sussex.
1961 *Cetti's Warbler* (March) Hampshire. *Calandra Lark* (April) Portland Bill. *Fox Sparrow* (June) Copeland. *River Warbler* (Sept) Fair Isle.
1962 *Fan-tailed Warbler* (Apr) Cape Clear. *Bimaculated Lark* (May) Lundy. *Bobolink* (Sept) Scilly.
1963 *Pied-billed Grebe* (Dec) Somerset.
1964 *Yellow Warbler* (Aug) Bardsey. *Eyebrowed Thrush* (Oct) Northants.
1965 (none).
1966 *Rufous-sided Towhee* (June) Lundy. *Spanish Sparrow* (June) Lundy. *Northern Parula* (Oct) Scilly. *Penduline Tit* (Oct) Spurn. *Brown Thrasher* (Nov) Dorset.
1967 *Cretzschmar's Bunting* (June) Fair Isle. *Little Swift* (June) Cape Clear. *American Redstart* (Oct) Cornwall.
1968 *Blackpoll Warbler* (Oct) Scilly. *Spectacled Warbler* (Oct) Spurn.
1969 *Evening Grosbeak* (March) Outer Hebrides. *Short-toed Treecreeper* (Sept) Dungeness.
1970 *Franklin's Gull* (Feb) Hants. *Hooded Warbler* (Sept) Scilly. *Scarlet Tanager* (Oct) Scilly. *Veery* (Oct) Cornwall. *Desert Warbler* (Dec) Portland.
1971 *Trumpeter Finch* (May) Minsmere.
1972 (none).
1973 *Ring-billed Gull* (March) Glam. *Ovenbird* (Oct) Shetland.
1974 (none).
1975 *Hermit Thrush* (June) Fair Isle. *White-tailed Plover* (July) Warks. *Tennessee Warbler* (Sept) Fair Isle. *Yellow-bellied Sapsucker* (Sept) Scilly. *Siberian Rubythroat* (Oct) Fair Isle.
1976 *American Kestrel* (May) Fair Isle. *Pallas's Reed Bunting* (Sept) Fair Isle.
1977 *White-crowned Sparrow* (May) Fair Isle. *Cape May Warbler* (June) Strathclyde. *Eleanora's Falcon* (Aug) Merseyside. *Rüppell's Warbler* (Aug) Shetland.
1978 *Pallid Swift* (May) Kent. *Semipalmated Plover* (Oct) Scilly. *Greater Sand Plover* (Dec) Sussex.
1979 *Aleutian Tern* (May) Northumberland.
1980 *Forster's Tern* (Feb) Cornwall. *Yellow-browed Bunting* (Oct) Fair Isle.
1981 *American Coot* (Feb) Cork. *Rock Sparrow* (June) Norfolk. *Pacific Swift* (June) off Norfolk. *Hudsonian Godwit* (Sept) Humberside. *Magnolia Warbler* (Sept) Scilly.

5: Movement and migration

Ronald Hickling

Yea, the stork in the heaven knoweth her appointed times; and the turtle and the crane and the swallow observe the time of their coming – *Jeremiah*

Doth the hawk soar by thy wisdom and stretch her wings toward the south? – *The Book of Job*

In 1964 Sir Landsborough Thomson wrote: 'The broad fact of migration has been known from ancient times.' The quotations from the Old Testament which head this chapter bear this out, for they were already received wisdom when they were written down some two and a half thousand years ago. The 'broad fact' has changed little since that time, although often encrusted with legend. Only in the past one hundred years or so have serious migration studies been carried out, and some progress made in elucidating details. Six broad areas of study were listed by Thomson within which he thought such progress had been made. The Trust has been actively engaged in three of them, and a summary of its discoveries is given in this chapter.

A knowledge and understanding of breeding distribution and of patterns of winter distribution are, Thomson emphasised, an essential part of migration studies. These subjects have always been an essential feature of the Trust's work. The Breeding Atlas (1976) has proved especially valuable in this connection, especially in showing the limits of the range of many species. Many detailed studies of the distribution of migrant species have also been made, of which the Pied Flycatcher is a good example. It is, perhaps, in investigations of birds in winter that the Trust's most important contributions have been made – into waders on estuaries, gulls inland in winter,

Starling roots, overwintering of 'summer' migrants such as the Blackcap, and so on. These have opened up new dimensions for the student of migration.

OBSERVING VISIBLE MIGRATION

To watch migration actually in progress at some particularly favoured observation point has long excited the imagination of men. Thus modern birdwatchers cross Europe in large numbers to gather at one such place, the Turkish Bosphorus, which was of course known long before the advent of the package holiday tour. Here in autumn are concentrated in enormous numbers most of the birds of prey and the storks of eastern Europe, which 'stretch their wings to the south' on the rising air of thermals, providing a spectacle hard to equal in this hemisphere. Those who pass from wonder to study, as have Richard Porter and his colleagues, have added enormously to our understanding of what R. E. Moreau called 'the Palaearctic–African bird migration system', here at the eastern gateway into Africa.

There is still much to discover about migration in this way in Britain. Those indefatigable Scottish ladies, the Misses Rintoul and Baxter, described a day on the Isle of May in October 1926 in their book *A Vertebrate Fauna of Forth* (1935):

> As soon as there was even an apology of daylight out we went, and found the island swarming with birds. No words can describe the multitudes: redwings were the most plentiful species, the island was thick with them, great flocks were coming in from the north-east, lighting on the island for a few minutes and then passing on to the south-west. Innumerable flocks passed over the island in the same line without stopping; looking up into the sky we could see them flock above flock as far as the eye could reach.

This passage is quoted by Sir Landsborough Thomson in his own book *Bird Migration: a short account* (1936), and he then goes on to describe an experience of his own on another October day at the observatory of Rossitten (now Rybachiy) on the eastern Baltic coast:

> Some twenty or more thousand [crows] must have passed in the course of the day. It was not merely the vastness of the numbers that made the scene so impressive, but the fact that all these thousands were moving together with one accord, without great speed or appearance of haste, yet without halt or deviation and still more noticeably without noise.

Observations such as these stimulated the enthusiasm for bird observatories which were such a feature of our islands in the 1950s and 1960s: the sight, perhaps, of the unceasing day-long passage of swallows over the mud-flats of the Wash, or on some fine autumn morning finding the *Suaeda* bushes of the north Norfolk coast alive with warblers, or watching at some south coast headland as flocks of small birds hesitatingly flew out and back until they overcame their fears and set off strongly over the sea.

Many important discoveries have been made by straightforward observation in this way. For example, David and Elizabeth Lack wanted to find out whether migrants crossed over the high passes of the Pyrénées. On a memorable day in October 1950 – David Lack described it in a volume entitled *Discovery* 'in which each naturalist contributor was asked to describe the most memorable day in his life' – they climbed to the summit of the Port de Gavarnie, high above the fearsome Cirque de Gavarnie, 7,500 feet above sea-level and only fifty yards wide.

> We settled in the shelter of a tall rock at the top of the pass, looking back down the valley, toward France . . . In the next three hours we counted, in all, some 200 Goldfinches, 100 Linnets, and 30 Serins . . . There were also a few Meadow Pipits, White Wagtails, and Skylarks, making in all nearly 800 small birds in the three hours . . . Flocks of Woodpigeons started passing at noon, and in all we saw 500 of them, together with a few Stock Doves . . . The steady passage of small birds at so high and bleak a spot . . . established beyond doubt that small songbirds migrate through the High Pyrenees.

More sophisticated methods of observing directly the migrations and movements of birds are now available. The outstanding example is the use of radar. For some years Lack directed an extensive research programme into migration over the North Sea by this method, and discovered things which could have been found out in no other way. It was, of course, only part of the truth, as he was himself always quick to point out. Nevertheless, it seemed to have an inhibiting effect on studies carried out at observatories, and this will be discussed later. Radio-telemetry is another technique which undoubtedly has an important future in studies of movement.

A form of direct observation which always seems slightly suspect to many British birdwatchers is moon watching. Our weather conditions in Britain are not conducive to this form of observation, but in the more stable weather conditions of the United States some remarkable studies have been carried out by this means.

THE STUDY OF MIGRATION THROUGH RINGING

The Trust has been deeply involved in this, the most important area of study selected by Sir Landsborough Thomson and a technique of which he was one of the great pioneers. Organised ringing in this country began in 1909, and it is astonishing that two separate and independent schemes were born in the same year: one by Witherby through his magazine *British Birds*, and the other by Thomson from Aberdeen University. The latter became a casualty of World War I, but Thomson then became active in the *British Birds* scheme. After the Trust assumed responsibility for ringing in 1937 he became Chairman of the Ringing Committee and retained that office until 1965.

During the first few years it was inevitable that ringing numbers were low and recoveries few. Nevertheless some of the early recoveries resulted in startling discoveries, and by 1926 Thomson thought them important enough to form the basis of his book *Problems of Bird Migration*.

In 1937, when the Trust took over management of the national ringing scheme, something over 500,000 birds had been ringed – a respectable total. But by the end of 1982 the number had grown to nearly 14½ millions, and recoveries numbered more than 330,000.

The handling of this enormous mass of data has been a major task for the Trust during most of its existence. It has needed more manpower than any other Trust project. For many years recording and analysis were manual – often (at certain times of the year) a boring routine, but accepted cheerfully by a staff composed of practical ringers, so that they appreciated and were motivated by the value of the end results. Eventually an adequate computer was installed and some of the boredom of routine was mitigated. Information can now flow more rapidly from the valuable store of ringing data. In spite of this it must always be remembered that the computer's ability to process rapidly a mass of complex material does not alter its essential role. It is a tool to aid the interpretation of data which must be gathered through fieldwork.

A comprehensive annual report presents a summary of the ringing scheme, and the most important feature of the report is a detailed list of important recoveries, with information on place of ringing and recovery, age of bird, speed of passage, and much other information in coded form. These reports are a basic source for migration studies carried out by many workers. The reports also summarise the whole ringing history of some species, with maps plotting all recoveries over lengthy periods. These invaluable items are difficult to produce and thus only a few can be prepared each year; here the computer proves an invaluable tool. Chris Mead's booklet 'Bird Ringing' (*BTO Guide* 16, 1974) presents some of the results for non-ringers in the form of similar maps, and some are reproduced later in the present chapter. For a number of years now the journal *Ringing and Migration*, published twice a year, has included papers based on ringing results and from the field experiences of individual ringers.

The act of ringing a bird is a brief interruption of its life journeyings. When a full-grown bird is caught, and identified with its individually-numbered ring, a point in time and space in its wanderings has been established. If the bird is later found dead then a final reference point has been discovered; if it is recaptured by a ringer and released after its ring number has been recorded there are opportunities for even further points to be discovered. If the bird is ringed as a nestling the beginning of its journeyings is known, and later perhaps the end of those journeys. But what happens in between is the great mystery. When these points are plotted upon a map there is an almost irresistible compulsion on the map-maker to join the two points with a line. This is a graphic device which should not be taken to show the route followed by the individual bird. Nevertheless, by these means a broad picture begins to emerge in time: slowly some of the mist begins to clear.

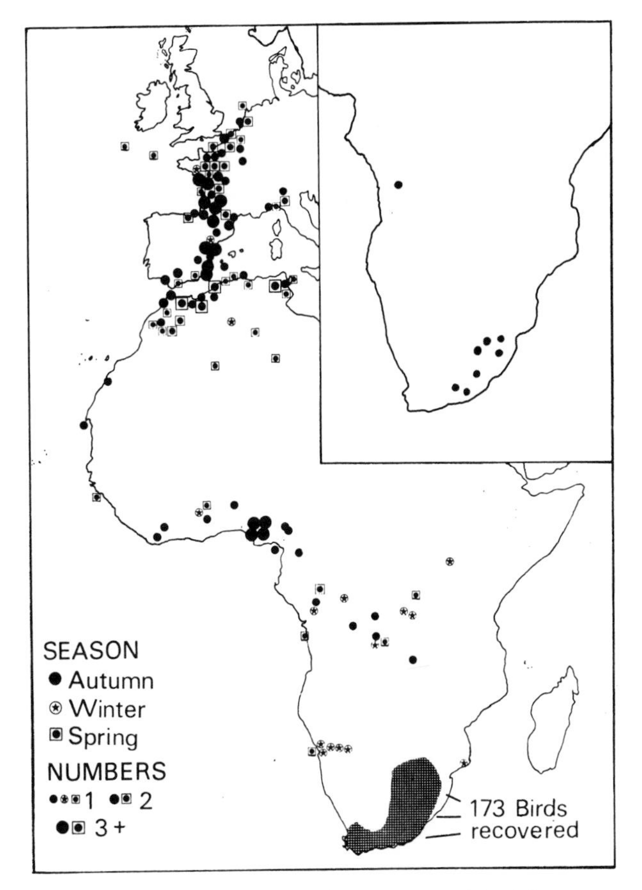

Fig 14 Swallows from Britain recovered in Africa.

WINTER IN AFRICA

The ornithological world was startled in 1961 when R. E. Moreau, in a paper published in *Ibis* that year, estimated the numbers of birds entering Africa each autumn 'from that part of Europe which lies directly to the north' at 600 million. 'A large proportion of all the insectivorous birds breeding in the Palaearctic region winter in Africa south of the Sahara,' (he wrote), a journey 'potentially the most arduous to be performed regularly by a mass of land-birds anywhere in the world.' He admitted later (1972) that they were figures 'tossed in the air'. Nevertheless they gave some indication of the enormous numbers involved. On this basis the number of birds leaving the western part of Europe through Iberia and France (thus including birds from, and passing through, Britain), and taking the African coast opposite that part of Europe as roughly 1,000 miles, would total some 250 million birds. Out of this enormous mass of birds we ringed in one year (1980) a mere 180,000. They leave our shores and few are ever heard of again. Where do they go? Ringing returns are few, very few; for examples, the recovery rates for Tree Pipit and Grasshopper Warbler are less than two birds for every thousand ringed. Yet such recoveries, however few, fire the imagination of every birdwatcher. And if some of the interpretations we build on these meagre African recoveries are speculative, is this not leading to an enlargement of our human attempts at understanding the lives of a group of animals who share our world and command our affections?

The Swallow, most delightful of birds, has always been an especial favourite of ringers. Its nests in farm buildings are easy to discover and are readily accessible; large numbers of nestlings can thus be ringed with little effort. In addition the mist-net has enabled many Swallows to be ringed at their autumn roosts, when for brief periods enormous numbers gather nightly in reed beds. By the end of 1980 over three-quarters of a million Swallows had been ringed. The recovery rate of birds from their winter quarters in southern Africa has also been gratifyingly high – partly because in that area there is considerable activity by South African ringers, and also because Swallows obligingly repeat there the communal roosting habit they show in Britain in autumn. The first Swallows were found in Africa soon after the ringing scheme was started. 'Few recoveries,' wrote Mead (1974), 'can have caused such excitement as the first Swallow found in South Africa. It was caught in a farmhouse at Utrecht, Natal, 27 December 1911, eighteen months after being ringed as a nesting adult.' Since then the total of ringed birds from a restricted area of South Africa has reached nearly two hundred, and some eighty birds ringed in that same area have been recovered here in Britain (Fig. 14). It could be argued that the preponderance of recoveries from that region reflects the activities of South African ringers rather than the winter distribution of our Swallows. However the first seven recoveries (before 1923) showed exactly the same distribution. Data from Continental ringing schemes suggest that Swallows from other parts of Europe may winter in different parts of Africa, with those from Germany (for example) being found mostly in central Africa.

Most small insectivorous birds winter in dry savannas, scrub marsh and semi-desert between latitudes 20°N and 10°S (Moreau 1972). There they are subject to many hardships, as insect life is dependent upon unpredictable rains. In such regions, with sparse human populations and many alert scavengers (bird and mammal) it is not surprising that so few recoveries of small birds are received. The meagre extent of these recoveries is shown by the Cuckoo; over 4,000 of this large and conspicuous bird have been ringed in Britain but there has been only one recovery in Africa in the winter period (Fig. 15).

Speculation of a high order solved the mystery of the crash of the Whitethroat between 1968 and 1969. Perhaps 'solved' is too definite a word.

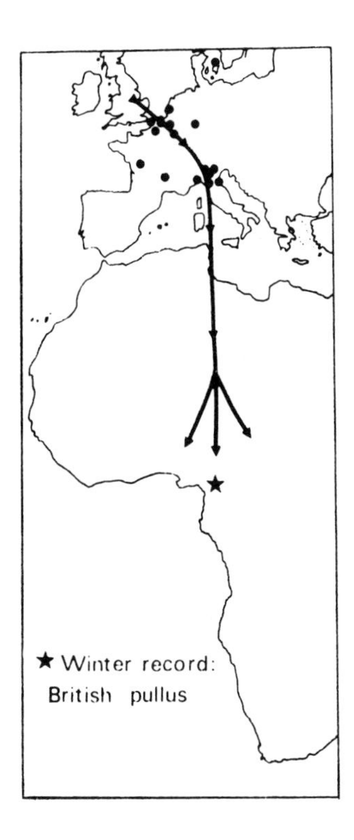

Fig 15 Cuckoo – the single recovery in winter from Africa.

It would be more accurate to say that the solution proposed by Winstanley, Spencer and Williamson (1974) is logical and based on much experience, and no alternative has yet been put forward. The population has not recovered from the sensational drop in this species in those few years. (Many of our young birdwatchers find it difficult to believe that the Whitethroat was once our commonest summer migrant.) The underlying facts were shown by the number of birds ringed: 1967, 8,842; 1968, 11,005; 1969, 1,897; 1970, 3,764. Unfortunately recoveries in Africa in the winter months of October to April were almost non-existent: just two birds from Sénégal, one in January and one in April. Ken Williamson and Bob Spencer had spent many hours debating this problem, and no reasonable solution had been discovered. It was a discussion with meteorologist Derek Winstanley about the drought conditions in the Sahel zone (below the Sahara), and its possible effects on birds, which suddenly made the significance of the few Whitethroat recoveries apparent. They summed up the position thus:

> The cause seems likely to be in the wintering area, the arid steppe on the southern fringe of the Sahara, between 12°–18°N. in West Africa . . . During the 1950s rainfall was substantially above normal, but since 1968 has been well below normal, resulting in severe drought . . . It is considered that this rapid and continuing deterioration is responsible for an unusually heavy mortality among wintering Whitethroats, and is probably affecting other Palaearctic

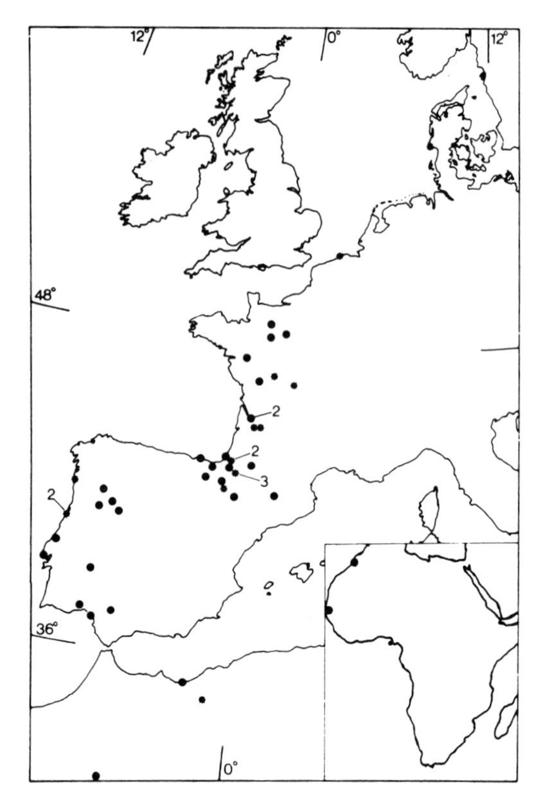

Fig 16 Recoveries of Whitethroats ringed in Britain and Ireland, 1909–1979.

> migrants less severely. The climatic change is thought to be long-term and the Whitethroat population may well stabilise at a relatively low level compared with pre-1968.

The last prediction seems so far to be true, and there is evidence that several other species which are known to winter in the Sahel zone have also suffered (Fig. 16).

JOURNEY TO THE SOUTH

> . . . migration certainly does subsist in some places as my brother in Andalusia has fully informed me. Of the motions of these birds he has ocular demonstration . . . .. GILBERT WHITE

Routes followed by migrants after they leave the south coast of England – whether they are birds which have bred in this country or those which have accepted our hospitality for a short period of the migratory journey – are known only from ringing recoveries. The maps of these recoveries, indeed, form our present day 'ocular demonstrations'. The general pattern is brought out clearly in map after map and species after species. After crossing the English Channel birds fly in a broad stream southwards adjacent to the Atlantic coast of France – where they are at the mercy of the bloodthirsty bird-catchers of that region – and often in a straight line west of the Pyrénées to the Mediterranean and beyond. Some, on the other hand tend to carry on towards the west coast of Portugal when, as Moreau (1961) put it, 'on reaching the western part of the Iberian peninsula, a change in direction is the only alternative to a suicidal plunge over the Atlantic' (a conclusion supported by recent experimental work in Germany).

Such generalisations are, of course, inexact. Each species has its distinctive pattern. For examples, the Spotted Flycatcher and the Swallow show a strong tendency to fly to the narrow crossing at the Straits of Gibraltar, although many birds drift westward into Portugal, before presumably making the necessary change in direction to avoid the 'Moreau suicide'. The Garden Warbler, on the other hand, is a species which follows a less direct route than many other warblers.

Not all species of summer migrant travel the south-westerly route. The Wood Warbler, for example, seems to take a path just east of south, the effect

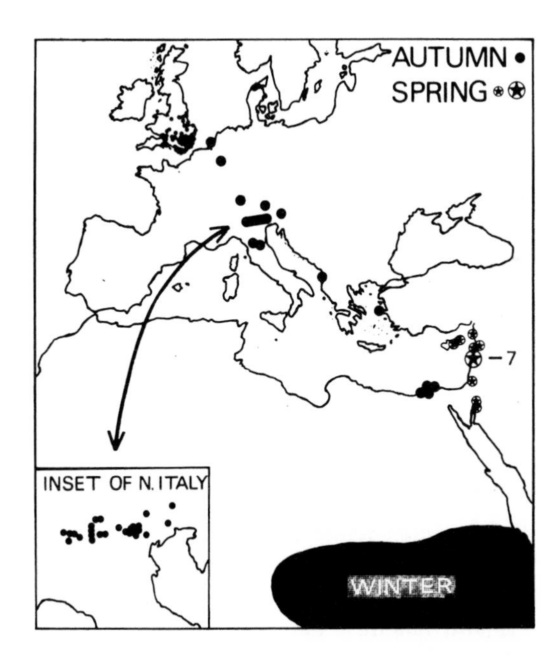

Fig 17 Lesser Whitethroat: recoveries abroad of birds ringed in Britain (at sites shown) on autumn passage. The species follows a south easterly route from Britain, in a narrow corridor. The spring return is by a different route.

of which is to give it a long sea-crossing over the Mediterranean. The Lesser Whitethroat also follows a strong south-easterly flight line, with many birds flying through a narrow corridor about 150 miles wide to enter Italy. The number of recoveries of this species make it the best documented example of a south-easterly route; it results in a long sea crossing from Italy (Fig. 17). However, there is another strong line disclosed to the east of this, through the Balkans and the Levant into Egypt, and so via the Nile to winter quarters in East Africa. Although there have been so many recoveries on the journey there has not yet been a recovery of a British-ringed Lesser Whitethroat from the presumed wintering area.

PARTIAL MIGRATION

The problem of partial migration emphasises the complexity of all migration, and exposes our inadequate knowledge. It is a loose term, and Jean Dorst (1962) prefers to call it 'winter dispersal' – which seems to cover those species which normally breed with us, and which in winter may stay put, may move varying distances from their home neighbourhood, or may make a genuine migration. These are also species in which there is a considerable immigration from Scandinavia or colder parts of the Continent. The Robin is a classic example; Figure 18 shows the recoveries of nineteen birds ringed as UK residents in the breeding season and recovered well to the south – three in Iberia. The dots show birds ringed on passage, having crossed over from Fenno-Scandia and then continued (some in subsequent seasons) to the Continent. There are also on this map many examples of Robins ringed in Britain in winter and recovered in their northern breeding areas. One recovery was quite sensational; in early October 1951 there was a great 'fall' of Robins on the east coast of England (more will be said of this later), when one ringed at Spurn was subsequently recovered in Italy.

In 1944 David Lack published a comprehensive review of this aspect of migration, based on the limited information then available. Only birds ringed as nestlings could be considered, 'those trapped as juveniles or adults being excluded, as some of the latter may have been hatched outside Britain'. Because one point which he was investigating was the relation of age to migration he had to allow for the expected life-span of the species studied, and therefore excluded from his analysis all those birds which had been ringed after 1936. He found, amongst other things, that in the species he studied females and juveniles tended to migrate south more than males, but in those birds which migrated west to Ireland there was no tendency for juveniles to migrate more than older males. He found much variation from species to species, and amongst the same species in different years. He summed up these variable patterns as the result probably of 'a balance between genetic, internal, physiological and external environmental factors, with natural selection exercising a delicate control'.

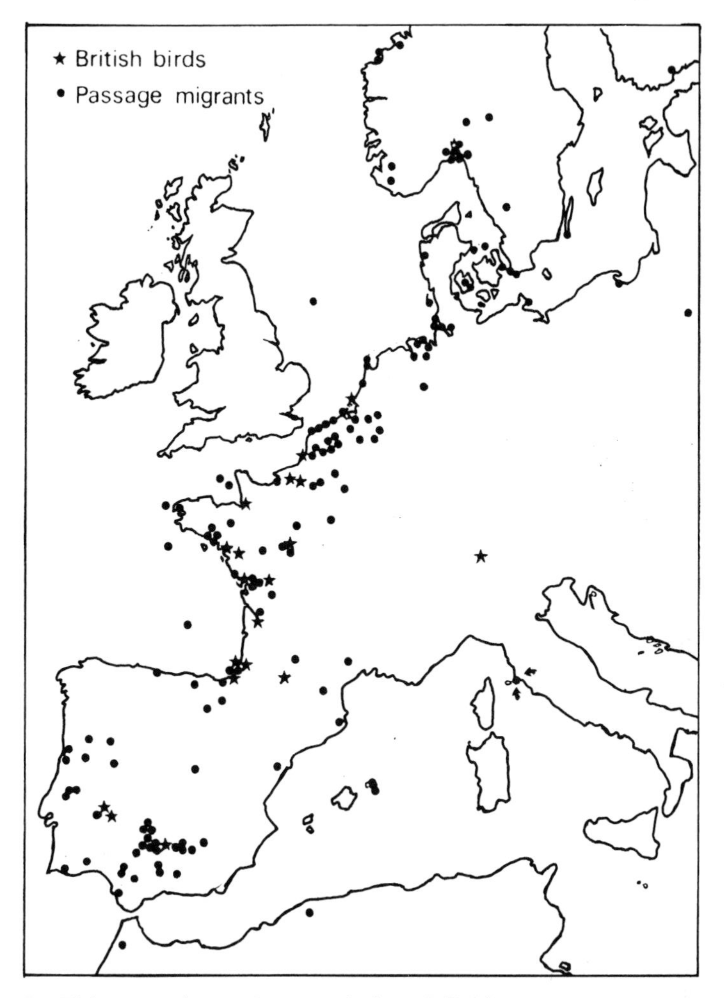

Fig 18 This map shows the complexity of Robin recoveries. The birds recovered in France and Iberia are birds ringed on passage in Britain, passing through from Fenno-Scandia. The recoveries marked by stars are those of birds ringed in Britain in the breeding season. One of the birds recovered in Italy was from the great Robin 'rush' of October 1951, and was ringed at Spurn Point.

Cornwallis (1959) and Williamson and Spencer (1960) showed the possibilities of studying specific bird movements when they were large and conspicuous. For example, Williamson and Spencer reported extremely large numbers of finches present in southern England in the late summer and autumn of 1959; it had been a good summer for seed-eaters, and the country seems to have been seething with Linnets, Goldfinches and other finches, and some large-scale movements were seen (Fig. 19). On 12 October 1,000 Linnets passed Selsey Bill (Sussex), on the 14th 700 Goldfinches moved at

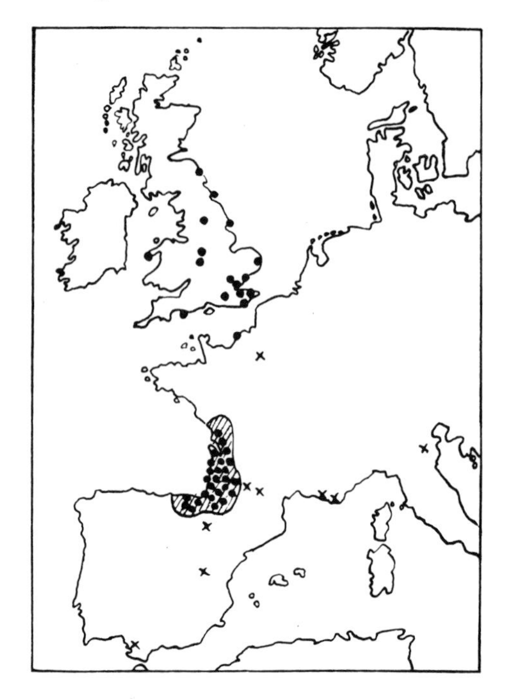

Fig 19 Linnet: recoveries in the autumn and winter of 1959/60 (solid dots). The shaded area is the main wintering area, as revealed by recoveries in earlier years, with the few recoveries outside this area shown by a cross. The dots in Britain show the origins of birds recovered abroad.

Portland Bill (Dorset), on the 25th at Frinton (Essex) Goldfinches were passing south-west at the rate of 1,200 an hour, and on the Isle of Wight on 1 November 1,130 were counted flying west. Ringing totals were high, and later there was a large series of recoveries.

WINTERING IN BRITAIN

Many of the winter visitors to which we play host come in large and conspicuous numbers. When Fieldfares and Redwings land on our east coast, or Barnacle Geese plane down to a Hebridean sea-loch, we have exciting 'ocular demonstration'. The Fieldfare map (Fig. 20) is particularly fascinating. This handsome thrush, a winter immigrant from Fenno-Scandia and points east, is a noisy and attractive part of our winter avifauna. The map shows all foreign recoveries of British-ringed Fieldfares to the end of 1972. They fall broadly into two groups: the north-easterly one represents the breeding area of birds which had been ringed in Britain; the southerly group includes birds which had been ringed here before moving further south later in the winter (perhaps as a result of hard weather conditions) and others which were wintering in different regions in succeeding years. An analysis of the recoveries for the years 1969 to 1980 shows that all recoveries within those thirteen years of birds ringed in previous seasons were found in different wintering areas. The southern and western penetration of this species into Spain and Portugal is also surprising. The scattered recovery points in south-eastern Europe are of outstanding interest; in the same thirteen years (1969–1980) there have been six of these exotic recoveries. Birds were ringed in eastern England, or near to the east coast, in winter: two at Spurn Point, and one each at Gibraltar Point, on the north Lincolnshire coast, in Yorkshire and in Huntingdonshire. They were recovered in later winters in Poland, Austria, Yugoslavia (2), Greece and Turkey.

Birds from the other side of the Atlantic – from Greenland, Iceland and even Baffin Island – are known to cross to Britain regularly, either to winter here or, as with the Greenland Wheatear, to pass through on migration. This remarkable passerine has to make a long and hazardous non-stop flight over the stormiest ocean in our hemisphere. If it flies direct to the Iberian peninsula – its shortest route to Africa – it must travel some 2,000 miles. Even if it passes through Britain – and at times many birds of the Greenland

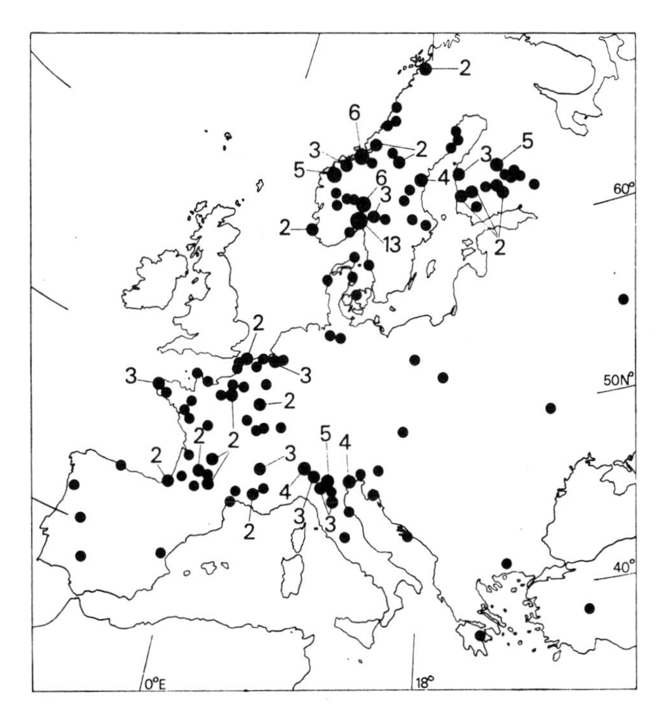

Fig 20 Fieldfare: recoveries abroad of birds ringed in Britain.

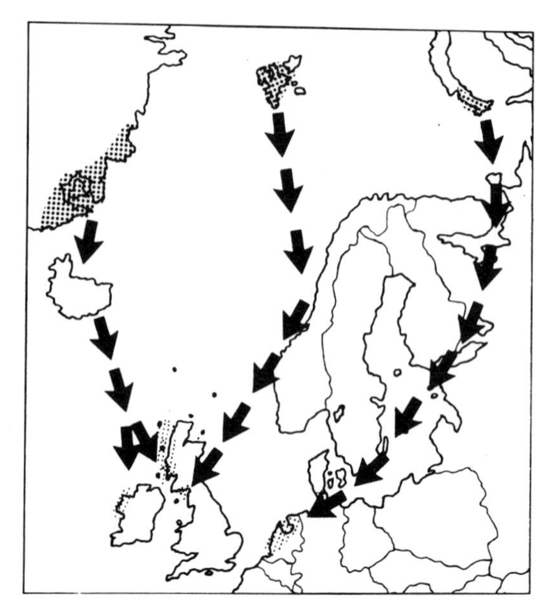

Fig 21 Barnacle Geese: the three populations each with its separate breeding and wintering grounds. From Owen (1976).

race *leucorhoa* have been caught here, and identified by measurement and weight – it must traverse some 1,600 miles of ocean. This race also occurs in Iceland and Faeroes, so that in the cases mentioned there is no absolute certainty that such birds have originated in Greenland. Only four birds ringed in Greenland have been recovered in Britain, and these have all been on spring migration. There is no doubt that many other birds – notably waders and geese – also make the crossing.

Barnacle Geese have been studied intensively by the Wildfowl Trust; birds have been ringed on the wintering grounds in Scotland, and on the breeding grounds in Greenland and Spitsbergen by special expeditions. Marking birds with large plastic rings, with a bold letter code, has enabled geese to be identified without need for further catching. By these means the extraordinary migratory pattern of this species has been worked out in detail. It is noteworthy that of 350 adults ringed in Spitsbergen in one year, no less than 343 (98%) were seen subsequently on the wintering grounds at Caerlaverock on the Solway.

SEABIRD MOVEMENTS

Seabirds which nest colonially in accessible places can often be ringed in large numbers. Those which nest in dangerous situations, however, are

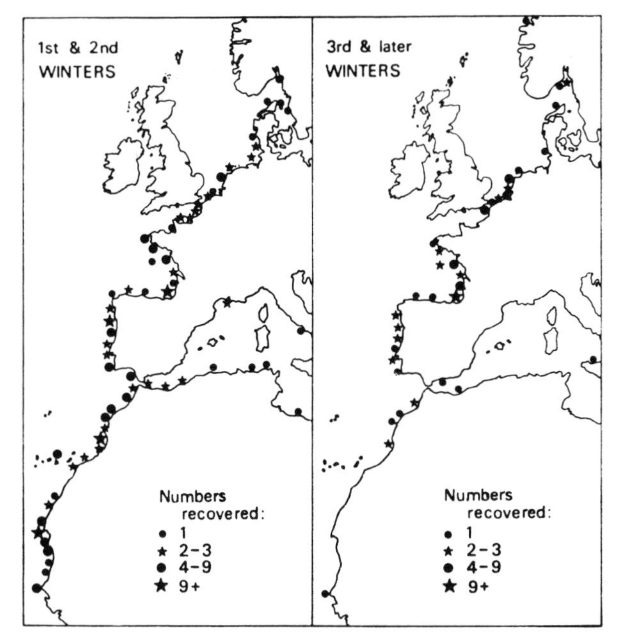

Fig 22 Gannet: young birds travel further than older ones on migration.

necessarily ringed in smaller numbers – although many ringers respond to the challenge. After their brief sojourn ashore for nesting most seabirds disappear into the stormy vastness of the ocean, where they wander and live in tune with their wild environment. But here also they die – though few ringed birds have been recovered at sea. Like small passerines in the deserts of Africa, few are found. The best ringing dividends are obtained from those species which frequent coastal waters and which are, moreover, conspicuous, like the Gannet, for 'the sea lanes around Britain and Ireland are always more or less busy with Gannets' (Nelson 1978).

Sir Landsborough Thomson began to analyse the recoveries of Gannets a long time ago, when few had been received, and published a paper as far back as 1939 when only about 200 were available. He re-assessed his conclusions later (1974), when over 1,700 recoveries had accrued; although he was able to correct a few of his earlier views, his main conclusions from the earlier study were confirmed. This shows how ringing results can work out the details of the life of a bird which would not be possible by any other means (Fig. 22).

Thomson found that the Gannet was a partial migrant; many remained in northern waters throughout the winter whilst others migrated to west European seas, and to Africa even down to the tropics. Yet others penetrated the western part of the Mediterranean. The really startling discovery was that young Gannets move much greater distances than adults, and then remain to

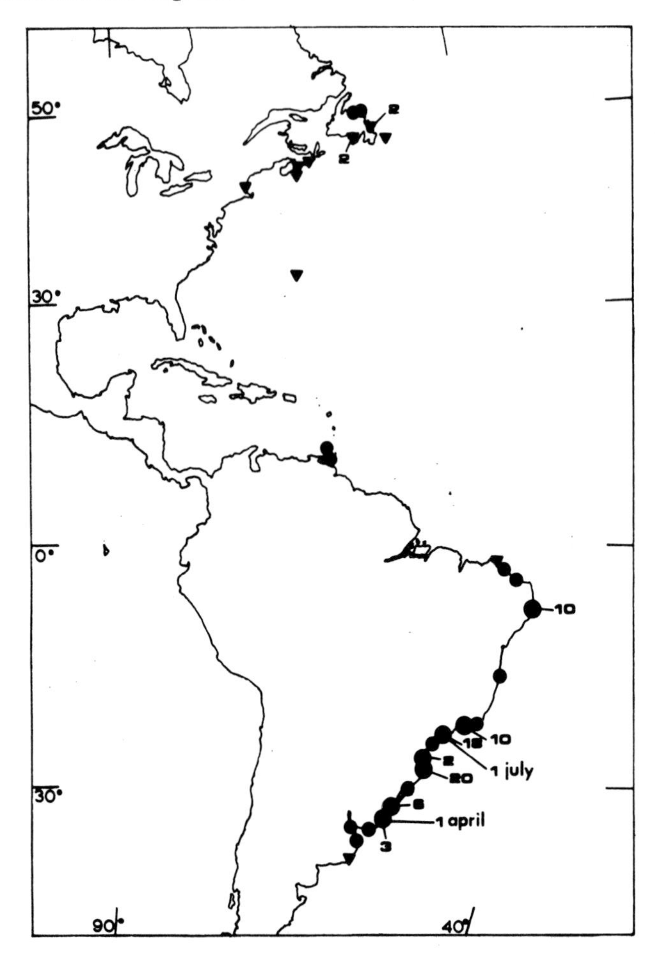

Fig 23 Manx Shearwaters: all New World recoveries to 1970. Circles represent recoveries in the months August to March, and circles April to June.

summer in their wintering areas. It is a year or two before these young birds re-appear in their home waters (Nelson 1978). Thomson summarised it thus:

> Birds in their first year of life are migratory to a markedly higher degree than those in their second year taken alone, or than all older birds taken together; this is shown in the proportion that quit northern waters in winter and in the numbers then found in north-west African and tropical waters. That there is any further decrease in the migratory urge after the second year is doubtful . . .

On the islands of Skokholm and Skomer, off the Pembrokeshire (Dyfed) coast, occurs the largest concentration of Manx Shearwaters in Britain. The Skokholm colony has been studied intensively since the early 1930s, when Ronald Lockley started the first British observatory there; since 1963 the study has been directed by the Edward Grey Institute (Oxford University). Ringing has been extensive – nearly 200,000 to 1980 – and from recoveries of these marked birds much has been discovered about this mysterious bird. Unfortunately, the ringing programme had to cease in 1980 when the ownership of the island changed hands. Recoveries of ringed birds in the breeding season in the Bay of Biscay convinced Lockley (1953) that birds were flying out from the breeding colony to feed, needing a round trip of between 600–1,000 miles; but Harris (1966) believed, based on further work, that the breeding birds were not in fact flying any further than the Bristol Channel or the coast of southern Ireland, and that the Biscay birds were either non-breeders or failed breeders. There have now been many birds recovered in winter off the coasts of Brazil and Argentina, several of them newly-fledged birds which had flown south probably without stopping (Lloyd 1976). Recoveries of Skokholm birds in summer off the north-east coast of the United States presumably are of summering non-breeding birds (Fig. 23).

The mist net has made possible the large scale ringing of Storm Petrels in recent years; the numbers ringed to the end of 1980 (over 144,000) have nearly all been ringed since 1953. Although most birds breed on inaccessible islands these offer a challenge to adventuring young ringers, which they have not been slow to accept. A further impetus was the discovery that Storm Petrels can be attracted to mist nets by the use of tape-lures, many being caught in this way on headlands away from breeding colonies.

Between 1976 and 1981 at least 22,000 were captured and ringed in this way on headlands away from breeding colonies. Analysis of figures so far available suggests that Storm Petrels are highly mobile and move randomly around the coastlines of the Northern Isles at night from the end of June onwards. Probably they are pre-breeders prospecting for nest sites (Fowler, Okill and Marshall 1982). It is to be hoped that this work will be extended to other areas. Ringing off Kintyre, for instance, suggests that these wandering movements are more than local and may extend over wide sea areas of western Britain and Ireland.

Ringing totals for some seabirds to the end of 1980

	Total ringed	*Total recovered*	*Percentage*
Gannet	41,315	2,539	6·15
Razorbill	46,920	1,385	2·95
Guillemot	42,614	1,080	2·53
Kittiwake	56,340	1,235	2·19
Manx Shearwater	228,453	3,130	1·37
Fulmar	42,448	525	1·23
Storm Petrel	144,880	1,418	0·97

OTHER MOVEMENT STUDIES DEPENDING ON RINGING

Long-distance migration, as revealed by recoveries abroad of birds ringed or controlled in the United Kingdom, can be shown on maps, and this is the glamorous aspect of ringing. There are, however, other kinds of movement, less definite than true migration, which are of important survival value – such as post-juvenile dispersal, food searching, hard weather movements, roosting movements and eruptions – and which are revealed by ringing. But these can rarely be shown by maps. Movements of these kinds are complex, and in most cases insufficient data have yet accumulated. A few examples are given here which will show that great opportunities for new discoveries from ringing are still before us.

Post-juvenile dispersal

That juveniles of many species tend to move away from their natal areas is now widely accepted. Ringers have first-hand experience of such movements. For example, at observatories and other ringing sites at the end of summer, before migration proper has got well under way, young birds preponderate in what are clearly local population movements. This kind of movement is shown clearly in the Sand Martin; ringers at breeding colonies in late July or August catch numbers of ringed juveniles which have moved in from other known colonies. An opportunity to examine post-juvenile dispersal in this species was provided by the results of the special Sand Martin enquiry, carried out between 1962 and 1968.

This highly successful venture had grown out of the discovery by a group of ringers in Essex that large numbers of Sand Martins, gathering to feed over a small river, could be caught readily by mist nets stretched across the river. At about the same time other ringers were discovering the possibilities of ringing large numbers at the great autumn reed-bed roosts. As a result the ringing of Sand Martins increased markedly. The Ringing and Migration Committee seized the opportunity and encouraged this ringing by establishing a formal enquiry, providing free rings for the purpose. As a result, during the seven years of the enquiry the number of Sand Martins ringed increased by over 400,000, and recoveries by over 10,000.

At the conclusion of the enquiry the Trust had acquired a mass of valuable data on this species. The problem of analysing it was formidable. It had to be carried out by a staff already hard-pressed to cope with their normal duties, and at that date there was no computer help available. As a result the writing-up took a long time; but eventually the results were published in a special issue of *Bird Study* (financed by a welcome grant from the Royal Society) in June 1979. It contained a number of important papers on movements in the Sand Martin, of which one (by C. J. Mead and J. D. Harrison) on movements within Britain discussed pre-migration dispersal. The authors summed up their paper thus:

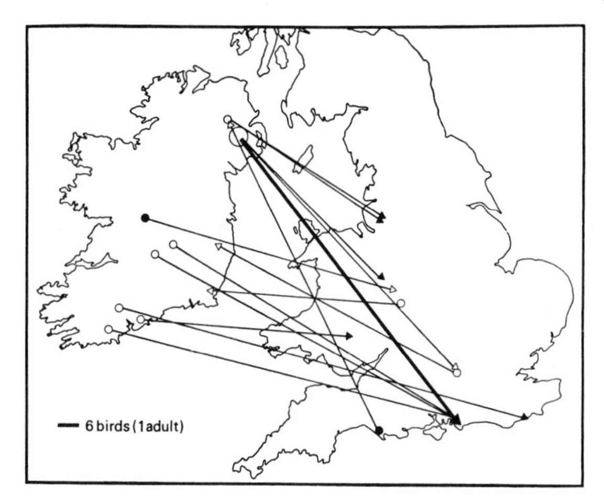

Fig 24 Recoveries of Sand Martins crossing the Irish Sea. Lines join ringing and recovery localities. Open circles are ringing sites at colonies, and closed circles are roosts. Open arrows are recoveries at colonies, closed at roosts. All except three were ringed as juveniles. From Mead and Harrison, 1979.

> The results of this BTO enquiry produced a very clear picture of the movements of Sand Martins within much of Britain during the late summer and autumn. Most breeding adults remain at their colonies, raising broods, until the second half of August, though some, which may have failed in or finished breeding, move earlier. Adult movements are normally oriented strongly just east of south . . . They spend about 10–14 days attached to a particular roost . . . but (unlike juveniles) there are few same-autumn retraps between British roosts, which suggests more direct and quicker passage through the country . . . The pattern of autumn movement is very different for juveniles. After reaching independence (from late June for early broods) they are not tied to their natal colony. They then wander extensively and are often caught visiting and roosting in colonies far from their own. They form the bulk of birds in large autumn reed-bed roosts . . .

In preparing their paper the authors drew some 200 working maps. It was unfortunate that lack of space prevented the publication of most of these, and only a few could be reproduced. A single example is given (Fig. 24) – one which shows how young Irish birds cross into Wales and southern England to join large roosts there before migrating southwards across the Channel.

We can now see, with benefit of hindsight, how unfortunate it was that the enquiry ceased in 1968, for the following summer showed a disastrous drop in the numbers of returning migrants. This was the year also of the Whitethroat crash, which we believe was caused by drought in the Sahel region of Africa. The Sand Martin was another species to suffer from the same disaster; and if we had only known, we were in a position to discover information which would have been of the greatest value in our attempts to understand the effects of that natural calamity on our bird populations.

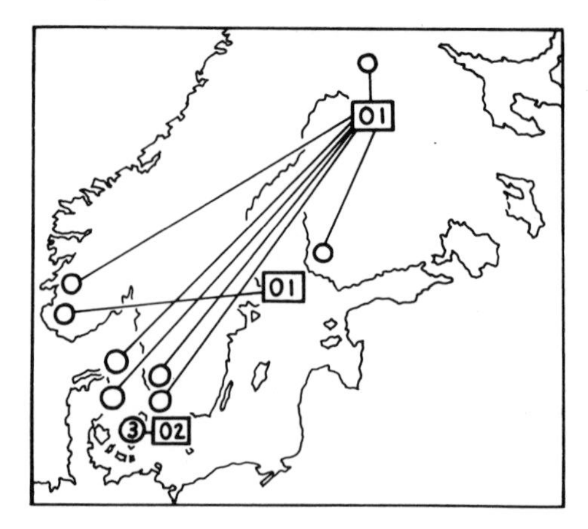

Fig 25 Recoveries of Waxwings in Europe in 1965 in October (○) from ringing in Finland and Sweden. From Cornwallis and Townsend, 1968.

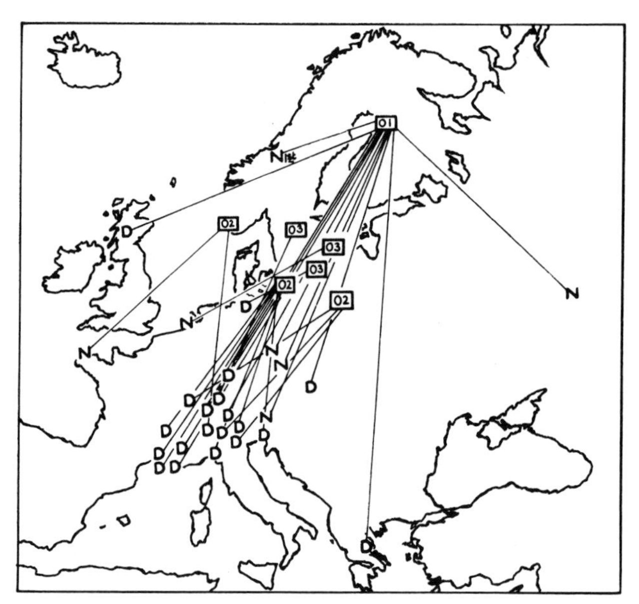

Fig 26 Recoveries of Waxwings in Europe in 1965, in November and December, from ringing in Finland, Sweden, Norway and the Soviet Union. From Cornwallis and Townsend, 1968.

Eruptions

The Waxwing is a showy and splendid bird – altogether a suitable representative of those species which exhibit that puzzling form of movement we call eruption (or 'irruption' in areas receiving the birds). So conspicuous is the Waxwing that when it occurs in sudden and unexpected numbers it is widely reported; but in spite of this wealth of records it has proved difficult to base on them any interpretations of its movements. Other eruptive species are even more difficult. The Siskin is one; its appearances in winter are predictable, as it frequents traditional feeding areas, and now that it has taken to feeding in gardens on peanut bags (Chapter Four) it is better known than before. But irruptive movements of this and similar species are masked because they result in nothing more than apparently local increases in numbers. Since so little is yet known about the total numbers of such species it has proved impossible to decide on visual evidence alone whether one sees merely a local concentration or a wide-spread irruptive increase. Few birds, ringed here in winter, have been recovered on their breeding grounds, and none found here in winter have been ringed in breeding areas abroad.

Birds subject to these strange movements are those which rely on a limited number of tree species for food – species which themselves are subject to wide variations from year to year in the quantities of seed they set. Thus finches, limited in this way, usually find enough food so that they need occupy only part of their overall range. A bad harvest however will cause them to seek out local abundances of food which allow them to concentrate there (Newton 1972); and in very bad years this searching can take them to the very limits of their range – often to Britain.

Four successive years of spectacular Waxwing invasions in the years 1956–60 offered a rare opportunity for research into this problem; this was seized by R. K. Cornwallis, who made a remarkable pioneer study (1961). It enabled him to summarise, on the basis of his studies, the characteristics of this type of movement and to distinguish it from regular migration and from sedentariness: 'True migration is an adaptation to a variation in conditions, usually food supply, that occurs annually. Sedentary habits are an adaptation to conditions that are reasonably stable throughout the year. The invasion type of migration is an adaptation to conditions that fluctuate not annually but irregularly.' The next invasion occurred in 1965/66, and Cornwallis was joined by A. D. Townsend in an analysis (1968). This time some ringing evidence was available – both from birds ringed here and abroad – and two of the informative maps they prepared are shown here (Figs 25, 26).

THE BIRD OBSERVATORIES

> Migration study, complex though it is, still depends – and always will depend – on the observatory and field man, the island lover, the cape-cliff-haunter, the bunk sleeper and the sandwich eater – JAMES FISHER

Headlands, peninsulas and islands – these are places where students of migration tend to gather. It used to be thought that migrants concentrated at such places. Radar observations have discounted that simple idea by showing that there are (spring and autumn) large-scale wide front movements of birds, often beyond visible range. This suggests that the birds seen on the ground at favoured places are a mere local or accidental assemblage. What is certain is that places of this kind have been known, by long experience, to be places where migration can be seen, year in and year out. They are, if nothing else, good for observation, and that is the reason our bird observatories have been located in such places. The Bird Observatories Committee in February 1946 defined an observatory thus: a field station co-operatively manned for the purpose of making continuous observations on migrant birds and for catching, examining and marking them. The emphasis, it will be noted, is on continuous observation; the observatories have therefore always put a high priority on meticulous log-keeping. Some, notably Cape Clear Island in Co. Cork, have specialised in this form of study.

In practice most observatories carry out their observations through ringing and the examination of handled birds. The typical observatory is built around a series of Heligoland traps – large structures designed to trap birds which arrive in the area with a directional urge which aids capture. Observatories are not therefore just 'ringing stations'. Their main strength is that they are handling birds which are actually in the course of migrating. This not only results in recoveries which are of great value to the general picture of migration, but enables recoveries from a single observatory to be analysed separately. Two maps illustrate this (Figs 27, 28) and show ringing recoveries from Gibraltar Point Observatory of two closely related species, Song Thrush and Blackbird. The east coast observatories handle large numbers of *Turdus* species in autumn which, although they come at the same time, may well show – as in these examples – a differing pattern between species. Song Thrushes recovered in winter after passing through Gibraltar Point (whether in the same or subsequent winters) show a strong tendency to continue south, as far as the Mediterranean, whereas it will be seen that many of the Blackbirds travel westwards into Ireland or to the north coast of France.

It will be apparent that a great quantity of similar information exists in the files of all the observatories. Since these are all independent, autonomous organisations, and in the absence of a central research worker such as the Trust was fortunate to have between 1958 and 1963, much information of this kind still awaits exploitation. A start was made in 1981 when a booklet in the *BTO Guide* series, 'Seasonal Movements of Summer Migrants' by Nick Riddiford and Peter Findley, brought together histograms from all the observatories for each of the passerine species being dealt with.

Sea-watching is also a profitable form of observation which the observatories pioneered. This work has now been intensified and extended by the work of the Seabird Group, and the observations of the 'Seabirds at Sea' team.

Masses of complex data call out for handling and analysis by computer. Ringing groups are beginning to find access to commercial computers through the work-a-day activities and interests of some of their members – and as the use of computers spreads (including current moves to put them

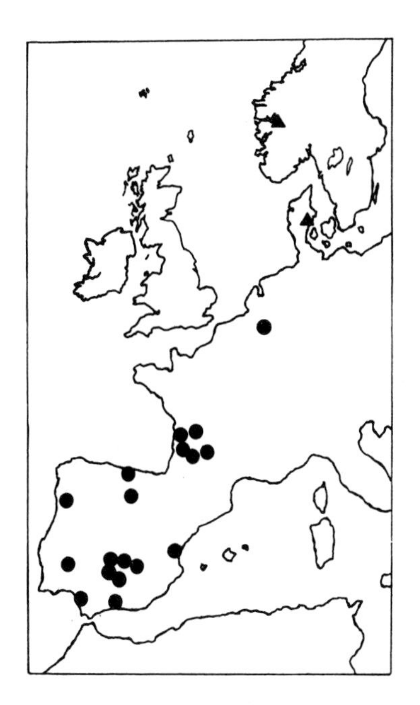

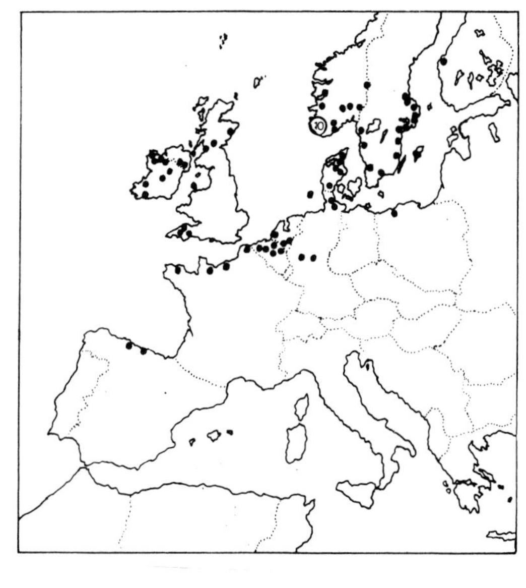

Fig 27 Song Thrush: foreign recoveries of birds ringed at Gibraltar Point. Circles: recovery October to March; triangle: recovery in July. From Evans, in Durman, 1976.

Fig 28 Blackbirds ringed at Gibraltar Point and recovered over 200 km distant. From Evans, in Durman, 1976.

into schools) there are sure to be many opportunities for the amateur birdwatcher to use his professional expertise and opportunities in this way. It is to be hoped that before long observatories will also benefit from this movement.

The chain of observatories round the coast of Britain was established after World War II, and their heyday was in the 1950s and 1960s. Ronald Lockley started it all in the early 1930s. He had gone in 1927 to the small rocky island of Skokholm, off the magnificent cliff-coast of Pembrokeshire, where he repaired the ancient farm buildings and combined farming with study of the island's birds. His evocative books brought a stream of visitors to Skokholm, including many famous ornithologists, and it grew into an 'observatory'. Lockley established it as such in 1933, began the daily recording of migrants on the island (in addition to the studies of seabirds already in full swing), and built a trap modelled on the famous design used on Heligoland. The example soon spread. Young enthusiasts of the Midlothian Bird Club, led by George Waterston, and inspired by the Misses Baxter and Rintoul, established the first co-operatively manned observatory on the Isle of May in the Firth of Forth. Already Yorkshire ornithologists had decided to establish an observatory on the peninsula of Spurn Point; but before they could put their plans into operation the war intervened – and this also closed the two existing observatories.

Plans to re-open these observatories, and many other exciting possibilities when hostilities had ended, sustained ornithologists through the dangers, horrors and boredoms of war. For example, two prisoners-of-war in a German camp, George Waterston and Ian Pitman, survived the privations and sickness of prison life by planning an observatory on Fair Isle. So, when the war ended, bands of enthusiasts began to establish the observatories, often in primitive living conditions and with no money, with traps constructed from war-time leavings; migration began to be studied with an unbelievable intensity. Soon this movement of enthusiasts began to throw up its leaders – including men who determined to make a career of observatory wardening. The first, and the undoubted leader of the movement, was Kenneth Williamson who went (with the enthusiastic support of his wife) as warden of Fair Isle. The Bird Observatories Committee, under the wise chairmanship of W. B. Alexander, organised an annual conference of observatory workers at Oxford, where enthusiasm ran riot. These were indeed great days.

The observatories were (and are) autonomous, each with its highly individual character and organisation. Yet they needed the kind of influence which the Trust was able to provide, and the links were close; the Chairman of the Bird Observatories Committee was appointed by Council of the Trust, and the Trust provided secretarial services, including the organisation of the annual meetings. The partnership has been fruitful. The Committee laid down its own minimum rules for each observatory, compliance with which was a pre-requisite for 'recognition'. They were simple and sensible rules, freely accepted, and gave a structure and coherence to the movement without imposing any further obligations.

As the movement grew, and surveyed the prospects of further co-operative migration studies, it was recognised that the potentialities of its work would always be limited unless there was a professional leader. The Committee, at the annual conference in 1957, passed a bold Resolution; it was 'of the opinion that the increasing number of observatories and the volume of work thereby produced now necessitates the services of an expert. We therefore recommend to Council the appointment of a full-time officer, charged with the duties of co-ordinating and advising on all such migration studies, and in view of the rapidly accumulating mass of data, urge immediate consideration of such an appointment.'

This was an audacious request – but it worked. The President of the Trust approached the Nuffield Foundation trustees and convinced them that an investment of money in this enterprise would yield results of the greatest importance in ornithology. They were indeed impressed and made a generous grant for a five-year period from 1 January 1958, to enable a suitable appointment to be made and also, as a part of the project, to permit the publication of a twice-yearly journal devoted to migration studies arising out of the appointment. The relationship between the Trust and the observatories was thus made ever closer. The conference had of course known the person they wanted for this appointment – Kenneth Williamson, who for personal reasons was about to leave Fair Isle. Robert Spencer notes, in the introduction to *Bird Observatories in Britain and Ireland* (1976):

> With his record of enterprise and leadership it was natural that Kenneth Williamson should have been chosen to fill this important post. The observatory system had now reached its hey day. Methods of recording were standardised; special log books were printed, routine microfilming of records was instituted and a twice yearly journal *Bird Migration* was established which published a wide variety of migration papers and in addition served as a contact medium for the still multiplying numbers of localities at which migration watches took place.

This fruitful five-year period reached its end too quickly, with the work still in full flood. By their constitution the Nuffield Foundation was unable to renew the grant (although they generously made available a limited sum to enable the work of the Migration Research Officer to be properly wound up). The Trust was in one of its recurrent periods of financial stringency and could not itself fund the continuation of the appointment. The work did not cease entirely, but had to be carried out by staff members as part of other duties. Ken Williamson himself went on to head the newly-formed Populations Section, and his involvement in census work, a new subject for him, took up his whole energies. For whatever reason – whether the results of the radar studies by Lack and his co-workers, or the advent of the mist net, or the package holiday calling birdwatchers abroad – the observatory movement went into decline. It eventually stabilised at a dozen observatories; but it must be emphasised that these were not a decayed rump, living on past glories, but were (and still are) working steadily and purposefully in the accumulation of long-term migration data.

One effect of the radar studies of Lack and his pupils was to emphasise that migration did not stop at the coast, but proceeded inland on wide fronts. Before the decline in the numbers of observatory workers had made itself felt, Ian Wallace suggested to the Conference (in January 1962) that a chain of inland observatories should be established. This proposal was accepted and the scheme, known as the Inland Observation Points, was organised by Humphrey Dobinson. It started an experimental period on 1 March 1962 with records from points in Berkshire, Buckinghamshire and Oxfordshire, lasting until November of that year. A report on this experiment was made by Dobinson, who said: 'Inland Observation Points are capable of keeping track of the variations that occur in numbers of our common passerine species in inland localities . . . More extensive data and further analysis are needed for these projects . . .' Unfortunately the scheme was not renewed, but remains another intriguing and rewarding possibility for migration workers when there is a resurgence – as most assuredly there will be – in migration studies.

MOVEMENTS AND WEATHER

On the Fair Isle Desert Wheatears crash like disappointed meteors.
Do such feathered vagrants ever
Board a boat and cadge a lift?
Cannot *Tringa solitaria* travel on the *Berengaria*?
'No!' cries Williamson, 'No, never.
All is wholly due to drift.'

M. F. M. MEIKLEJOHN

Birds are creatures of the air. Both in their daily lives and in their migratory journeys they are subject to sudden changes in the behaviour of the circumambient atmosphere, to deteriorating weather, to wind and rain and cloud. Thus breeding Swifts, dependent upon airborne insects for food, may suffer severely when bad weather causes insects to disappear. 'It has now been shown that big summer movements of Swifts occur during the passage of a depression, the birds flying against the wind round the southern edge of the depression, and thus moving away from bad weather into better weather . . . Recoveries of marked birds suggest that they may travel at least four hundred miles from home on such movements' (Lack 1965). When the bird is driven by biological imperatives to travel long distances, as on migration over the sea, the effects of adverse weather can be severe.

Annual weather pattern has been the ultimate factor in the evolution of migration. 'In general, the spring migration of each species appears to be so timed that the birds arrive on their breeding grounds at almost the earliest moment that they have a reasonable chance of surviving there . . . Again, the autumn migration of most species appears to be so timed that the birds leave their breeding grounds ahead of the period when their continued survival there would be precarious' (Lack 1960). Long-term cycles in weather or climate can change the breeding distribution of many species. 'Several recent ornithological developments in Britain seem less likely to be isolated phenomena than closely integrated responses to a pattern of climatic change. These developments embrace an increasing volume of spring migration, colonisation – of Scotland especially – by boreal elements, a greater frequency of North American waders and passerines on the eastern side of the Atlantic, prolonged winter stays of some Arctic birds, and a great diminution in numbers of summer visitors which have their main wintering area in West Africa' (Williamson 1976).

As the bird observatories grew in experience, and as they began to compare notes one with another, they came to see distinct patterns of migratory movement. These, it was soon realised, were often connected with weather – more specifically, with bad weather. This did not come as a surprise. In these islands, with our changeable and unpredictable weather – the subject of daily conversation – we accept that all life is affected by these conditions. But it was the relationship between large-scale movements of birds and certain weather patterns which attracted attention. Thus at our east coast observatories the 'falls' or 'rushes' of birds following easterly or south-easterly winds brought excitement to those lucky enough to be present. On the other hand, the complete absence of movement often experienced during prolonged spells with south-westerly winds was a boredom which had to be endured.

Serious studies of these relationships had been going on intermittently for many years. In the early years of the century the noted ornithologist, William Eagle Clarke (*Studies in Bird Migration*, 1912), had spent many years visiting islands and lighthouses (often in hazardous conditions) to observe migration in progress. One of his conclusions was that in autumn birds followed a regular path – the so-called 'trunk line' – from Scandinavia through Britain to France and Iberia. Birds, he believed, followed fixed routes, in great numbers, involving two dangerous sea-crossings. This was a reasonable assumption to base on the observations he had made. He also noted that the largest numbers, particularly in such places as Fair Isle, occurred with south-easterly winds. Hence he concluded that this kind of weather actually favoured migration.

The Scottish ornithologists Miss E. V. Baxter and Miss L. J. Rintoul, who had worked for so many years in the Forth area and particularly on the Isle of May, had also noted these weather effects, but put a different interpretation on them. They believed that such birds would not normally have passed through Britain, but had been displaced by the south-easterly winds. Here was the first exposition of the theory of migrational drift, published in *Ibis* in 1918, but overlooked by ornithologists for thirty years. Then Kenneth Williamson, in a prolific series of papers which began in 1952, and Dick Cornwallis in 1954, and many other observatory workers, set the observatory movement alight. The concept of drift migration took us all over.

At first these studies were mainly concerned with what happened when birds landed on our own shores. It was soon realised that it was equally important to know the weather at the point where the migrants began their journeys across the sea, and the weather conditions which initiated migration. Attention was directed towards Scandinavia; not only was there now a considerable amount of work being carried out which could help in this way, but some British ornithologists were travelling to Scandinavia especially to study this.

It is clear that passerine migrants leave Scandinavia in fine settled weather. Until times are propitious birds tend to wait, taking advantage of this period to feed and build up body fats to be the energy supply for the impending journey. It is suggested by most workers (for example, Svardson 1953) that they wait for weather which includes clear skies, very light (or no) winds, and (in autumn) a drop in temperature – conditions usually found in anticyclonic weather. Most workers believe that it is the favourable components of the weather system which are important, rather than the pressure system as a whole, for these conditions in Scandinavia may be found in both cyclonic and anticyclonic systems. It seems that when birds have left, particularly if they are night migrants, they often leave the area of the anticyclone and may hit strong winds, with low clouds completely destroying visibility. 'The peripheral easterlies (on the south side of the high pressure system) may be strong enough to drift the birds to westward of their standard SW or SSW if fog intervenes at the Skagerrak sea-crossing or along the North Sea coasts. Usually under anticyclonic conditions . . . the adult part of the movement should be able to maintain goal-orientation, so that the easterly winds will more effectively displace the young during their post-juvenile dispersal, and any non-oriented irruption flocks which may be moving' (Williamson 1969). This idea of birds displaced westward, even by light winds, when disoriented by cloud, rain or fog, was generally accepted. Williamson went further. He postulated that the disoriented bird could detect wind direction (perhaps by noting the direction of wave movement) and would then turn to fly downwind, 'for by adding wind-speed to its own flight-speed it would cover the greatest distance in the shortest time and would have a better chance of reaching land before its energy-giving resources ran out' (Williamson 1965). This attractive and ingenious theory, which he called 'downwind directed drift', was unacceptable to many other workers. In particular, the differences between Lack and Williamson polarised about this contention.

After Lack had ended his radar studies he published a number of papers (especially 1959, 1960a, b) summarising his discoveries. He was unable to find anything on his radar screens which supported Williamson's 'downwind directed drift'. Yet more important for migration workers, he was able to show that 'the number of night migrants alighting need not be proportionate to the number passing overhead'. Lack further showed how in spring but to a lesser degree in autumn, migration at night was often heavy and continuous irrespective of weather conditions, with most birds flying beyond human vision even with the aid of optical instruments. The numbers of birds which were grounded at observatories were almost accidental, and it was this conflict with what Spencer called 'the laboriously built up hypotheses of the observatory migration workers' which was so demoralising to them. But a look at some specific examples might show that the truth was many sided. For example, let us look at the great Robin rush of 1 October 1951 and the weather map, Figure 29. A large anticyclone had moved from Russia in late autumn to come to rest over Scandinavia. The next morning, along the whole east coast of Britain from Fair Isle in the north to Kent in the south, Robins abounded in great numbers (with other species in smaller numbers). The greatest concentration was from Yorkshire to Norfolk. The Isle of May ringed 300 in the days following, Spurn Point 500, and Gibraltar Point another 500. Of the birds ringed at Spurn five were recovered later that same winter: two in Minorca, two in France, and one in Italy. It is not unreasonable to suggest that these birds, recovered in winter to the east of the normal wintering range for Scandinavian birds, were of an eastern population, landing accidently in Britain and trying to recover their normal

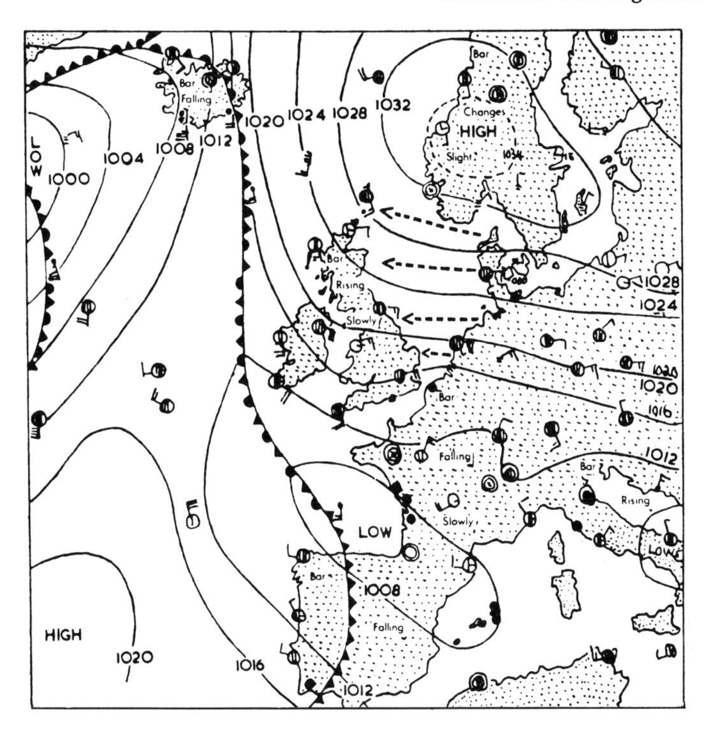

Fig 29 The great 'Robin rush' of 1st October 1951. From Williamson, 1965.

wintering area. As another example, the presence of young birds of species breeding in eastern Russia and Siberia is now regular on the east coast – Yellow-browed Warbler, Pallas's Warbler, Red-breasted Flycatcher, Siberian Lesser Whitethroats and others. Kenneth Williamson's weather map for a day in September 1949, when a number of these sub-rarities occurred at Fair Isle is shown. Perhaps after all, there may be validity in the concept of regular long-distance vagrancy, and that it is weather which brings them, along with birds such as the stranger Robins, and causes them to make the first available land-fall on our eastern shores.

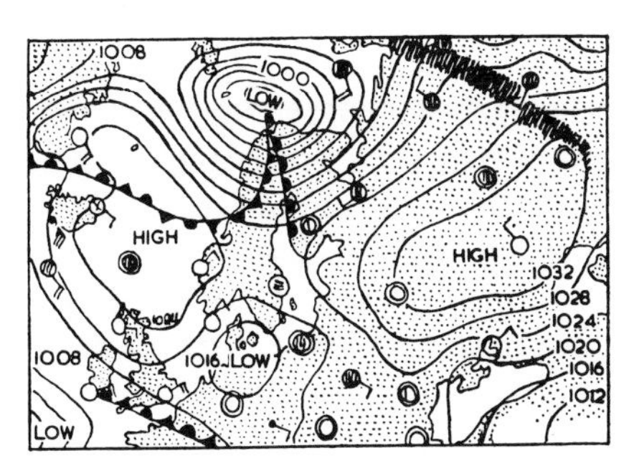

Fig 30 Yellow-browed Warbler weather, 1949. 'An autumn of strong anticyclonic developments over Europe and western Asia, with light easterly breezes to carry the birds hundreds of miles across the Continent. The wind was so light and the sky generally so clear that true migrants are unlikely to have been displaced and the drifted birds were probably young on dispersal.' From Williamson, 1965.

6: Conservation and sister organisations

The Royal Society for the Protection of Birds

NICHOLAS HAMMOND

At the birth of the BTO the RSPB, forty-four years old, was well into middle age. The infant in Oxford at first appears to have received little attention from the RSPB, perhaps because the Society was an organisation run by elderly people. Many of them were those worthy pioneers who founded the Society in 1889. Their early contribution had been almost beyond praise: they, respectable ladies and gentlemen, had fought in the face of fashion to change public attitudes and the use of wild birds' feathers in hats.

Socially, the membership of the Society was well established as an upper middle class organisation with a sprinkling of aristocracy. Indeed, the Vice-President's list read like a combination of Debrett, Crockford's and the more senior part of the Army List. The Council was scarcely less grand, which had been just as well in the early days when the Society needed influence if it was to achieve anything. In those days charities were not proscribed from attempting to change laws and much of the Society's effort was aimed at producing legislation for the better protection of birds. These efforts had been successful to some extent, with a series of Protection of Birds Acts gradually improving the lot of British wild birds.

By the 1930s a hazard to birds unimaginable in 1889 was being seen as a growing problem. The Society had first begun to draw public attention to oil pollution at the end of World War I, and in 1922 the Oil in Navigable Water Act was passed. Four years later there was an international conference in

Washington, which recommended that discharge of oil within 50 miles of land should be made illegal. *Bird Notes and News* in 1933 was fulminating against the inability of maritime nations to come to any agreement to put the recommendation into practice.

In 1929, the RSPB had acquired its freehold land at Dungeness, and in 1932 a reserve (then called a sanctuary) was established at East Wood, Stalybridge in Cheshire. In addition, there was an established network of voluntary and paid watchers who looked after the birds in particularly sensitive places, many of which subsequently became nature reserves: Sandwich Bay, Portland Bill, Radipole Lake, Ainsdale Dunes, Skokholm, Skomer and Ramsey Island among them.

After 40 years or so the Society's 4,000 members could look back with some satisfaction on what had been achieved. Perhaps they even looked back with too much satisfaction. The vigorous, young people who had taken on the plumage trade and set about improving bird protection laws in the last years of Queen Victoria's reign were ageing by the 1930s. They had become vulnerable to the attacks of the young, and in 1926 a young man, who more than 50 years later was to be elected President of the RSPB, criticised the Society's approach to bird protection in his book *Birds in England*, whose sub-title was 'An Account of the State of our Bird-life and a Criticism of Bird Protection'. The author, Max Nicholson, did not question the goodwill of the Society and credited it with recognising the true position as to bird protection fairly well, except for its 'exaggerated faith in sanctuaries'. However, he felt that this goodwill did not produce solid achievement, largely because the members did not realise that the problems of protection could not work on a piecemeal basis; in other words, at that time the Society was unable to keep up with the times. Nicholson claimed the branch secretaries publicly advocated views that were widely different from those of its Council: one of them had written to *The Times* advocating that protection be removed from Peregrines because they killed other birds, and her heresy had to be publicly rebuked. Clear and strong leadership was required, claimed Nicholson. It patently was not there, when the Society was seen to equivocate on birds'-nesting and the shooting of birds of prey.

By the early 1930s certain Council members began to express doubts about the conduct of the Society's administration. At its London headquarters was a staff that consisted of a secretary and two assistant secretaries, all of whom were female, helped by a very small clerical staff. The secretary, Miss Linda Gardiner, was due to retire after 35 years' service (a long-service record that will not be beaten for another 10 years at least). In addition, a regular attender at the office was Mrs F. E. Lemon, wife of the Honorary Secretary, a founder member and secretary of the Watchers' Committee. Some elements on the Council felt that a man's hand was needed and that a male secretary with ornithological knowledge should be appointed.

The idea of a male secretary was not greeted with total enthusiasm, especially by the two assistant secretaries (Miss Phyllis Barclay-Smith and Miss Beatrice Solly), both of whom felt their abilities were being ignored. Even in those days Phyllis Barclay-Smith was involved in international bird protection and was well regarded in ornithological circles. She could, therefore, perhaps fairly expect preferment. Indeed, within a few days of Miss Gardiner's retirement in 1935, both she and Miss Solly asked that they should be regarded as of equal standing with the new secretary, although they realised that he would be *primus inter pares*. If their requests were not met, they would regretfully be forced to resign. Both must have been well aware of the character of Mrs Lemon, who had recently been widowed and was Acting Hon. Secretary in her late husband's place, and cannot have been surprised that such a threat was taken as a challenge. Born in 1860, Mrs Lemon was one of the founders of the Society in 1889 and, being a formidable lady, was undoubtedly the driving force in its formative years. But she could be a very difficult lady with strong prejudices and she set a high value on personal relationships, so that the action of the assistant secretaries infuriated her.

The resignations were accepted, and the brief note Mrs Lemon wrote about them in *Bird Notes and News* did not even mention them by name. Mrs Lemon had won the first round, but the disaffection of the assistant secretaries was a manifestation of a widespread feeling in the Society that all was not well. Public airing came in February 1936 in a leader in *The Field*, then the most influential country magazine, when it criticised the organisation of the Society. This started a one-sided correspondence criticising the Council and its ability to run the Society.

At a packed AGM in March that year awkward questions were asked by Captain Adrian Hopkins and Mr E. G. Bentley. The published report of the meeting went into detail about speeches by the Duchess of Portland, Sir Montagu Sharpe, Sir Henry Richards, Lords Desborough and Forester and Field-Marshal Viscount Allenby, but there was no mention of Captain Hopkins' questions about the Society gambling in real estates, inaction over cagebirds, excessive administrative expenses, the excessive ages of ladies involved with the Society, and the dismissal of officers at a moment's notice. There was, however, a reference expressed as laconically as possible to Captain Hopkins' motion, seconded by Eric Parker (editor of *The Field*), that a committee be appointed to investigate the organisation of the Society. That motion had been passed, and a six-man committee set up under the chairmanship of Julian Huxley (then Secretary of the Zoological Society). Their subsequent report made various proposals for reorganisation, most of which were adopted. Some, however, were fought very hard, not least the suggestion that a fixed proportion of Council members should retire each year. That did not come about until twenty-four years later!

The Society had barely settled down under the new secretaryship of Robert Preston Donaldson when World War II began. Five and a half years of hostilities did little for the day-to-day running of the RSPB whose offices, close to the Houses of Parliament, twice sustained severe air raid damage. Nevertheless, the social upheaval of wartime must have helped to spread an interest in and a sympathy for birds. Town-dwellers posted to remote radar stations, far from pubs and dancehalls, found themselves with little in which to take an interest beyond birds. The exploits of Peter Scott in the Royal Navy and the ornithological pursuits of Alanbrooke, one of the country's most popular generals, helped to make an interest in birds acceptable to many of the public. The Society's membership had fallen to 3,558 in 1942; yet by 1946 there were 6,000 members, which suggests that a large number joined or rejoined to celebrate peace.

Some good publicity for birds and the RSPB came as a direct result of the war. The deliberate flooding for defence purposes of some coastal pasture on the Suffolk coast beneath Dunwich Heath, and the accidental flooding (because a stray shell hit a sluice) of an island in the mouth of the River Orwell a little further down the coast, created saltmarshes. On each of these two marshes Avocets were discovered breeding and local conservationists, fearful that their eggs would be stolen, called in the RSPB. Agreements were reached with the landowners and reserves set up. The resulting publicity brought the name of the Society to many people and the Avocet was chosen as its symbol. It was also on these reserves, Minsmere and Havergate, that the RSPB developed the techniques of wetland management for which it is now internationally renowned.

Education had always been an important part of the Society's work. Indeed, in its widest sense it is the prime object of the Royal Charter. In addition to the publication of leaflets, the educational effort had been aimed at children and had been carried out in two main ways. For many years there were two schemes – the Bird and Tree Scheme aimed at elementary schools, and the Public School Essay Competition which was brought up to date in 1945 by being made the Open Essay Competition. Even more important was the founding in 1943 of the Junior Bird Recorders' Club. Its emphasis was on members recording what they saw and many people active in ornithology and conservation today owe a debt to the encouragement given them by the JBRC.

The 1950s were not dramatic years for the Society, but there were some significant events. Membership recruitment had tailed off after the post-war boom; by 1950 there were 6,265 members and by the end of the decade the figure had reached only 8,101. But things were beginning to warm up. First there was the Protection of Birds Act 1954, which covered almost all the points for which the Society had been struggling for most of the century. Then came the successful breeding of Ospreys on Speyside. The attacks by egg-collectors and the impossibility of keeping the presence at Speyside of such a dramatic bird quiet meant that the Society had to announce its presence and set up a major wardening scheme. The newspapers loved the story and there must have been thousands of column inches written about the

Speyside Ospreys over the years. It was during this decade that radio and television showed a serious interest in nature with the founding of the BBC Natural History Unit.

The year 1960 was significant because it was then that deaths of birds due to agricultural toxic chemicals first came to the Society's notice. Since the BTO had been getting similar information, a joint committee was set up to investigate the matter. This forged a strong link between the two organisations. For many years they had shared Council members, who at this time included such influential people as Stanley Cramp, James Ferguson-Lees, James Fisher, Bruce Campbell and Tony Norris. The campaign against persistent chemicals was waged throughout the 1960's and it was a story that received enormous press coverage. It was certainly coverage from which the RSPB benefited in terms of members recruited. In 1960 a record 1,478 new members were recruited.

The following year the RSPB moved offices. Since 1898 they had been in London, convenient for the Houses of Parliament and the clubs of St James's, but by 1960 the composition of Council had changed and the need for these conveniences was no longer so pressing. Besides, office space in London was expensive and the lease on the Eccleston Square offices could be sold profitably and a place in the country be bought with the proceeds, so argued a far-sighted group of Council members. And they were right. The RSPB bought a country house in Bedfordshire for far less than they sold their London property. Three advantages came with the move to Sandy: room for expansion, a position with good communications in all directions, and grounds where the staff could actually see birds.

During the secretaryship of Philip Brown, appointed in 1952, the Society had gone from a neo-Edwardian organisation to one that reflected the new Elizabethan era. When he resigned in 1963, his place was taken by Peter Conder, under whom the Society grew in influence and effectiveness as well as membership, which was more than ten times as large when he retired as when he was appointed. Supported by a far-seeing Council he set about improving the effectiveness of the Society by building up a team of staff professional in their expertise but truly amateur in their enthusiasm. Thus, by 1966 the staff included a reserves manager, an administrator, a research biologist, an education officer, an editor, a films officer, a development officer to increase membership participation and a sales officer. Membership was increasing at an annual rate of three and a half to four thousand, and stood at 31,738 at the end of 1966.

The appointment of a reserves manager signalled the acceleration of reserve acquisition. Coombes Valley came in 1963, Leighton Moss in 1964 and Arne in 1966. The last two were both leasehold and it was not until a million-pound appeal was launched in 1976 that the freeholds were bought. An earlier appeal was launched for money to purchase Vane Farm on Loch Leven, The Gwnffrwd and Ynys-hir in Wales and land at the Ouse Washes in

Cambridgeshire. The reason given in the appeal literature in 1967 for buying the Washes was its breeding Black-tailed Godwits. Today the emphasis would no doubt be different and the Society would appeal on the ground that it was wetland internationally important for its wintering wildfowl, because the accent is now on scarce habitats rather than individual species.

The aim of educating people about birds was not forgotten. The JBRC was given a new look as the Young Ornithologists' Club in 1965, and *Bird Notes* was revamped as *Birds* in 1966. Both these aspects have since developed, with the YOC having 100,000 members today and *Birds* becoming a colour magazine with an important role in retaining members. Both these aspects of the Society have been widely used as models for conservationists abroad: the national organiser of the YOC has been on all-expenses paid trip to the USA to advise the National Audubon Society on setting up a young persons' organisation; and *Birds*, too, has proved a pattern for the magazines of other conservation bodies, both here and abroad.

The RSPB may be unique in that it is probably the only charity in the UK capable of making its own films. The film unit produces films that are seen on television and win awards in competitions with major industrial companies. The tradition goes back to the 1950s when the first RSPB films were made in black and white. Today there are experiments in 35 mm films for showing in the commercial cinema and with RSPB videos, as well as public showings of 16 mm films throughout Britain and Northern Ireland.

Countrywide film shows grew out of the determination in the mid-1960s to involve members more. Another way of doing this was to revise the system of local representatives. In many cases these were merely nominal, being a legacy of the pre-war system of local secretaries, so criticised by Max Nicholson. A new network was built up and it was made clear that to be a local representative meant hard work. Then this was strengthened by the formation of local groups, and today there are more than 160 such groups involved in a variety of activities from fund-raising to beached bird surveying.

A monumental year for the Society came in 1970. During the previous decade a combination of events made public opinion very receptive to the publicity thrown at them from all quarters during European Conservation Year. Added to the continuing saga of the effects of persistent organochlorine pesticides, there had been the *Torrey Canyon* oil pollution incident and the first recorded breeding of Snowy Owls in 1967, and a massive seabird kill in the Irish Sea in 1969. Membership leapt from 43,669 to 65,677 but it wasn't just a result of the ECY publicity. Faith in a professional approach to membership recruitment and an ability to pick the brains of experts were paying off and the society was beginning to learn the best techniques of promoting membership.

Although much of the effort of the 1970s was building on earlier foundations, there were some new departures. International involvement became greater, with a great deal of help given to conservationists abroad, and the Society has been involved with the European Economic Community. Its international reputation is very high and the present director, Ian Prestt, has recently been elected chairman of the Executive Committee of the International Council for Bird Preservation, whose Cambridge headquarters is only 20 miles away from Sandy.

As the number of staff at Sandy grew, it was decided to set up regional offices in other parts of England, to complement those established earlier in Scotland, Northern Ireland and Wales; the process of regionalisation has continued ever since. This helped another development of the 1970s: involvement in planning issues, for which there is now a department.

Throughout the 1960s and 1970s the RSPB and the BTO have worked closely together on several projects. First there was the investigation into the effects of pesticides, which was followed by the joint Birds of Estuaries Enquiry, the RSPB's funding of the Register of Ornithological Sites during the latter's crucial initial period, and now the two organisations are involved in a new survey of the Breeding Waders of Wet Meadows. A high proportion of BTO members also belong to the RSPB; some are so active in both organisations that it would be hard to say to which they feel the most loyalty. Perhaps an aim of the next fifty years would be to see even more members of this sort.

The Wildfowl Trust

MYRFYN OWEN

Founded by Peter Scott in 1946 as the Severn Wildfowl Trust, the new name was adopted in 1954 in recognition of the wide range of its interests in the field of research and conservation. Sir Peter Scott, knighted in 1973 for his contribution to worldwide conservation, continues as the Honorary Director. The aims of the Trust can be summarised under three headings:

(a) education, in the broad sense of creating better awareness of wildfowl (ducks, geese and swans) in particular and nature in general;
(b) conservation of wildfowl and their habitats;
(c) research into wildfowl biology both in the wild and in captivity.

The Trust's headquarters are at Slimbridge, on reclaimed land on the eastern bank of the River Severn in Gloucestershire, chosen because of its wealth of wildfowl and especially the flock of several thousand White-fronted Geese which traditionally come in winter to graze the wet pastures. Initially a few acres were leased from the Berkeley Estate to house the collection of captive birds, and a wardening arrangement agreed with the landlord over the 500 ha (1,250 acre) refuge. In later years farmland was leased and managed for the birds and the Trust's present holding extends to some 320 ha (800 acres).

A much smaller centre was established in 1956 at Peakirk, Northamptonshire, with the object of providing finance for the running of the duck ringing station at Borough Fen Decoy, operated by the Trust since 1951. In the following few years the ringing effort was intensified when decoys at Orielton (Pembrokeshire) and Abbotsbury (Dorset) and trapping stations at Deeping Lake (Northamptonshire) and Abberton Reservoir (Essex) became part of the Trust's sphere of influence. Other ringing stations were later operated by the Trust, the main ones being at Loch Leven (Kinross), which was the site of major research projects initiated by the Trust in the mid-1960s, and Nacton Decoy (Suffolk), the last commercial decoy in Britain. Nacton began its conversion from a centre providing ducks for the market to a ringing station in 1967 and was leased by the Trust in 1968.

The first major wildfowl refuge outside Slimbridge was established in 1967 when the Trust bought 106 ha (260 acres) of land at the Ouse Washes in East Anglia. The holding increased rapidly to 230 ha by 1973 and to 350 ha by 1981. Another refuge was established in 1970 when the Trust leased 340 ha (850 acres) of land, including the 240 ha sanctuary area of Caerlaverock National Nature Reserve, on the Solway Firth in Dumfries-shire. Expansion continued in the 1970s when three major centres were opened, at Martin Mere (Lancashire) and Washington (Tyne and Wear) in 1975 and at Arundel (Sussex) in 1976. As well as collections and educational facilities these centres provided newly created wild areas, and the refuge at Martin Mere within two years held internationally important concentrations of Pinkfeet, Pintail and Teal. The New Grounds at Slimbridge and the Martin Mere refuge are both recognised as Sites of Special Scientific Interest by the Nature Conservancy Council and are in the NCC's list of sites qualifying for designation under the Ramsar Convention.

EDUCATION

The need for the Wildfowl Trust to be deeply involved in education was seen early on as a means of creating a greater public awareness of nature and the need to conserve wildlife and their habitats, under constant threat from man's activities. An educational service has been developed which is particularly directed towards the younger generation visiting the Trust centres, usually on planned school visits. Before the visit preparatory material is sent to the school and on arrival parties are given lectures and escorted walks with qualified teachers and other trained staff. Groups are encouraged to undertake projects on wildfowl biology during their visits and to follow this up with school-based projects. Trained teachers are on the staff of each of the five major centres and many are partly supported by grants from local authority education committees. The number of children catered for on such organised visits is usually in excess of 100,000 a year.

Courses are also run for groups of older students from colleges of education and university education departments. The Trust has strong links with several university zoology departments, and the Research Department at Slimbridge is recognised as an associated institute of Bristol University. Several members of the Trust's scientific staff take part in university teaching programmes, and several PhD. students carry out projects supervised by these staff or use material and facilities provided by the Trust.

The wider public are reached through outside lectures and exhibitions established at major recreational and other events, as well as by the public visiting Trust centres where they are exposed to informative displays, film shows and other educational material. The centres give people an introduction to wildfowl, providing access to the birds at close quarters. The wild areas and refuges supply the opportunity of observing wildfowl in their natural habitat. The Trust has concentrated on providing facilities for large numbers of people to observe wild birds by constructing hides overlooking prime wildfowl habitat and providing screened access. The birds are lured within view of observational facilities by suitable land management and in some cases by providing supplementary food. The number of people visiting centres and refuges rose to 600,000 in 1980, and the growth in active participation is shown by the increase in the proportion of those visiting in winter to view the wild birds, and by the growth in membership, from 5,000 in 1960 to 20,000 in 1981.

CONSERVATION

The early emphasis of the Trust's conservation effort was on reviving by breeding in captivity those species which were threatened with extinction. The Trust played a large part in the programme to change the fortunes of the Hawaiian Goose, down to only 50 individuals in the late 1940s. Many releases of birds reared in captivity (200 from Slimbridge) resulted in the relatively safe number of 1,500 in the wild today. Such efforts continue; the rare White-winged Wood Duck, from Assam and Malaysia, whose status in its native forest habitat is uncertain, has successfully been bred by the Trust in recent years.

Through its refuges the Wildfowl Trust is safeguarding some of the most important wildfowl habitat in Britain. The Ouse Washes at times hold 50,000 wildfowl, including up to a quarter of the western population of Bewick's Swans, and the Trust's reserve forms an important part of this key site. The whole population of Barnacle Geese breeding in Spitsbergen spends the early winter at our Caerlaverock refuge, and the wild refuge at Slimbridge still holds the vast majority of British-wintering European White-fronted Geese, as well as large numbers of Wigeon and Bewick's Swans.

Most of the Trust's work is directed towards wildfowl conservation and by far the largest contribution comes through the education and research programmes. The research work provides basic data on numbers and distribution on which conservation decisions at local, national and international levels are based. Much of our efforts are directed towards obtaining conservation legislation that insures thriving wildfowl stocks while at the same time allowing sensible harvesting of the surplus (by shooting) and ensuring that farmers can protect their crops from severe damage.

The headquarters of the International Waterfowl Research Bureau are at Slimbridge and its Director, Professor G. V. T. Matthews, is also Deputy Director and Director of Research at the Wildfowl Trust. The IWRB is working for the conservation of water birds and their habitats worldwide, and through an international convention for the protection of wetlands and waterfowl – the Ramsar Convention – has made a major contribution in recent years.

RESEARCH

The research work of the Wildfowl Trust falls into three broad categories. Surveys and monitoring includes wildfowl counts, ringing and habitat surveys aimed at assessing present distributions and numbers and at detecting population trends. More detailed studies examine environmental and behavioural factors affecting distribution and numbers. The Trust also undertakes studies of behaviour and other aspects of the life of wildfowl not directly applicable to conservation but adding to our understanding of the birds.

Wildfowl counts

The National Wildfowl Counts were started by the International Wildfowl Inquiry Committee in 1947, and in 1954 the Wildfowl Trust took on responsibility for the counts and appointed George Atkinson-Willes as central organiser. By this time the number of waters covered by the scheme had risen to more than 500. The aim was to obtain counts from each site at monthly intervals at least during the winter, so that the pattern of movement of the different species could be established as well as estimates of their numbers. All the counting at this stage was undertaken by enthusiastic amateurs, and when the counts were taken over by the Trust about 700 individuals were involved in the network. Data were fed through regional or county organisers who took responsibility for the coverage of their particular area. A high level of enthusiasm was maintained by the production of regular reports and by personal contact between the organiser and his team. In the late 1950s a start was made on a major stock-taking exercise – the preparation of *Wildfowl in Great Britain* – a monograph examining in detail the habitats available for wildfowl, the population levels of the different species and the importance of key sites. The book was published in 1963 and still provides the best basic reference work on British wildfowl.

A major impetus for the British counts was the establishment, by IWRB, of an International Wildfowl Count scheme, the first full survey being undertaken in 1967 and organised from Slimbridge. This survey aimed to establish, once or twice during the winter, the distribution of ducks and swans in Europe, western Asia and North Africa, including the whole of most populations wintering in north-west Europe. New observers were recruited and the number of waters counted regularly in Britain jumped from 500–600 to more than a thousand.

Count coverage continues at a high level, and in 1971/72 the Wildfowl Trust combined with the BTO on the Birds of Estuaries Enquiry while continuing the countrywide counts. The two organisations still combine in the production of an annual report on the winter wildfowl and wader counts, those of wildfowl including counts of inland as well as coastal habitats. As the number of reserves owned or managed by local or national organisations has

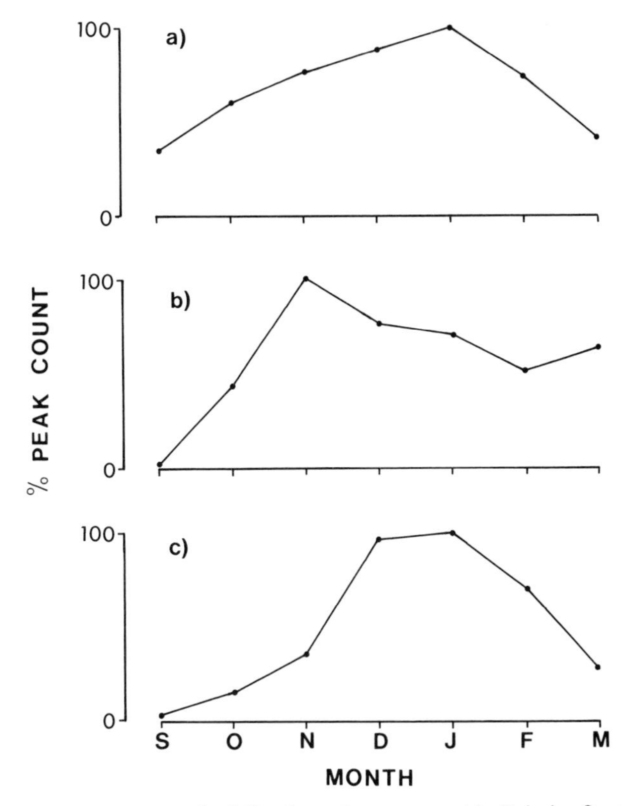

Fig. 31 Monthly pattern of wildfowl numbers counted in Britain, September–March. Values are mean numbers counted in the five years 1976–6 to 1979–80, expressed as a percentage of the peak count in that period. (a) All wildfowl; (b) Whooper Swan; (c) Scaup. All wildfowl includes ducks, geese and swans but is largely made up of dabbling ducks.

increased so has the contribution made to the count network by professional ornithologists. Nevertheless the vast majority of the work is still carried out by amateurs – the total number of counters involved in 1981/82 coverage was over 1,100. Twenty years after *Wildfowl in Great Britain*, a major reassessment is now taking place and the monograph being rewritten. The use of computers makes it possible to analyse the mass of data received between 1960 and 1980 – over 100,000 individual counts from 3,663 waters.

Although the coverage in each winter month is not quite even, most large sites are counted regularly so that the monthly totals can be used to examine the movements of migrant species to and from Britain as shown in Fig. 31. Most species show a gradual build-up in autumn and somewhat more rapid decline in spring (a). Whooper Swans (b), however, originate from Iceland and reach their November peak rapidly before falling in midwinter as many of the birds move on to Ireland. There is a slight increase again in March as

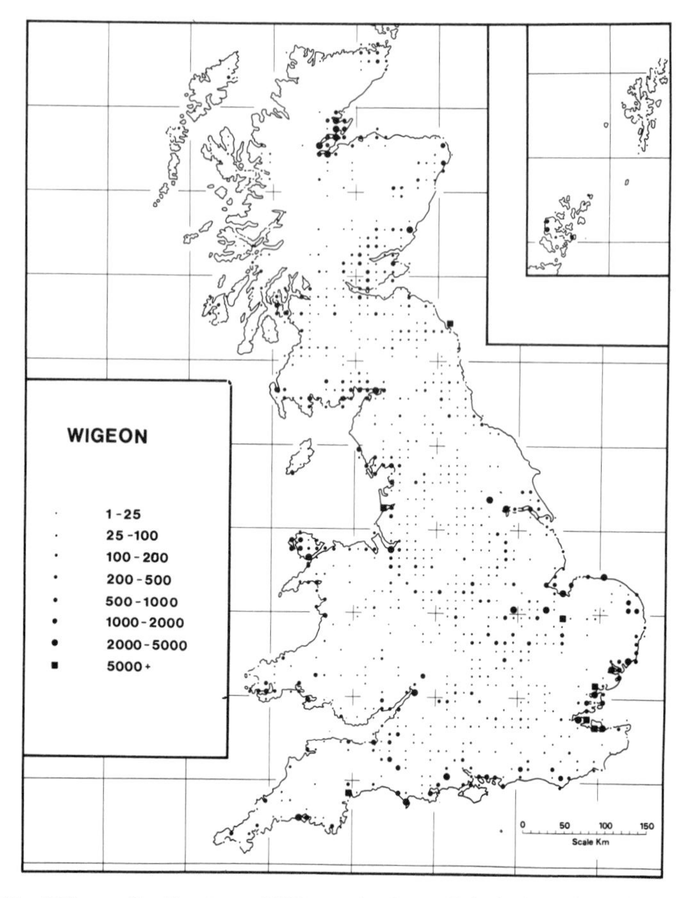

Fig 32 Winter distribution of Wigeon in Great Britain based on the average count for the last five years covered in the month when peak numbers were present. Squares indicate internationally important concentrations (holding 1% or more of the north west European population).

they stop in Scotland on the return journey. Scaup (c) are slow to arrive and are only here in substantial numbers in midwinter.

More accurate data than ever are now available for mapping the distribution of wildfowl species. It is preferable to map on a 10-km square basis since it avoids the problem of delineating sites – always a tricky business where large estuaries or interlinked water complexes are concerned. It also allows the smallest qualifying unit to be a single individual in all cases. As an example, the distribution of Wigeon is shown in Fig. 32. The numbers used for plotting are the mean of the last five counts at a site (usually 1975–80) in the month when peak numbers are counted. Adjacent sites are amalgamated to give totals for each 10-km square. The squares indicate the area holds a concentration of international importance, i.e. one per cent or more of the flyway population of that species.

One of the most important functions of the Wildfowl Counts, and the main reason why they were established, is to indicate trends in wildfowl numbers. These were initially obtained using counts from a sample of 'priority sites' whose returns were sent in during the winter, but this was rather a costly operation and one which proved a rather inaccurate way of establishing trends. With the data now computerised, species totals and trends are readily produced soon after the end of the winter. A report is published within six months of the end of the winter, edited by the present National Organiser, David Salmon. Fluctuations in numbers of three species – Pochard, Tufted Duck and Scaup – from 1960/61 to 1979/80 are shown in Fig. 33.

In common with many other ducks, the Pochard and Tufted Duck have increased dramatically in numbers in the last 20 years. The increase in

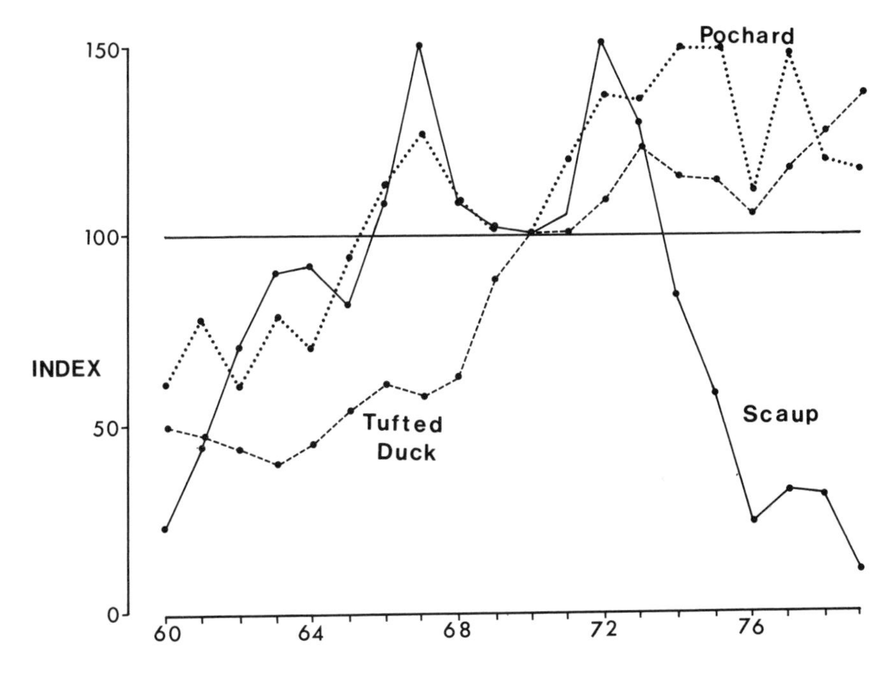

Fig 33 Trends in numbers of three *Aythya* diving ducks in Great Britain, 1960–61 to 1979–80. The index is calculated on the ratio between counts of sites counted in two adjacent years applied to the index of the previous or following year. In each case the index is calculated forward and backwards from 1970–71. The year given is the autumn year of the winter (i.e. 60 = 1960-61).
Solid line: Scaup in January (the peak month).
Dotted line: Pochard, average of December and January index, each months of high population.
Dashed line: Tufted Duck in September, representing the post-breeding population from British breeding pairs.

Pochard numbers reflects an upsurge in the population as a whole and this is probably due to the long series of mild winters since the early 1960s. The September Tufted Duck trend is the result of an increase in the British population, now estimated at about 7,000 pairs, ten years after the Atlas survey estimated 4,000–5,000 pairs. The increase may be due in part to the mild period, but is only made possible by the increase in breeding and wintering habitat for this inland duck in the form of newly created gravel pits and reservoirs.

The Scaup is the only wintering duck to have shown a major decline in recent years, but this is only a return to the level of the early 1960s. The rise and fall of the flock on the south side of the Firth of Forth accounts entirely for this change; the recent decline may be caused by the cleaning of Edinburgh's sewerage system, on whose outfalls the birds largely depended for food. Unfortunately, because there have been no aerial surveys in recent years in the Baltic, where most European Scaup winter, we cannot tell whether the decrease reflects a real decline in the population or merely a distributional shift.

Geese are not well covered by the wildfowl counts because they feed away from water during the day, and their counting is organised separately. Britain holds the whole of the Icelandic population of Greylags and the Iceland/Greenland population of Pinkfeet. They are censused in November each year, again by a network of volunteer observers but with a sizeable contribution by the organiser, Malcolm Ogilvie, from Slimbridge. The counts are complete enough not only to keep track of total numbers but also (by age ratio estimates) the number of young produced and the annual

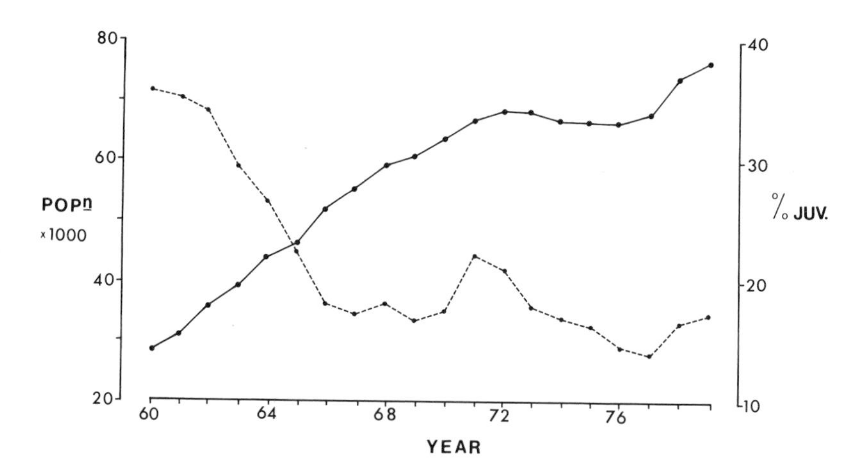

Fig 34 The number of Greylag Geese in the Icelandic population (solid line) since 1960 and the percentage young (dashed line) in the autumn flocks. Both are based on 5-year running means (i.e. figure for 1960 is an average of 1958–62 etc) to even out annual fluctuations.

mortality rate. Both species have increased considerably since the early 1960s but production has declined (Fig. 34). The increase in both species was made possible by a reduction in mortality, with restriction on the sale of dead geese and more controlled shooting; but clearly density-dependent factors are now operating to limit the number of young produced and these probably operate on the breeding grounds. Similar effects have been noted in both Barnacle Goose populations wintering here, but the increase in the numbers of the Dark-bellied Brent have not apparently diminished their reproductive potential in good seasons although the proportion of poor seasons has recently increased.

The wildfowl count system, despite some shortcomings, in that regular and comprehensive coverage of all sites is impossible using an amateur network, has provided us with very good information on the distribution of wildfowl in Britain and fairly accurate indices of trends and estimates of total population. Enthusiasm among amateur counters continues to be high and the system will provide us with counts for as long as there is a need for such information.

Ringing

It was one of the early aims of Peter Scott to discover the origins of all the wildfowl species wintering in Britain, and through the efforts of the Wildfowl Trust and others that aim has very largely been achieved. The most readily available method of catching ducks was the decoy and the one at Slimbridge was put into action as a ringing station in the late 1940s. Decoys provided the bulk of the catch in the 1960s and 70s, when not less than 4,000 ducks were caught annually, with a peak of nearly 11,000 in 1967. Decoys were so successful because they were quiet havens for resting birds amid heavily disturbed areas. With disturbance reduced in many places and with new havens being provided in the form of gravel pit nature reserves, reservoirs and flight ponds their performance has diminished; of the six decoys used extensively for ringing only the one at Slimbridge now catches large numbers. That at Abbotsbury (Dorset) catches a few hundred ducks a year, whereas only a few are trapped at Nacton and Borough Fen; the latter is also preserved as an Ancient Monument.

The trapping station at Abberton continues to be effective and ducks are caught there throughout the year. Particularly encouraging has been the increase in the number of diving ducks, particularly Pochard, caught there recently. A notable increase in the numbers of this species caught was made by the operation of cage traps in gravel pits at Blunham (Bedfordshire), where the 471 caught in 1979 boosted the British total by 50%. The total ringed for each species of wildfowl is given in the Table overleaf.

Mute Swans are relatively easy to catch in baited traps or while being hand fed, but recently Bewick's and Whooper Swans have been lured successfully into traps at Slimbridge, Welney and at Caerlaverock. Mute Swans have also

Total numbers of ducks, geese and swans ringed by the Wildfowl Trust since establishment in 1946. The totals include geese caught and ringed by Trust expeditions overseas and a small number of geese and swans which have been marked with plastic rings only

Mute Swan	2,842	Bewick's Swan	1,201
Whooper Swan	148	Pink-footed Goose	21,716
White-fronted Goose*	581	Greylag Goose	1,786
Canada Goose	1,321	Barnacle Goose	3,548
Brent Goose†	1,217		
Shelduck	446	Wigeon	4,895
Gadwall	1,875	Teal	51,199
Mallard	99,192	Pintail	4,323
Garganey	393	Red-crested Pochard	8
Shoveler	1,810	Tufted Duck	9,725
Pochard	3,403	Scaup	68
Ring-necked Duck	2	Common Scoter	1
Eider	65	Smew	9
Goldeneye	24	Red-breasted Merganser	8
Ruddy Duck	13	Goosander	4

TOTAL SWANS	4,191
TOTAL GEESE	30,169
TOTAL DUCKS	177,463
GRAND TOTAL	211,823

* *A. a. albifrons* plus 3 *A. a. flavirostris*
† *B. b. bernicla* plus 1 *B. b. hrota*

been rounded up during the flightless period – at Loch Leven, where over 200 were ringed in the late 1960s and early 1970s, and at Abbotsbury, where the largest ever swan catch in Britain was made in 1980, when 831 flightless birds were rounded up.

Early attempts at goose catching used clap nets but not much success was achieved until the development, in co-operation with the army, of rocket-propelled nets in the early 1950s. These nets, covering half an acre, were used later with great success and more than 500 geese have been taken at a single firing. Pinkfeet were the major quarry in the early years; Greylag, White-fronted, Barnacle and Brent Geese have also been caught by this method.

The Trust organised expeditions to the breeding grounds of geese to round them up during the flightless period. In Iceland in 1953 no fewer than 9,000 Pinkfeet were rounded up, the majority in 10 days of catching. Recently, trips to the Spitsbergen breeding grounds of Barnacle Geese yielded catches of 1,241 in 1977 and 881 in 1981.

Ringing of geese and swans is nowadays restricted to those populations which are being specially studied and the birds are marked with plastic rings and sometimes with plumage dyes. Of the population of over 1,000 Mute Swans in the vicinity of Abbotsbury almost all are ringed, and a quarter of the 8,000-strong Spitsbergen Barnacle population are individually marked with plastic leg rings.

Population studies

Whereas counts and ringing provide valuable information on numbers and distribution, more detailed studies are necessary to determine how changes in numbers are brought about. Studies of whole populations allow changes in recruitment and mortality to be monitored as well as the factors inducing those changes. Two such projects are currently in progress: the Abbotsbury Mute Swan study began in 1969 and the Solway/Spitsbergen Barnacle project in 1970. Individual marking and considerable effort in following the ringed birds enables their mortality rates at different ages to be measured through their life cycle. In both populations there is competition for nesting sites and only a small proportion of the pairs are successful in rearing young. Breeding success of individuals is related to environmental conditions and their own performance in relation to other members of the population, influenced by age and breeding experience.

Nearly all Mute Swans which are alive and ringed are seen each year, and the annual resighting rate of marked Barnacle Geese averages a remarkable 94%. These geese travel 2,000 miles from their wintering grounds to Spitsbergen, stopping to refuel in Norway on the way. Observers from the Trust have visited Norway and Spitsbergen regularly since 1977, keeping track of marked birds.

Both these study populations are protected (though shooting still accounts for substantial mortality in the Barnacles), but the results of the detailed population data will help in the management of other species through a fuller understanding of the processes of the control of numbers. Wildfowl are long lived and such investigations are necessarily long term. The Mute Swan study is a low-cost one but the Barnacle project involves a large amount of travel overseas. Most of the finance for this work comes from outside, from research councils and other grant awarding bodies. The Trust makes its contribution by maintaining a core of research staff to organise projects and supervise students and other field workers, and by providing unique facilities at its centres and refuges to study the birds at close quarters.

Ecological studies

Achieving an adequate food supply is the major preoccupation of wintering wildfowl, and determining the requirements of each species is a key item in the understanding of their distribution and conservation needs. With the co-operation of wildfowlers who provided duck stomachs for analysis, the diet of most species was investigated countrywide in the 1960s. Later work concentrated on detailed observational studies especially on geese, relating the diet to food availability and numbers and movements to ecological factors such as disturbance, weather, food quality and quantity. Experiments were carried out both in captivity and on a large scale on refuges to determine feeding preferences and the effect of some management practices.

This information was put to practical use in improving habitats by management. The Sevenoaks Gravel Pit Reserve was established jointly by the Wildfowlers' Association (now BASC) and the Wildfowl Trust and proved a very successful experiment in habitat creation. On Trust refuges grazing, flooding and cutting practices are sensitively managed to the needs of the birds. The result of this management, together with the reduction of disturbance to a minimum, has been to increase the use of the areas by wildfowl, spectacularly so at the Ouse Washes and Martin Mere. At the same time the land has been kept in agricultural production and let out to tenants or graziers.

Wild geese, and to some extent swans and ducks, are in conflict with farmers at certain times and the Trust has been involved deeply in trying to reduce this conflict as far as possible. As well as carrying out experimental work to assess damage, studies also involved testing scaring devices and assessing various other means of reducing damage. The use of refuges to lure birds away from conflict situations is a method which has been tried little in Britain but experience at several Wildfowl Trust refuges indicates that it could provide a long term solution in some cases.

Many of the most potent ecological factors influencing wildfowl behaviour are caused by man, and the effect of shooting and disturbance have long been a subject for study. Recently, the effects of water-based recreation on inland sites was scrutinised over three years, using data from special surveys as well as from the Wildfowl Counts. Although recreational pressures have local deleterious effects because of the disturbance they cause, on a national scale the effects have not noticeably affected population levels despite an enormous increase in recreational activity in the last two decades. Many species, such as Mallard and Mute Swan, live happily in close proximity to man, but shyer ducks such as Goldeneye and Teal are affected. The extent of the ingestion of lead shot by wildfowl in Britain has also been investigated recently. All these studies have important implications for wildfowl conservation.

In addition to these investigations, which have an applied basis in conservation terms, the Trust also undertakes and fosters studies of wildfowl biology which have no immediate application. Detailed behavioural studies on the collection birds have provided valuable information on taxonomic relationships, and material from the extensive museum kept at Slimbridge has provided data for many university and other projects. Classic studies have been carried out on orientation of Mallard released from decoy catches, and important advances have been made in the understanding of waterfowl eggs and incubation requirements using egg and nest telemetry. The long term study of Bewick's Swans' social relationships and family histories has provided unique data on the behaviour of long lived species.

All the activities of the Trust are geared towards safeguarding the variety and quantity of wildfowl. We realise that to do this we must create a greater awareness in the public of the value of this natural resource as a source of enjoyment, and the recreational aspects of the Trust's activities are a vital part of this education. More and more, the camera and binoculars are taking over from the wildfowler's gun. The Wildfowl Trust fosters this change in public attitudes, and provides outlets where the pursuit of wildfowl watching and study can be carried out without detriment to the birds and preferably even without their knowledge.

The Royal Society for Nature Conservation and the Nature Conservation Trusts

A. E. SMITH

The growth of the voluntary nature conservation movement in Britain since World War II has been a remarkable scientific and social phenomenon. In the case of the Nature Conservation Trusts its origins lay in the strong tradition of local natural history – not least in ornithology – and in the concern felt by many people for the future of wildlife and wild places. The Trusts have thus combined naturalist and non-naturalist, amateur and professional. They have provided a new focus for concern about the use of land and natural resources and have aroused keen awareness of the political and economic issues involved. Moreover, practical involvement in habitat management in nature reserves has helped to stimulate new approaches to ecological studies, research and experiment.

The time-scale of the County Trust movement has been a short one. It is one of the tragedies of nature conservation in this country that no other county followed the remarkable pioneering example of the foundation of the Norfolk Trust in 1926. Had they done so many sites subsequently lost might have been saved. But the 1920s and 1930s were lean years for nature conservation and it was not until after the war that the second and third Trusts were established in Yorkshire (1946) and Lincolnshire (1948). Even then the movement was slow to gather momentum, only four or five more Trusts being created in the 1950s. Then suddenly around 1960 it caught fire, and within five exciting years 30 more Trusts were launched and virtually the whole country was covered. There are now (1983) 44 Trusts with a total membership exceeding 140,000, each of them dependent on voluntary support and participation but each now employing a small staff to support the administrative and conservation aspects of their work.

This explosion of activity in the 1960s was due in large measure to the stimulus provided by the Royal Society for Nature Conservation (then the Society for the Promotion of Nature Reserves), which had been founded in 1912 under the dynamic and far-sighted leadership of Charles Rothschild. It had made a promising start, with ambitious plans for establishing reserves in Britain and many parts of the Empire, and in spite of the difficulties caused by World War I the Society published in 1916 the first list of areas 'worthy of protection' in the United Kingdom.

Unfortunately the promise of those early years was not fulfilled. In the aftermath of a devastating war government and public were apathetic about nature conservation. The Society failed to attract any popular support and most of its plans came to nothing. Rothschild's untimely death in 1923 was a further setback for it, and its undemocratic structure (Council members were elected for life) was a serious impediment to the introduction of new blood and new ideas. Shortage of money was another difficulty. Opportunities to acquire important sites – St Kilda, for example, was offered to the Society in 1927 for £3,000 – were lost and the Society had difficulty in managing effectively those reserves which it did acquire, like Woodwalton Fen.

Planning for peace during World War II created new prospects for nature conservation, and the SPNR, having failed to persuade government to take action after the Great War, readily responded to a suggestion from the government in 1942 by appointing the Nature Reserves Investigation Committee. The primary purpose of the Committee was to consider the selection, acquisition and management of a series of National Nature Reserves and to identify where they should be. The NRIC, however, subsequently established a network of county sub-committees to collect information about other potential reserves, and it was those bodies which laid the foundations of the vastly increased knowledge of habitats and sites which has facilitated the identification of the statutory Sites of Special Scientific Interest and so provided the basis upon which the Conservation Trusts have selected many of their reserves.

The NRIC indeed, in drawing attention to the hundreds of sites identified by its sub-committees, expressed the view that these 'should be entrusted to the energies and local patriotism of those who may be expected to derive the greatest benefit from them'. It was not, however, until the advent of the Trusts' movement that the Committee's hope was realised. The NRIC's report, published by the SPNR in 1945, prompted the Government to set up its own Wildlife Conservation Special Committee whose famous report (Cmd. 7122) provided the framework for government policy in nature conservation, including the eventual creation of the Nature Conservancy in 1949.

Unfortunately, the SPNR failed to capitalise on its own achievements. In particular, the NRIC county sub-committees, which could have been used to promote conservation in their own counties, were disbanded. They had succeeded, however, in arousing local concern for site protection, and the Trusts' movement owed some of its early inspiration to their work. It was in fact the Trusts themselves which gave the Society a new lease of life. Recognising the close affinity between their aims locally and those of the Society nationally, and needing an umbrella organisation, the six or seven Trusts then in existence approached the Society in 1958 to seek a place within its structure. The Society responded by establishing a Trusts' liaison committee which set about the task of promoting the formation of more Trusts, with results already described. Gradually the Society was adapted to become the Trusts' association, a process completed by a new Royal Charter in 1976 which established the Trusts as the Corporate Members of the Society and effectively gave them control of its affairs.

The Society thus provides the Trusts' movement with a national identity. It promotes their common interests and represents their views on national issues; it gives them a forum for the exchange of ideas and experiences; it has helped them significantly in the search for financial resources (from government and voluntary sources); it provides important services – for examples, a sales business, a members' magazine *Natural World*, a national organisation (the WATCH Club) for their juniors, and a handbook to a selection of their reserves which may be visited by all members. For all these purposes the Society maintains a full-time staff of around 20 based at its headquarters at Nettleham, near Lincoln.

As the spokesman now for a vigorous nation-wide movement, the Society is able to exercise considerable influence on national conservation policies. It has campaigned consistently for many years for stronger legislative protection for habitats and sites, and has sought to draw that aspect of legislation into closer and more meaningful relationship with species protection. The site protection provisions of the Wildlife and Countryside Act 1982 go some way to meeting those objectives and the Society will be much concerned in the next few years with monitoring the working of that Act, especially as it relates to the Sites of Special Scientific Interest. The Society has also made a special study of the problems associated with the decline of the Otter and it plays a major representative rôle on behalf of the Trusts in the Badgers and bovine tuberculosis issue. It was one of the founders of the Farming and Wildlife Advisory Group and retains a leading place in the direction of the Group. In the last two years it has given much thought and attention to the complex and urgent problems of modern agriculture and the conservation of wildlife habitats. Its consultative report 'Towards 2000 – a place for Wildlife in a Land-use Strategy' suggests ways of reconciling those conflicting interests.

Land drainage and water storage have far-reaching effects on wildlife, not least on birds, and the Society has helped to establish liaison arrangements between the Conservation Trusts and Regional Water Authorities. In these and many other ways the Society fulfils an indispensible promotional and co-ordinating rôle for its associated Trusts, enabling them to exercise a corporate strength and influence whilst retaining the local autonomy and concentration of effort which is the key to their success.

The Trusts for their part pursue their objectives in two main and closely related directions: through education and the provision of information and advice on the one hand, and through practical action to safeguard and manage sites and areas of wildlife interest on the other. The balance between these, the emphasis given to one or the other, varies from Trust to Trust and from time to time within individual Trusts. It is indeed one of the great strengths of their local organisation and independence that they are able to respond to local needs and opportunities, to appeal to local loyalties, and to make appropriate use of the voluntary resources available to them. All of them are involved, however, in creating greater awareness and understanding of the natural world among the public at large. They played a leading part in pioneering the nature trail and the visitor centre, and they now provide nearly 30 such centres in reserves where information is available and where exhibits interpret landforms and wildlife and the effects on them of human activities. The total number of visitors to these centres each year is probably in excess of half a million, with tens of thousands more using nature trails and visiting reserves open to the public. Many Trust reserves are used for field studies by schools and other educational institutions and by amateur naturalist bodies. On some particularly suitable reserves, special facilities have been provided for such use – as at Gibraltar Point in Lincolnshire, Skokholm in West Wales and Woods Mill in Sussex.

Advice and representation to local planning authorities and other statutory bodies, and to land owners and users, are of increasing importance to the Trusts. Most of them are closely involved in the work of the county FWAGs and have many direct contacts with individual farmers and landowners. Two Trusts – Gloucestershire and Somerset – employ special officers to give advice to farmers and prepare plans for farm conservation schemes. Liaison procedures between Trusts and Regional Water Authorities, referred to earlier, provide for consultation on river 'improvement' schemes and by this means Trusts are able to seek modifications and make proposals to mitigate the effects of such schemes on riparian habitats. In such ways – however modest and unostentatious they may be – Trusts are influencing the practical treatment of wildlife habitats and features in the wider landscape, many of them of special importance for birds.

Trusts find it equally important to maintain close relations with local planning authorities and to make known their views on structure, local and subject plan proposals, many of which are likely to affect landscape and wildlife interests. Conflicts between such interests and those of agriculture, industry and recreation have resulted in recent years in a number of major public enquiries in which Trusts have been involved, usually in association with the RSPB and the NCC. Many of these enquiries have concerned areas of national ornithological importance – ball clay excavation in the Arne peninsula in Dorset, land drainage at Amberley Wild Brooks in Sussex, saltmarsh reclamation at Gedney Drove End on the Wash in Lincolnshire, and the extension of ski-ing facilities in the Cairngorms, to mention only a few.

Evidence for the conservation case presented at such enquiries has been based on a mass of survey, monitoring and research carried out by professional scientists and amateur naturalists over the years. The impressive evidence for the Gedney Drove End saltmarsh reclamation inquiry, for example, drew heavily on the ornithological and other studies undertaken in connection with the Wash water storage scheme, on the results of ringing by the Wash Wader Group, on the wildfowl counts, on the BTO's Birds of Estuaries Enquiry, and on particular breeding bird surveys conducted by the Lincolnshire and South Humberside Trust and the RSPB. Evidence prepared for all such enquiries on land use issues clearly demonstrates the value of ornithological and other surveys and studies for conservation. BTO enquiries are proving especially valuable in this respect.

The importance of survey is also apparent in the process of selecting sites for protection and management for conservation. In the case of SSSIs, designation is the statutory duty of the NCC whose scientists have carried out much of the survey work involved in the selection. But the Conservation Trusts have made a major contribution to the identification and surveying of these and other sites, through the accumulated records and studies of their members, and in recent years through the employment in many counties of survey teams under the various Manpower Services Commission's schemes for the unemployed.

In this type of survey work also there has been close correlation with the results of such BTO enquiries as the Common Birds Census, the Sites Register, the Waterways Bird Survey and the Birds of Estuaries Enquiry. The current Winter Atlas project, like its Breeding Atlas predecessor, will also yield much new information to throw fresh light on site conservation problems and possibilities.

For several years Trusts have used a sites recording scheme designed for them by the RSNC and the Biological Records Centre of the former Nature Conservancy. The system is being revised in association with the NCC, and it is hoped that it will be adopted by all bodies involved in site conservation and management. The need to collect and make available some of the site data on a national basis and the facilities which would be required for this are also being investigated.

The acquisition and management of nature reserves remains one of the primary objectives of the Conservation Trusts. By the end of 1982 they had established some 1,400 reserves covering more than 112,000 acres. In about a third of these cases they have acquired the freehold and for that purpose have raised at least £2½ million since 1970; the others are held by lease or by agreement in almost equal proportions. The achievement is impressive in quality as in number. A study conducted by the RSNC, and published in 1979, revealed that more than half the Trusts' reserves were SSSIs and some 18% were assessed as Grade 1 or 2 in the NCC's *A Nature Conservation Review*. Thus the Trusts' reserves are making a substantial contribution to habitat and rare species conservation on a national basis. Locally, too, their spreading network of reserves plays an increasingly important part in sustaining populations of localised and specialised plants and animals, and of such habitats as woodland, scrub, heathland, reedbed and coastline. The value of this is often overlooked because the Trusts are not concerned primarily with bird conservation, but with whole plant and animal communities of which, of course, birds are an important and conspicuous element.

Among the 1,400 reserves belonging to Trusts and to RSNC there are many of special ornithological interest. Coastlands of all kinds support particularly rich bird populations and significantly they are the largest habitat group within the Trusts' reserves. Cliff-nesting seabird colonies are found on the Pembrokeshire islands of Skomer and Skokholm, and on St Abbs Head, Longhaven Cliffs and the Eigg reserves in Scotland. Many lowland coast reserves give protection to nesting terns and shore birds such as Shelduck, Oystercatcher, Ringed Plover and Redshank, and these and others support large numbers of migrant and wintering wildfowl and waders. Nationally important examples of shingle beach, sand-dune, saltmarsh and estuary reserves include Spurn Peninsula in Humberside (Yorkshire Trust); Donna Nook, Saltfleetby, Gibraltar Point, and the Wash saltmarshes at Frampton, all in Lincolnshire; Holme and Cley in Norfolk; Landguard Common in Suffolk; Colne Point, Fingringhoe Wick, Northey and Two Tree Islands in Essex; Sandwich Bay (South Swale) in Kent; Farlington Marshes and Keyhaven and the Pennington Marshes in Hampshire; Brownsea Island and West Bexington on the Chesil Beach in Dorset; the Fal-Ruan and Tamar estuaries in Cornwall; Peterstone in Gwent; Cemlyn in Anglesey (North Wales Trust); South Walney in Cumbria; Loch Fleet, Ardmore and the Montrose Basin in Scotland; the Ayres in the Isle of Man; and the Umbra in Northern Ireland.

Lowland coasts are subject to many threats ranging from recreational and shooting pressures to reclamation of saltmarshes and industrialisation of estuaries. In addition to their involvement in the land use issues of coastal areas Trusts are also giving close attention to the practical conservation of breeding sea and shore birds. Little Terns, in particular, receive special protection in several of the above-mentioned reserves and have thereby been saved from the extinction which has befallen so many British colonies. A great deal has been learned in this process about conservation techniques and also, incidentally, about the breeding behaviour of Little Terns.

Wetlands, already reduced to remnants and almost everywhere under threat, are represented in Trusts' reserves by sites of national importance: Grafham Water (Beds. and Hunts. Trust); the Ouse Washes in Cambridgeshire; the Lower Test Valley in Hampshire; Rutland Water in Leicestershire; Barton Lakes and Reedbeds in South Humberside (Lincs. & South Humberside Trust); Cley and Salthouse Marshes, and Barton, Hickling, Martham and Ranworth Broads in Norfolk; Attenborough Gravel Pits in Nottinghamshire; Carlton Marshes and Redgrave and Lopham Fens in Suffolk; Amberley Wild Brooks in Sussex; Wheldrake Ings in Yorkshire; Loch of Lowes, Balgavies Loch and Loch of Lintrathen in Scotland; and Talybont Reservoir in Brecon. Woodwalton Fen, one of the finest fragments of the great fenland, belongs to the RSNC and is leased to the NCC who have restored open fen conditions over much of this famous National Nature Reserve – an impressive example of what can be achieved by management. In addition to these relatively extensive sites, which are important for rarer breeding species of aquatic, reedbed and wet pasture habitats, there are many smaller wetland reserves – gravel pits, ponds, lakes, lochs, flashes, small reservoirs, reedbeds, wet meadows and bogs – which maintain characteristic plant and animal communities including populations of such birds as Little and Great Crested Grebes, Snipe, and Reed Warbler.

Heathland is another fast-disappearing habitat in lowland Britain with rare and endangered bird species, such as Stone-Curlew, Nightjar and Hobby. Among the most extensive heathland reserves belonging to Trusts are the Breckland reserves of the Norfolk Trust, Thursley Common in Surrey, and Skipwith Common in Yorkshire. Many smaller tracts of heath and associated scrub and woodland are protected in lowland English counties from Yorkshire to Devon. Elsewhere, upland moors and mountains are well represented in reserves at Glenmuick and Lochnagar in the Cairngorms and at the RSNC's reserves in Scotland at Benmore Coigach (Ross-shire) and Rahoy Hills in Morvern (Argyll), both of which are managed in association with the Scottish Wildlife Trust; Harbottle Crags in Northumberland; the Bridestones in Yorkshire; Earls Hill in Shropshire, and at Mynydd Ffoesidoes in Radnor Forest (Hereford and Radnor Trust).

Broad-leaved woodland, one of the richest bird habitats, figures prominently in county trust reserves. There are extensive areas of ancient forest in the Sussex Weald at the Mens and at Ebernoe Common, in the New Forest at Brockenhurst Woods, in the Wyre Forest reserve in Worcestershire, and at Great Breach Wood in Somerset. The traditional coppice-with-standards system of management, which produces woodland of great diversity, is a largely obsolete commercial practice. Fortunately, it is being maintained or restored in Trusts' reserves in many counties, notably among larger ones at Bradfield Woods in Suffolk (a reserve owned by the RSNC and now leased to the local Trust), at Hayley Wood in Cambridgeshire, and Waresley Wood (a Beds. and Hunts. Trust Reserve) and Treswell Wood in Nottinghamshire. Heronries are a notable feature of woodland reserves of a number of Trusts, and others are the subject of protective agreements between Trusts and private landowners. Woodland reserves on upland and acid soils, with their specialised avifauna, include the Dart Valley and Dunsford Woods in Devon; Stoneycliffe and Grass Woods in Yorkshire; the Holystone Woodlands in Northumberland; the Caledonian pine forest remnant at the Pass of Ryvoan in the Cairngorms; and the Coedydd Maentwrog and Pengelly Forest Reserves in North and West Wales respectively.

The Trusts' capacity to manage reserves has increased steadily as resources have grown, as volunteer managers have gained experience, and as more conservation officers have been appointed and more full and part-time wardens have been employed on larger sites. In many reserves enhancement of the bird interest is one of the primary aims of management. Ponds and scrapes have been created and in some cases – as, for examples, at Potteric Carr in Yorkshire, Witton-le-Wear in Durham and Hickling Broad in Norfolk – large-scale re-creation of wetland habitat has been undertaken.

Some of Britain's best known bird observatories are closely associated with

Trust reserves. Skokholm, where an observatory was established as long ago as 1933, has for many years been managed by the West Wales Field Society and its successor, the West Wales Trust. Two more of the early observatories – Spurn (1945) and Gibraltar Point (1949) – operate within the security of Trusts' reserves, and both have had a long association with the BTO, including facilities for holding ringers' training courses. The observatory on South Walney also operates within the nature reserve there; and this site is even better known for the work on gull behaviour which was conducted there by Professor N. Tinbergen and members of the Animal Behaviour Department of Oxford University.

Woodland and other habitats on Trusts' reserves provide numerous opportunities for distribution, ecological and behavioural studies, and these have often been used in the course of BTO enquiries and surveys. The use of nature reserves for ornithological studies exemplifies the vital relationship between research and practical conservation. Thus there is a close affinity between the work of the Nature Conservation Trusts and that of the BTO. They have another common interest, too: both depend on a tremendous volume of voluntary effort. The BTO has demonstrated throughout its fifty distinguished years how amateur knowledge and enthusiasm can be harnessed in the interests of research by means which enhance rather than diminish the enjoyment and excitement of birdwatching. For their part, the Trusts are providing opportunities for people to support and become involved in the conservation of their local wildlife and landscapes. It must surely be one of their major tasks in the years ahead to expand the process of creating throughout the community a greater awareness of the natural environment and a sense of practical responsibility for it.

The Scottish Ornithologists' Club

ALASTAIR PEIRSE-DUNCOMBE

The Scottish Ornithologists' Club was founded three years after the British Trust for Ornithology, but it can be traced back to 1929 when (as a schoolboy) the late Dr George Waterston founded the Inverleith Field Club, subsequently to become the Midlothian Ornithological Club, which had as its sole objective the serious study of birds. The SOC was officially formed on 24 March 1936, with a wider base aimed at attracting the support of ornithologists throughout Scotland. George Waterston was its first Secretary, the Misses Baxter and Rintoul its first joint Presidents, and Arthur (later Sir Arthur) Duncan its first Chairman. Sir Arthur was also one of the founders and an original Trustee of the BTO and he, together with Miss Baxter and Miss Rintoul, organised most of the Scottish work in the 1928 Heronry Census of which Max Nicholson was the overall organiser. Co-operation between Scotland and England on census work had therefore started five years before the BTO was founded, and continues to this day.

By 1939 SOC branches had been formed in Edinburgh and Glasgow, but naturally all club activities ceased during the war. The club resumed its meetings in 1945 and in 1947 a third branch was formed, in Aberdeen. Expansion continued and there are now thirteen branches in Scotland from Thurso to the Borders. Membership increased steadily to its present level of just over 3,000.

Since the war the club has passed a number of important milestones. By 1955 a paid part-time secretary had become necessary to cope with the growing membership. George Waterston took on this job at the same time as he was appointed part-time Scottish Representative of the Royal Society for the Protection of Birds. Both organisations continued to grow rapidly and in 1959, on being appointed full-time Scottish Director of the RSPB, George resigned the SOC secretaryship. His wife Irene was appointed in his place and she handed over to the present Secretary in 1969; therefore the SOC has only had three secretaries in its history.

1959 also saw the establishment of the Scottish Centre for Ornithology and Bird Protection, through the generous purchase by an anonymous donor of the house at 21 Regent Terrace in Edinburgh. The offices of the SOC, RSPB and Fair Isle Bird Observatory Trust then came under one roof. In 1968 continued expansion of both the SOC and RSPB forced the latter to seek new premises; they purchased 17 Regent Terrace, only four doors away, so that the close connection between the two organisations continues to this day. The Scottish Centre is the focal point for SOC activities as well as Scottish ornithology in general.

The Club's reference library was started in 1949, largely with books from George Waterston's own collection. Over the years it has expanded considerably and is now one of the leading ornithological libraries in Britain. The Club journal, *Scottish Birds*, is exchanged with many other journals from home and abroad, and the library now includes a most comprehensive range of periodicals. In 1981 the reference library was named the Waterston Library in memory of its founder.

One of the objects of the Club is to publish material relating to Scottish ornithology. Originally papers were published in the *Scottish Naturalist*, but when this ceased publication in 1957 the SOC decided to establish a journal of its own, *Scottish Birds*. The late Professor M. F. M. (Maury) Meiklejohn was editor of the first number, published in the autumn of 1958. *Scottish Birds* appears quarterly and since 1968 has included the annual Scottish Bird Report; from 1978 the SBR has been published separately.

In June 1947 the SOC and the British Ornithologists' Union jointly organised, in Edinburgh, the first weekend ornithological conference held in Britain. The SOC has held an annual weekend conference ever since, and the success of each one is due in part to the programme, which is never too full or rushed, but also to the warm and friendly atmosphere which George Waterston engendered from the start. It has long been one of the highlights of the year. Another of his innovations was a weekend visit to the Solway goose grounds. On one of the first, in 1959, the SOC was invited to join the annual conference of BTO Regional Representatives being held in Dumfries and to attend its open meetings.

The co-operation between Scottish and English ornithologists, started before either the SOC or BTO had been founded, has continued through the years. In the early days of both organisations there was youthful rivalry, but recent years have seen much co-operation and the SOC has often provided a Scottish national organiser for BTO work. The very successful Atlas of Breeding Birds was organised in Scotland by Christopher Headlam; Malcolm Castle organised the Rookery Survey; and this year the Scottish organisers of the Silver Jubilee Mute Swan Census are Allan and Lyndesay Brown. In recent years another aspect of co-operation has been the annual weekend meeting of Scottish ringers; while the weekend is arranged by the BTO, almost all who attend are also SOC members.

The versatility of the SOC is further demonstrated by two other events. In 1966, when the 14th International Ornithological Congress was held in Britain, the Club organised a Scottish Bird-Island Study Cruise. Nine hundred ornithologists from many countries, of whom 400 were delegates to the Congress, enjoyed a week sailing round the north of Scotland from the Clyde to the Forth, taking in most of the famous bird islands on the way. In the official report of the Congress the Cruise was described as 'the longest, most ambitious, and most imaginative excursion that has ever been provided for an International Ornithological Congress. Through a combination of superb organisation, favourable weather and general goodwill it was an immense success'. For those fortunate to have been on it, the Cruise is a memory they will never forget.

Earlier, in 1963, the club established its Bird Bookshop, as there was a need for a really good specialist bird bookshop. It has grown out of all recognition from those early days and now has a worldwide mail order business. Since 1965 the SOC has very gratefully accepted an invitation from the BTO to bring a collection of books to its annual conference. BTO members are given the opportunity to browse over a wide selection of books in the informal and relaxed atmosphere of the weekend.

The standard work on the history, status and distribution of Scottish birds, *The Birds of Scotland*, published in 1953 and now out of print, was written by the club's eminent founder-Presidents – Miss Baxter and Miss Rintoul. It is fitting, therefore, that a successor to this book is now being prepared by Miss Valerie Thom, whose term of office as President of the SOC finished in October 1981. Publication, on behalf of the club, of *Birds in Scotland*, is planned for 1985, adding another chapter to Scottish ornithology, and in time for the club to celebrate its own Jubilee in 1986.

In wishing the BTO every success in the future, the SOC looks forward to continued co-operation in the field of ornithological research during the next fifty years.

The Irish Wildbird Conservancy

CLIVE HUTCHINSON

In the year that the BTO celebrates its fiftieth anniversary the Irish Wildbird Conservancy celebrates its fourteenth birthday. An outsider might have thought that the coming together of three diverse Irish conservation and ornithological bodies to form one united organisation would have resulted in a reduction of the influence of the BTO on Irish ornithology. The BTO had for many years provided a focal point for the few active field ornithologists. The pages of *Bird Study* in the 1950s and 1960s indicate how few they were; all the papers on Irish birds were either by Major R. F. Ruttledge or a British author. The wide-ranging enquiries into single species normally left out Ireland altogether; the few, like the Fulmar enquiry, which did cover Ireland, depended on visiting British observers for most of the results. Even the bird observatories at Saltee and Cape Clear relied for their survival on visits from English observers, almost invariably BTO members.

Ornithology in the Republic in the 1950s and 1960s was organised into the Irish Ornithologists' Club, a small club based in Dublin, and the Irish Society for the Protection of Birds, a dormant reflection of the RSPB. In the mid-1960s a threat to the Wexford Slobs posed by the purchase of this famous goose wintering area for intensive farming provided the motive for yet another body, the Irish Wildfowl Committee. This organisation attracted a large number of members very rapidly and established a reputation for aggressive publicity. In late 1968 the young, vigorous body and the older, staid bodies merged to form the present IWC with the objectives of (a) conservation, (b) education, (c) research, and (d) encouragement of field ornithology in relation to wild birds and their environment in Ireland. The overall aim was to capture the entire bird conservation and birdwatching market in Ireland for one vigorous and influential body which would pursue the same objectives as both the BTO and the RSPB in Britain. Indeed, the unspoken ambitions of those responsible for the merger were greater: the unwieldy title was chosen carefully so that in due course the new body could grow into an Irish 'Wildlife' Conservancy.

In contrast to what an outside observer of these developments might have thought, the close relationship with and influence on Irish ornithology of the BTO did not diminish. Instead, it increased enormously and the prime reason was the success of the BTO in persuading the IWC to adopt the Breeding Atlas project. At the time, few Irish ornithologists thought there was much chance of completing coverage of the country, but a combination of factors resulted in the project being a wonderful success. Trust members from Britain spent holidays in Ireland atlassing, Tim Sharrock spent several months atlassing here, and the IWC was remarkably lucky in having David Scott to organise the survey and carry out months of fieldwork from his caravan base each summer. More than anything else, the Atlas showed Irish birdwatchers that, despite their small numbers, large-scale surveys were possible throughout the country.

The very success of the project produced a rush of requests for Irish participation in surveys, but the BTO Council agreed that all such requests should be channelled through the IWC. The Irish ornithological establishment was keen on getting Common Birds Census work going but birdwatchers failed to react. Instead, the next successful co-operative project was the Birds of Estuaries Enquiry. After a visit by Tony Prater to eastern and southern Ireland in 1970, counting waders, Irish interest was stimulated and the IWC adopted the survey with enthusiasm, expanding it to cover lakes, rivers and marshes and calling it the Wetlands Enquiry. This was a case of the IWC showing a new self-confidence, modifying a BTO-sponsored enquiry to suit Irish conditions and expanding its terms of reference to seek information on the relatively unknown but immensely rich inland habitats of the west of Ireland. The Irish contribution to this survey appeared in a separate book (Hutchinson 1979) in the additional detail required by Ireland's circumstances, but there were separate chapters on the Republic and Northern Ireland in the BTO's book (Prater 1981).

The excellent relationship between the IWC and BTO was strengthened by the reaction of the BTO and Scottish Ornithologists' Club to Irish suggestions for a Corncrake breeding survey in 1978. This declining breeding species is much more widespread in Ireland than in Britain and a decision to carry out a survey in Ireland was followed rapidly by the BTO Council agreeing to survey those breeding in Britain. Although the results of the survey indicated a gloomy position for the Corncrake, the project did show that Irish birdwatchers were as keen as those anywhere to carry out co-operative surveys. Indeed, they may well be more enthusiastic and hardworking than their representatives give them credit for. The IWC Council was less willing (because of shortage of funds) to commit itself to the Winter Atlas than was the BTO Council, but the huge response from members in 1981/82 and the BTO's generous financial assistance persuaded the IWC Council to agree to complete the survey. The first year's fieldwork for the Winter Atlas was far more successful than most expected in Ireland. It now seems that it will be a very worthy successor to the Atlas of Breeding Birds.

Another example of the advantages to the IWC of co-operation with the BTO is the area of bird-ringing. It may be difficult for most BTO members to comprehend the problems for a country with a mere handful of qualified ringers in developing a broad ringing base; and there were very few qualified ringers in Ireland before the first BTO ringing course was held at Dundrum Nature Reserve in 1970. Since then a series of BTO-run courses has been almost entirely responsible for building up a nucleus of keen ringers who produce an *Irish Ringers Bulletin*, an Irish Ringing Report and ring

25,000–30,000 birds per annum.

In many ways Irish ornithology differs from that in Britain. It is perhaps more competitive and less aware of the urgent need to monitor common bird populations; it has far fewer financial resources for conservation; it has been described as narrowly based on the energies of a few really active ornithologists whose drive carries others along (O'Connor 1980c). But it has developed rapidly over the past fourteen years and much of the progress achieved has been influenced by the example of the BTO and the willingness of its staff and members to advise and assist in many ways.

Bird reserves of the Scottish Wildlife Trust

BERNARD GILCHRIST

The Scottish Wildlife Trust has established fifty-eight reserves covering some 37,500 acres of land and water. They include a wide selection of the habitats to be found in Scotland, thus bringing within the Trust's estate a very broad range of bird species, whether or not the object of creating the individual reserves was the protection of any particular bird.

The Trust, like its equivalents in England, Wales and Ulster, works to a broad remit, covering all forms of wild plants and animals and the habitats in which they live. It therefore attracts a great many ornithologists (among others) interested in nature conservation, including many who are also members of the Scottish Ornithologists' Club and the British Trust for Ornithology, and some who also operate with the Royal Society for the Protection of Birds. Such persons take part in the various surveys of birds promoted by these bodies, whilst some members gather information independently. Hence all information gathered in Scotland is readily available to the Trust, which is able to assess each site for its ornithological qualities and to quantify these in conjunction with other interests.

The Trust has taken over some sites as reserves with the safeguarding of particular birds in view. In response to general concern for the Little Tern the Trust created reserves at two sites on the west coast at Ballantrae (Ayrshire) and Rhunahaorine Point (Kintyre). The first of these is exposed to visiting by the public and therefore is wardened in the breeding season. When the Loch of Lowes (Perthshire) was purchased for a reserve in May 1969 the presence of five pairs of breeding Great Crested Grebes, and the knowledge that when this species returned to nest in Scotland (in 1870) it was to this loch, were factors in its selection. However, within two months Ospreys moved in to build an eyrie and have returned each year since, so that the reserve may now be said to be also for the protection of this rarity. Elsewhere, Grey Herons nest on Eilean na Creige Duibhe reserve in Wester Ross and Manx Shearwaters at one of the reserves on the island of Eigg. Golden Eagle, Peregrine Falcon, Greenshank, Black and Red-throated Divers, Ptarmigan and Dotterel nest on some of the Trust's wilder upland reserves.

The native pinewoods of the Pass of Ryvoan reserve contain a full complement of Crested Tit, Crossbill and Redstart typical of that habitat, and the broadleaved woodlands of the Falls of Clyde (Lanarkshire) and Roslin Glen (Midlothian) similarly contain woodpeckers, tits and warblers among other birds. Unfortunately there is no gannetry among the Trust reserves and the *machairs* of the west, with their breeding wading birds and Corncrakes, are missing too.

Open water, and wetland sites within reserves, include Loch of Lowes

(Perthshire), Loch Libo (Renfrewshire), Possil Marsh (Glasgow), and Duns Castle, Yetholm Loch and Hoselaw Loch in the Borders. These are all in lowland situations with fringing and locally extensive marsh vegetation. They are breeding localities for Great Crested Grebe and Little Grebe, Tufted Duck, Mallard, Pochard, Coot and Moorhen. In winter they are the home of greater numbers of these species, and are joined by Goldeneye.

Six reserves are major bird sites: two are inland, two are coastal seabird breeding cliffs, and two are estuaries. They are all in the east of the country, and are: Balgavies Loch (Angus), Loch of Lintrathen (Angus), Longhaven Cliffs (Aberdeenshire), St Abb's Head (Berwickshire), Loch Fleet (Sutherland), and Montrose Basin (Angus).

The Scottish Wildlife Trust advises the Scottish Development Department on wildlife conservation in Royal Parks, which include Linlithgow Loch and the Duddingston Loch Sanctuary in Holyrood Park, Edinburgh, both excellent places for viewing waterbirds, including Great Crested Grebes.

7: Pollution, problems and pests

Agriculture and birds: the present and the near future

NORMAN W. MOORE

Britain was once largely forest, but 80% of it is now farmland. The present distribution and the numbers of land birds in Britain closely reflect agricultural practices and an understanding of changes in these practices is essential for an understanding of changes in our avifauna.

Basically, Britain has gone through three ecological stages since the withdrawal of the ice. The first stage was when forest covered most of the country – pine forest in mid-central Scotland, deciduous forest elsewhere. Man had relatively little effect on the environment at this time. The avifauna must have been predominantly a woodland one. Most of the land which was not forest was wetland, and species such as the Skylark, which are restricted to dry open land, must have been very limited in numbers and distribution. The second stage was that of traditional agriculture. It started in Mesolithic times and continued into the lifetime of many today. Of course, there were immense differences between a neolithic farm, a medieval farm and a farm of the 1930s; but they shared fundamental characteristics: they were largely dependent on renewable resources and on human and animal labour.

By the end of Saxon times most of the forest had been cleared in England, and by the end of the 19th century only about 4% of the total land surface of Britain retained its original woodland cover, but highly modified. To some extent the loss of woodland was made good by the planting of hedges during the enclosures from the 16th to the 19th centuries. The numbers of those bird species which were entirely dependent on woodlands must have declined considerably during the change from forest to traditional agriculture. Yet, surprisingly, the avifauna of farmland remained an essentially woodland one, although many species which nested in woods and hedges fed extensively on crop lands. The few species pre-adapted to living on open land must have increased enormously during this period – notably Skylark, Meadow Pipit, Corn Bunting, Lapwing, and Grey Partridge.

The third stage of agriculture is the industrial stage, which already predominates over most of lowland Britain. It is characterised by the replacement of human and animal labour by machines, and farmyard manure by artificial fertilisers. Pesticides, based on new synthetic substances, are used extensively to control weeds and fungal and insect pests. Machines, fertilisers and pesticides are largely dependant on fossil fuels. Industrial farming necessitates complex marketing, economic and political activities, which in turn favour uniform treatments of land. Hence agriculture becomes less tailor-made to suit local conditions. The rapid change from traditional to industrial farming is likely to produce considerable changes in the avifauna, but they will not be as great as those caused by the original clearance of the forests.

The BTO was founded at the end of the traditional farming era. Many of its investigations have been or could be used to measure the effects on birds of the transition to industrial farming; the Common Birds Census was inaugurated with that aim in mind. The following section attempts to relate the complex relationship of the factors at present at work in order to provide a basis for predicting what may happen in the immediate future. Agriculture affects bird populations in two ways. First, it alters and destroys habitats; second, its tools of fertilisers, pesticides and biological control agents have direct or indirect effects on bird populations. In addition, agricultural land and the birds on it can be affected directly or indirectly by industrial processes sited on non-agricultural land.

LOSS AND ALTERATION OF HABITAT

Throughout most of the period of traditional farming, woods formed an integral part of a farm. They supplied fuel and timber for building, ships, fences, implements, and supports for hops and other crops. The larger woods provided pannage for pigs and a habitat for deer and other game. When they ceased to have significant value in providing timber for local needs, many were retained as cover for Pheasants. The woods which exist today usually do so because:

(a) they still have economic value for forestry;
(b) they are valuable for game preservation;
(c) they provide shelter for stock in the uplands;
(d) they occur on steep or rocky ground, and so are difficult to reclaim.

These reasons have not been strong enough to conserve many woodlands; many have disappeared and have been replaced by barley or grass leys. When this happens the original woodland bird fauna is totally destroyed.

Modifications of woodland management also have profound effects on woodland birds. The ancient practice of coppice-with-standards was particularly favourable to wildlife, since it provided a rotation of cleared woodland, scrub and high forest, and so catered for all types of woodland bird. This practice is now rare; it is virtually restricted to sweet chestnut coppicing in the south-east of England and as a result the populations of species (such as Nightingales) which are dependent on the scrub stage have declined. The widespread conversion of much deciduous woodland to conifer plantation has also been inimical to most woodland species, though it has favoured others, for examples, Goldcrest and Coal Tit.

Many plant and insect species are confined to ancient woodland, but birds are more adaptable and most woodland birds can breed successfully in plantations of broadleaved trees and in gardens. Therefore their future is less dependent on the conservation of ancient woodland than is the case for plants and insects. It is unlikely that the small wood will ever become an essential element of the industrial farm; therefore their future in the lowlands will largely depend on game conservation. Most lowland woods are on land which could grow arable crops or grass; if field sports were no longer practiced many more woods would be converted to farmland unless they could be conserved deliberately for nature conservation and landscape.

Hedges have been an important feature of much farmland for many centuries. However, they came relatively late to areas such as the East Midlands. Their greatest extent was reached by the mid-19th century, and this peak was retained until World War II. Then, field sizes which were related to the horse became too small for machines, and one of the inevitable effects of the industrialisation of agriculture was to reduce the number of farm hedgerows. Approximately one-quarter of the hedges present at the end of the enclosures were removed during and after World War II, mostly in the late 1950s and 1960s. As with the loss of woods, the loss of hedges caused the loss of birds nesting in them, and also greatly reduced the amount of food available for wintering species such as Fieldfares and Redwings. If the field boundary remained after clearance, and the hedge was replaced by grass and a wire fence, this still provided suitable habitat for Grey Partridges and Corn Buntings and (if the ground vegetation was allowed to become very rank) for

Yellowhammers, Reed Buntings, Sedge Warblers and Whitethroats.

The traditional method of hedge management known as laying is labour consuming and therefore expensive. Today it is only practiced extensively in some stockfarming areas where hedges retain the function of an efficient fence, and in some fox-hunting counties where layed hedges provide jumps. Layed hedges ensure thick bottoms and so they are more suitable for birds than some other types. To reduce costs most hedges today are cut mechanically; a good many are coppiced to ground level. These treatments result in a loss of future hedgerow trees, and in a great reduction in the number of fruits. Therefore they are much less good for birds although the effects of modern hedgerow management have not yet been quantified. Few studies have been made on the rate of hedge removal in recent years, but it must have declined in eastern counties where few hedges remain. However, corn-growing is increasing at the expense of animal husbandry in the West Midlands, for example, so in such areas the rate of hedge removal may have increased. Few new hedges are planted anywhere in Britain today and, overall, we can expect a continual decline in hedges but probably at a slower rate. As with woods their survival in many lowland areas will depend on game preservation. If oil prices, and hence the price of pesticides, continue to rise there will be pressure on farmers to control pests using biological methods. If it can be shown that hedges support enough predatory insects to have significant effects on pest species farmers may be more easily persuaded to retain hedges or even plant new ones. Recent work suggests that hedges and field boundaries may be more important in this respect than has been supposed.

Changes in grassland husbandry have had most profound effects on the flora and fauna of Britain because most of the herb-rich meadows and pastures, which were such a feature of traditional farming, have been ploughed up and re-sown as monocultures of highly productive strains of grass such as Italian rye-grass. While the effects on the invertebrates dependant on the plants have been immense, those on birds have been less spectacular: Meadow Pipits have probably declined for this reason but Skylarks and Lapwings have remained abundant.

The development of earth-moving machines has made it much easier to reclaim heathlands and wetlands, and these habitats have been reclaimed on a vast scale throughout Britain, with the result that heathland species such as Stonechat and Dartford Warbler, and wetland birds such as Snipe and Redshank, have lost a large proportion of their total available habitat. Reclaimed heathland is poor in nutrients and so requires large inputs of fertiliser to maintain fertility. Increases in the cost of fertiliser may lead to the abandonment of some reclaimed heathland, but it is more likely that the latter will be used for industrial and urban development and forestry than that it will revert to heathland. By contrast, the drainage of wetlands is bound to remain financially advantageous in the foreseeable future, especially where arable crops can replace grass. Thus, both heathlands and wetlands will continue to be under constant threat, and their survival will depend almost entirely on their being acquired as nature reserves by the NCC, the RSPB and the County Trusts.

Upland heaths and moorlands lost their forest birds when they were converted by fire and sheep to their present state, but they have gained populations of a number of interesting species, such as Red Grouse, Golden Plover and Merlin. The need to reduce timber imports is likely to favour increased afforestation in Scotland, Wales and northern England; already there is more land under planted conifers than under broad-leaved woodland. The general effects of afforestation of moorland are obvious – the moorland species decline and the forest ones increase. The present trend towards the substitution of trees for sheep is likely to continue. This can hardly fail to cause a decline in such species as Red Grouse, Golden Plover, Merlin, Golden Eagle and Raven, and an increase in such others as Goldcrest, Crested Tit, Coal Tit, Scottish Crossbill and Goshawk.

Much grassland in river valleys has been lost to gravel and sand extraction. Where pits are allowed to remain wet they provide valuable habitats for numerous species, notably Coot, Great Crested Grebe, Tufted Duck, Little Ringed Plover and Common Tern.

Arable farming now depends on the annual application of fertilisers, herbicides, fungicides and insecticides, rapid harvesting with combines and early ploughing after harvest. The period when land is under stubble is very short and straw or stubble is usually burnt to reduce disease and to provide nutrients. As a result many plant and animal foods of birds have been greatly reduced. This must have affected many species, but it has only been studied extensively in the Grey Partridge. This species has declined conspicuously since the advent of industrialised farming, the loss of invertebrate food for the young being the main cause. In the Grey Patridge the effects of pesticides have mainly been indirect, in other species they have been direct.

THE EFFECT OF AGRICULTURAL AND OTHER CHEMICALS

Pesticides are chemicals used to control organisms which compete with crops or with man. None are specific to pests and so all affect populations of beneficial or neutral species of wildlife to some extent. They can kill birds by direct poisoning or through the food-chain, and they can also affect them indirectly (as we have seen in the case of the Grey Partridge) by reducing their food supply. Some pesticides can have sub-lethal effects on reproduction and they may make birds more susceptible to other stresses.

In general, herbicides and fungicides have little direct effect on birds but since they greatly affect insect populations it is unlikely that the Grey Partridge is the only bird to have been affected indirectly by these substances. On the other hand, many insecticides are toxic to birds and have killed many individuals. The extent to which a bird is under threat from an insecticide depends on its own genetic make-up and the amount of the insecticide which it consumes, and hence on the availability of the insecticide to the bird. Thus, while many birds eat corn dressed with the organophosphorus insecticide Carbofenothion, this chemical has only caused significant casualties among Greylag and Pink-footed Geese, which are both unusually sensitive to it. When corn dressed with Dieldrin was properly buried at sowing it had no effects on birds, but when the ground was wet and corn got left on the surface it acted like a poison bait and killed thousands of pigeons, gamebirds and seed-eating passerines.

Dieldrin was not only a very toxic substance but, like some other organochlorine insecticides, was very persistent since it was fat-soluble. This meant that when animals consumed food contaminated with it, it became concentrated in their body fat. So long as they did not mobilise their fat, as in hard weather, this did them no harm, but it made them extremely dangerous to predators which consumed their whole bodies and hence their accumulated residues. Secondary poisoning by Dieldrin in this way was the principal cause of the catastrophic declines of the Peregrine and Sparrowhawk and the decline in the fertility of the Golden Eagle in the 1950s and the 1960s. These species were saved from probable extinction by restrictions put on the use of Aldrin and Dieldrin in the 1960s and 1970s. The much less toxic but very persistent DDT had similar effects. Until its use was prevented it killed many Blackbirds and other species in orchards. Its principal metabolite (DDE) caused egg-shell thinning and this, together with other sub-lethal effects, reduced the rate of recovery of those species whose populations had been reduced by Dieldrin. Recent work shows that despite severe restrictions on the use of DDT in the United Kingdom, and indeed in Western Europe, many Sparrowhawks in Britain still contain levels of DDE which indicate hazard. It is not known whether this is due to DDT being used on a larger scale than suggested by the MAFF and DAFS surveys of pesticide use, or to Sparrowhawks eating migrant birds which have picked up DDT outside the United Kingdom, or to the continued cycling of DDT in British ecosystems. Thus, while the persistent organochlorine insecticides no longer provide a serious threat to British birds, the problem of their use has not been completely solved. As the Pesticide Safety Precaution Scheme became increasingly sophisticated in the light of experience, the dangers were reduced of particular pesticides producing harmful effects on the scale of the organochlorine insecticides. Doubtless new problems will arise; at present the main worries are over the extremely toxic carbamates used on sugarbeet and potatoes and some of the synthetic pyrethroids which are particularly toxic to aquatic organisms. But the principal concern today is about the effect which the sum total of all pesticides may be having on the farming ecosystem; this is likely to be considerable but is extremely difficult to investigate. However, the monitoring studies carried out on North Farm by the Game Conservancy (with support from ARC) and more recently the studies by

MAFF and others at the Boxworth Experimental Husbandry Farm in Cambridgeshire are the first steps in tackling it. If these studies show that it is possible to make better use of natural predators, and if the cost of pesticides increases, there is a very real possibility that pesticide use on farms will decline.

Biological control of introduced pests has been successful in many parts of the world. In Britain, it has been used successfully on glasshouse crops but, of course, this has had no effect on bird populations. The drastic reduction of the British rabbit population by the introduced myxoma virus had considerable effects on plants and hence on insect populations. The decline of rabbits probably reduced Wheatear habitat on the remaining unimproved grasslands; it certainly reduced the food supply of the Buzzard and, as was shown by the BTO surveys of 1954–56, it temporarily reduced breeding success of that species. Though predation by native invertebrate predators almost certainly prevents outbreaks of pests occurring, deliberate use of biological control to control native pests has proved difficult. The research mentioned above may conceivably make it more possible in the future. If so, this is likely to favour bird species which at present suffer from the total effects of pesticide use.

The great increase in the use of artificial fertilisers has had an immense effect on the flora and invertebrate fauna of Britain, principally by reducing acid conditions in the lowlands and by causing the eutrophication of ponds, ditches and rivers. Their effects on birds have not been studied in the lowlands. It has been shown experimentally that Red Grouse populations in the uplands can be increased by the addition of fertilisers to heather moor. However, higher application rates which turn moorland into grassland must have had deleterious effects on Golden Plover.

Industrial pollutants such as mercury and cadmium can have severe local effects near factories or effluent outlets. Doubtless many small areas in Britain support fewer birds than they otherwise would because of industrial pollution. Polychlorinated biphenyls (PCBs), which have chemical affinity to DDT, are widely distributed in the environment, but there is no evidence to suggest that they have had significant effects on terrestrial bird populations. If coal burning greatly increases, and measures are not taken to reduce the amount of acid rain which results from it, many bird habitats might become affected adversely.

CONCLUSIONS AND THE FUTURE

Birds are much more adaptable than most animals, and as a result the change from traditional agriculture to industrial agriculture during the last 40 years has not had the catastrophic effects it has had on plants, invertebrates, amphibia and reptiles. However, like other wildlife, they are becoming increasingly dependent on the uncropped areas of farms which are no longer connected functionally with the business of farming. Therefore habitats and birds increasingly depend for their survival on activities other than farming, whether these are forestry, game conservation, recreation or nature conservation. So long as the nation decides to produce most of its own food this situation is likely to continue and farming and conservation to become increasingly polarised. There is very little likelihood that agriculture in Britain will return to traditional methods and low productivity, because even if Britain needed to produce less food on her own account, she and other nations in the temperate regions will probably have to provide food for the Third World; hence governments of all complexions will continue to support highly productive, industrialised agriculture in Britain. New farming methods will become increasingly sophisticated and will make use of electronics.

Biological and cultural methods will become better integrated with chemical methods and will reduce pesticide use, but they will not do so by using semi-natural habitats on a large scale. Hence these changes will have relatively little effect on bird populations. In the past, wildlife existed as a by-product of what were then good agricultural practices. In the future, wildlife will have to be catered for by deliberate conservation measures: woods, hedges, heaths, marshes and ponds will then exist primarily for the conservation of wildlife and to produce a landscape which includes both productive agriculture and the elements from which it evolved.

SOURCES: Alexander (1932); Arnold (in press, *J. Appl. Ecol.*); Bull, Mead and Williamson (1976); Campbell (1953); Chapman (1939); Colquhoun and Morley (1941); Davidson and Lloyd (1977); Flegg (1975); Fuller (1982); Fuller and Youngman (1979); Godwin (1975); Hoskins (1977); Mabey (1980); Mellanby (1970); Moore (1967, 1974); Moore, Hooper and Davies (1967); Morgan and O'Connor (1980); Moriarty (1975); Murton (1971); Newton (1972); Osborne (1982); Pollard, Hooper and Moore (1974); Potts (1980); Rackham (1976); Ratcliffe (1977, 1980); Sage and Vernon (1978); Sharrock (1976); Sheail (1971); Shrubb (1970); Snow and Mayer-Gross (1967); Southward (1961); Warren and Goldsmith (1974); Williamson (1967); Wyllie (1976).

Woodland and forestry

JOHN ANDREWS

Forestry in the United Kingdom now presents great challenges and exciting new opportunities for bird conservation. In the past, relations between forestry interests and 'countryside organisations' have varied from a state of suspicious truce in some cases to open hostility and conflict in others. Sadly, this is still generally the case, but there are realistic prospects for combining interests in both the uplands and the lowlands.

Of course, there are aspects of forestry that still concern us and which will undoubtedly continue to pose problems in the future. Paramount amongst these is the afforestation of open moorland which hold important populations of such characteristic breeding birds as Merlin, Greenshank, Golden Plover and Dunlin; but, because most of Britain's uplands have never been properly surveyed by ornithologists, the importance of specific areas is not documented. This is why the Royal Society for the Protection of Birds and the Nature Conservancy Council started upland surveys in the late 1970s, concentrating first on those areas where there might be new planting over the next few years. We are also looking at the particular requirements of different upland bird species so that we can give the best possible advice to foresters on integrating new plantations into uplands without any significant detrimental effects on birds.

Possession of the information is only part of the story – there has to be the intention on both sides to put it to good use. At present, the economic and political framework within which forestry operates makes it almost inevitable that there will continue to be instances when forestry and nature conservation will clash over land use. One vital and influential fact we have learnt about forestry is that conservationists and foresters are still suffering from mistakes made up to 60 years ago, when the Forestry Commission was first charged with the duty of restoring something of Britain's ravaged tree-cover. Now, as these forests are due to be felled, there are abundant opportunities to learn from the past and improve their visual appearance and value for wildlife. The picture of even-aged blankets of forest stretching for miles across the hills will alter as individual blocks are felled and replanted and a patchwork develops with more open spaces, wet areas, stands of self-sown or cultivated native trees, all providing habitat for a wider range of birds. It is particularly encouraging that the Forestry Commission has appointed someone to work on birds and forestry so that the next generation of forests will be better for birds.

However, we have to recognise that alien softwood forests, no matter how sympathetically managed, are no substitute for the original native tree-cover of Britain and Ireland. Before man came on the scene most of the British Isles was clothed with forest, with only the wetlands and rivers and the tops of the higher hills breaking the vast, rolling canopy. The forests of the British Isles today have been so fragmented and modified by man that it is hard for us to imagine what they must once have been like. For one thing, they would have contained a much wider range of tree species than most woodlands today – oak, birch, ash, beech, maple and lime and others, giving way to alder, willow and poplar in the wetter areas. For another, each tree would have lived to its natural span instead of being harvested in its prime, so that there would have been many ancient giants and decaying and fallen trees creating gaps in the forest where a new generation of seedlings could spring up. This great, rich mixture of growing plants provided different niches for all sorts of woodland birds.

Man's management of the woodlands affected birds in a number of ways. The fragmentation of woods into ever smaller areas separated by largely inhospitable farmland hit woodland birds of prey, which demand large areas of habitat if they are to find sufficient food to breed successfully. Direct human persecution was a factor which only became significant in quite recent times, when the woods were fragmented and many became game and fox coverts – an important factor in the retention of woodlands in lowland Britain. Economic management of woodlands means removing timber before it can decay naturally and that means a reduction in nest sites for a great number of woodland species which nest in holes. The number of tits or flycatchers in a wood can be greatly increased by providing nestboxes which suggest how much greater the densities of these birds must once have been in natural woodlands. Equally adverse to birds must be man's tendency to grow woods containing only one or two tree species; the character of the beechwoods and oak woods which we admire today is far from natural and, because they contain so few tree species, they are less able to support woodland birds.

Fortunately, across the British Isles as a whole, the diversity of uses to which man has put woodlands has meant that enough examples of different woodland types and conditions remain to support a rich avifauna. Indeed, it seems unlikely that Britain has lost any broadleafed woodland bird species in historic times. The real trouble now is that even these remnants of woodlands are steadily disappearing. Many are on farms where they are no longer seen to have any use in the farm economy and where the skills necessary for their management have disappeared. Of course, if they were just left alone to revert to nature there would be nothing to worry about in the long term. Unfortunately, all too often the woodland is cleared for agriculture or for replanting with conifers.

Recently a House of Lords Committee, looking at scientific aspects of forestry, noted that between a third and a half of the ancient semi-natural woodlands in Britain had been lost in the last 30 years – as much as in the previous four centuries. The Committee recommended that the amount of broadleafed woodlands in Britain should not be allowed to decline further, that selected woodlands should be managed as nature reserves, and most of the rest managed productively but compatibly with wildlife and amenity interests. The RSPB wholeheartedly supports this recommendation and feels it has a threefold role to play.

First, we must help to safeguard the prime remaining woodland sites as nature reserves, because it is only with specialised conservation management that they can be gently brought back to a more natural state. Second, our research work must continue to develop our ability to advise forest owners on the best ways of managing woodlands to strike a good balance between timber production and bird conservation. Third, we must encourage more government support for forestry in lowland Britain, with greater emphasis on the production of high-quality hard and softwoods for the long-term benefit of the economy and of the birds.

Reservoirs and gravel pits – some compensation

MYRFYN OWEN

Man's activities have been responsible for the loss of many important bird habitats, not least of wetlands, both inland and on the coast. The vast East Anglian fens and the peatlands of Lancashire have disappeared and the largest remaining inland marsh area – the Somerset Levels – is following rapidly. On the coast reclamation for agriculture has eaten deeply into our saltmarshes and industrialisation of most of our larger estuaries continues. Pollution from agricultural and industrial chemicals and from oil degrades what habitat remains in many places.

Yet wetlands, in the form of reservoirs and wet mineral workings, are being created inland and these develop, often with man's help, into valuable habitats for wildfowl both in winter and summer. For the purposes of this account 'reservoirs' include impoundments of various sorts, whether for drinking water or industrial use, canal feeder or agricultural water storage. Unless otherwise stated 'gravel pits' include other wet mineral workings such as brick and clay pits, although those created by gravel extraction form the overwhelming majority.

RESERVOIRS

These are of a very wide variety of types, differing in value for various species of wildfowl. High-altitude dams in Wales and northern England are over poor soils and are rather unproductive; they are not stocked with fish and are of relatively little value. Lowland reservoirs, particularly in south-east England, are productive and well placed to hold continental immigrants as well as our native wildfowl.

Our migratory geese and swans largely feed on dry land, but often use reservoirs for roosting. Several of the reservoirs in east-central Scotland hold very large flocks of Pink-footed and Greylag Geese in autumn and the creation of these water bodies has made new feeding areas accessible to the birds. Pinkfeet, in particular, used to be largely restricted to the coast, but now range widely inland. Mute Swans and Canada Geese use reservoirs both for breeding and as winter roosts, though they are not important habitats for either species.

Many types of ducks rely on reservoirs as feeding areas and roosts. Those constructed by damming lowland valleys are especially important for both dabbling and diving ducks because they provide a wide variety of water depths and usually have long perimeters. Bunded reservoirs, such as many in the London area, are used by dabbling ducks as roosts, but are most important for diving species which can feed at depths of up to 6 m (20 ft).

Most British reservoirs were created in the second half of the 19th century and the first three decades of the 20th, but many of the most valuable ones are much more recent. Counts from the most important waters, having a regular peak of over 2,000 wildfowl, are given in Table 1. Only two of these were built before 1930 and half in the last 30 years. It is significant to note that several are either managed as reserves or are subject to zoning whereby recreational activities are restricted to part of the area and other parts are reserved for wildlife.

Table 1: Total wildfowl (swans + ducks + geese) at peak in three recent seasons, and the three-year average for those reservoirs holding 2,000 or more birds.

Reservoir	*Date flooded*	*1979–80*	*1980–81*	*1981–82*	*Mean*
Abberton (Essex)	1939	9,328	10,333	12,239	10,633
Rutland Water (Leicester)	1975	6,336	6,821	8,350	7,169
Blithfield (Stafford)	1955	4,194	4,064	3,705	3,988
Staines (Surrey)	1902	9,333	890	1,866	4,030
Grafham Water (Cambridge)	1966	4,830	2,750	3,411	3,664
Loch Ken (Dumfries & Galloway)	1936	3,171	2,444	2,752	2,789
Pitsford (Northampton)	1934	2,291	2,229	3,500	2,673
Chew Valley Lake (Avon)	1956	2,269	3,005	1,496	2,557
Tophill Low (Humberside)	1959	1,947	2,838	2,666	2,484
Belvide (Stafford)	1834	2,491	2,313	2,178	2,327
Arlington (Sussex)	1970	1,524	1,999	3,064	2,196
Eyebrook (Leicester)	1934	3,160	1,837	1,554	2,183

Note: Four Scottish reservoirs – Westwater in Borders (6,521 wildfowl), Gladhouse in Lothian (6,511), Monikie in Tayside (5,241) and Cameron in Fife (4,564) – are important in autumn chiefly as goose roosts.

Table 2: Numbers of selected species and total wildfowl counted at Rutland Water (winter maximum) since flooding began in 1975.

	1975	*1976*	*1977*	*1978*	*1979*	*1980*	*1981*
Mallard	1,038	2,961	2,448	1,982	1,685	1,857	2,544
Teal	263	2,038	1,180	1,090	1,458	1,139	1,398
Wigeon	293	4,518	2,327	2,902	2,205	3,540	3,070
Gadwall	0	20	55	135	351	141	380
Shoveler	126	231	450	404	471	316	317
Pochard	331	1,556	1,298	484	689	540	739
Tufted Duck	252	703	949	2,287	2,208	1,523	1,804
Total wildfowl	1,742	10,989	5,787	6,735	6,336	6,821	8,350
Coot	513	1,998	2,709	2,846	2,883	1,136	2,636
Great Crested Grebe	46	32	27	134	99	54	90
Little Grebe	11	25	33	51	57	71	113

The most recent and best example of the effectiveness of conservation management on reservoirs is that of Rutland Water, constructed in the early 1970s, in an arable area of Leicestershire. The reservoir was designated a nature reserve before there was any water and a management plan drawn up, which included the maintenance of existing habitats around the perimeter as well as creating bunded areas and lagoons in the shallower parts. Sailing and boating were limited to the deeper areas of the reservoir. Flooding began in 1975 but top water level was not reached until March 1979. This made Rutland Water the second largest lake in England and the largest man-made water in Britain. Placed as it is in the East Midlands, close to some large concentrations of inland wildfowl and on east–west flight-lines, it was soon adopted as a wintering site by large numbers of water birds. The numbers counted at the site each season since 1975/76 are shown in Table 2. Clearly wildfowl numbers of most species have now stabilised, somewhat below their early peaks, but some are still increasing. The reserve is used by a wide variety of other aquatic species in winter, and breeding populations are still increasing. The bird list for the reserve has well over 200 species.

In Britain as a whole, reservoirs hold between 12% and 20% of all wildfowl, depending on season. The numbers counted (on about 270 reservoirs annually) in January since 1968 (when the sample increased with the advent of the International Wildfowl Counts), are shown in Fig. 35. During this period the increase in numbers has been of the order of 50%. There has been some increase in existing sites but much has been due to the 7,300 ha of water created as new reservoirs since the mid-1960s, notably at Grafham and Rutland Water. Most of the increase has been in the two inland diving ducks, but the use of reservoirs by Wigeon has led to the spread of this traditionally

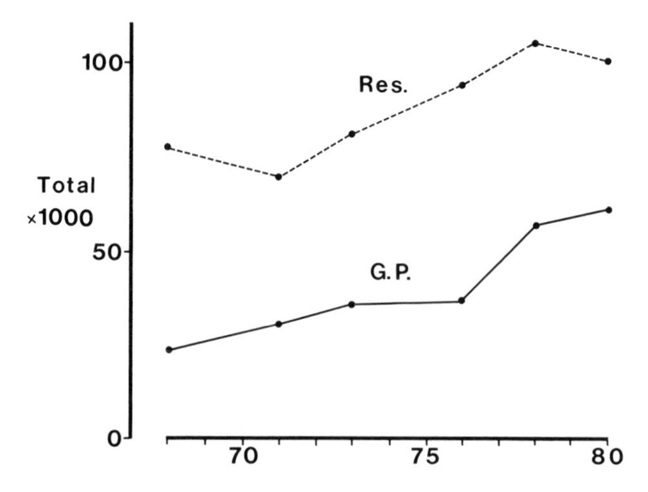

Fig 35 The number of wildfowl counted on reservoirs, dotted lines (c. 270 sites counted annually), and gravel pits, solid lines (c. 150 sites), in January from 1968 to 1980.

coastal species to many parks of inland Britain.

As breeding areas for water birds, reservoirs are not as productive as more natural waters. In the 1980 BTO/Wildfowl Trust breeding survey, which included grebes and rails as well as wildfowl, reservoirs accounted for 28% of the sites and 39% of the area covered, but in midsummer held only 20% of adult birds and 22% of young. Since reservoirs were well counted in the survey their real value in the British context is overestimated by this count. Nevertheless, they do hold substantial numbers of breeding Mallard, Tufted Duck, Coot and grebes.

There has been an increase in the use of reservoirs in Britain by ducks for moulting in recent years. Mallard gather in the safety of large water bodies to moult, and large numbers are found on such reservoirs as Abberton; up to 4,500 Pochard have also used this water for moulting, though numbers have recently declined to about 1,000 birds from the high levels of the late 1960s and early 1970s. Hanningfield Reservoir (also in Essex) holds as many as 1,000 Tufted Ducks and several hundred Pochard in moult, while London reservoirs have similar numbers. High September concentrations at several other impoundments not counted in summer indicate that there are probably more sites of importance during the moult.

GRAVEL PITS

The demand for sand and gravel for buildings has greatly increased in recent decades and most of this has been obtained from valley gravels, particularly from the deposits in the Thames and Trent Valleys and from the floodplains of the Ouse and its tributaries. Quarrying has, in many places, given rise to wet gravel pits and the area available has increased dramatically. The tonnage of inland gravel extracted since the 1940s is shown in Fig. 36 together with an index of wet gravel pit area obtained by summing the area of wet pits in the counties of Berkshire, Cambridgeshire, Greater London, Leicestershire, Norfolk and Surrey at various points in time.

The annual rate of extraction increased rapidly in the 1950s and 1960s, reaching a peak at 110 million tonnes in 1972, at the height of the era of motorway construction. Thereafter it declined slightly but is still running at a level of around 90 million tonnes. Despite this the area of wet pits continues to increase although the rate of increase is no longer accelerating. Because the thickness of many of the best gravel deposits means that extraction extends well below the water table, restoring wet pits to agriculture or other land use is difficult and expensive. In any case, as the demand for leisure increases, there is a growing need for water areas close to centres of population and many pits are designed to provide water recreation as well as natural history interests as legitimate after-use.

Gravel pits usually provide areas of relatively shallow water and are often worked in smallish blocks so that most gravel complexes consist of numerous

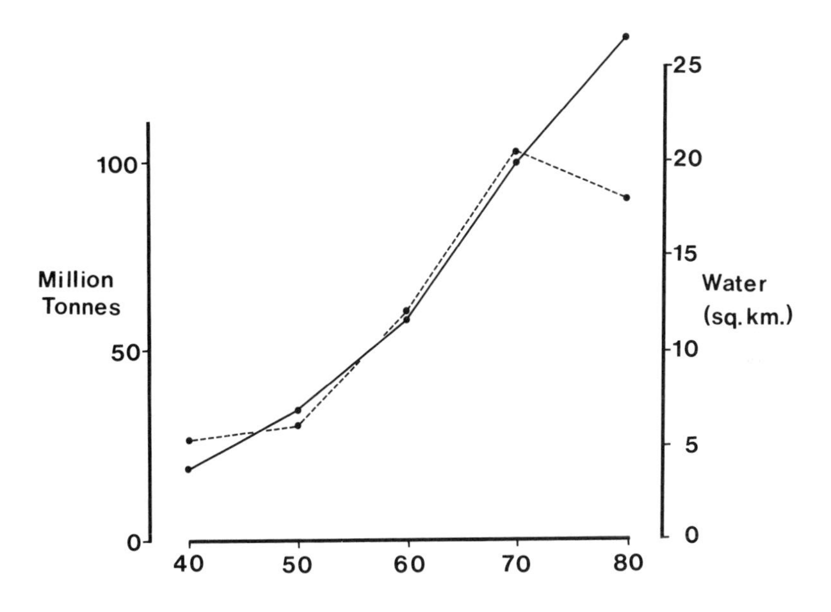

Fig 36 The number of million tonnes of gravel extracted annually in early parts of the last five decades (dotted lines), and the area of wet pits (solid lines) in six English counties (solid lines). Information on pit areas was provided by the planning departments of the councils of Berkshire, Cambridgeshire, Greater London, Leicestershire, Norfolk and Surrey.

pools, some including peninsulas and islands, with a long perimeter relative to the area of water. Valley gravels are in the fertile river plains and rich aquatic and marginal vegetation slowly develops. This process can be accelerated by planting and dumping organic matter in the water and a well-known example of such management, as well as gravel-pit design sympathetic to conservation interests, is that of the Sevenoaks Experimental Reserve in Kent.

Largely as a result of the enthusiasm and energy of Dr Jeffery Harrison, the Sevenoaks reserve was established in 1956 under a management agreement with the Kent Sand and Ballast Company. Gravel continued to be extracted from the site but the Company agreed to alter their strictly commercial requirements in order to provide islands and spits to aid the management effort. Floating islands were also provided for nesting wildfowl and grebes, and the perimeter was planted with seed-bearing plants and waterside trees such as alder. Submerged plants were also introduced and the invertebrate life increased as a consequence. The wildfowl population grew rapidly, especially in winter when 2–300 Mallard and over 100 diving ducks were regular. In summer, by the early 1970s, the complex served as a breeding area for more than a hundred pairs of ducks, chiefly Mallard, as well as introduced Greylag Geese and many other water birds. Wader habitat was created by blasting and applying manure, and the reserve was visited by large numbers of Snipe and a wide variety of other waders. Passerines also increased tremendously, largely as a result of management of the water margins and the surrounding land, particularly the maintenance of diversity of habitat types.

There is no doubt that the management carried out at this gravel pit reserve achieved its aims spectacularly, but not many areas receive such concentrated effort; instead, they are left to develop naturally, usually with some of the smaller pits being reserved for fishing while water-skiing and sailing are allowed on the larger waters. Provision is also often made for nature conservation and some waters are managed by local conservation bodies.

The development of the wintering wildfowl population in relation to the area of water at Chichester Gravel Pits (Chichester Leisure Centre, Wyke and neighbouring pits), West Sussex, is shown in Fig. 37, which can be regarded as a more typical pattern for the development of wet pits. Extraction began at the site in 1930 and ceased completely in 1975. Most of the pits remained wet but 6 ha were filled between 1970 and 1982. Total wildfowl numbers followed fairly closely the area of open water, also related, of course, to the age of the pits. These included some Mallard and Teal which roosted on the pits but which fed in the nearby Chichester Harbour or on farmland. The numbers of Pochard and Tufted Duck, which rely on the pits themselves for feeding, were slower to build up and later stabilised at just over 500 as the growth in water area ceased. The number of Tufted Ducks in September largely

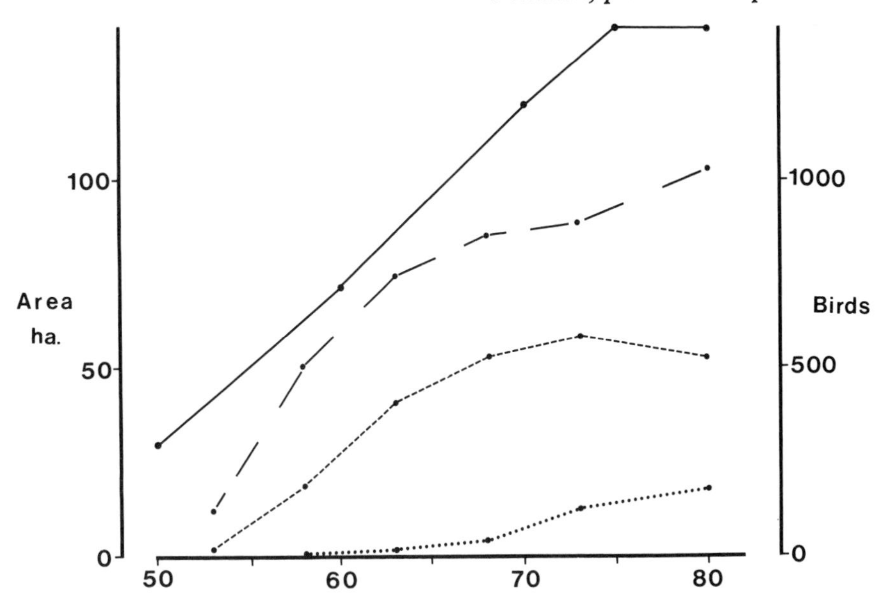

Fig 37 The area of water at Chichester Gravel Pits (solid line: data from West Sussex County Council), and the numbers of wildfowl counted there since the early 1960s. Wildfowl numbers are the mean of the three highest counts in each of five winters (each point is a mean of 15 counts). Large dashes: total wildfowl; small dashes: Tufted Ducks plus Pochard; dotted lines: Tufted Ducks in September.

reflected the local breeding population and their young; these built up very gradually as the workings became mature.

Many other complexes have grown in area and importance in the last two decades, particularly in the Thames Valley where several large groups near Reading are extremely important for diving ducks and Canada Geese. The Cotswold Water Park, on the borders of Gloucestershire and Wiltshire, is also extremely important, holding several thousand ducks, especially Pochard and Tufted Duck, at peak.

In Britain as a whole the number of wildfowl held on gravel pits has doubled since 1968 (Fig. 35). The proportion of all British wildfowl housed on gravel pits has risen from 2–3% in the early 1960s to 7–10% today. They are important for Tufted Ducks (30–40%), Pochards (25–35%) and Canada Geese (25–30%) in particular. These figures are derived from winter wildfowl counts which favour waters in the lowlands of England; nevertheless, gravel pits are clearly important habitats for several species and their increased area has doubtless been responsible in part for the substantial increase in the numbers of inland diving ducks and Canada Geese in recent years.

Gravel pits are no less valuable as breeding places for these inland species. Although they constituted only 12% of sites and 11% of the area covered in the 1980 summer waterfowl breeding survey, they accounted for 22% of adult birds and 18% of young in June and included a quarter of the Tufted Duck broods. Gravel pits also held a third of all adult Great Crested Grebes and a quarter of the young in midsummer.

Reservoirs and gravel pits, created by man to supply his own needs, now provide major refuges for wetland birds and, in the case of gravel pits, for other wildlife as well. Many of these same habitats, being as they are commonly in the lowlands and close to urban areas, are also in great demand for recreation. There has been an explosion of interest in water sports and other forms of outdoor recreation in the last two decades and these gave rise to fears that, since many sports are disturbing to wildlife, this increase might have an impact on wildfowl. Were these fears justified and can we ensure that these new habitats will continue to be valuable wildfowl refuges?

A three-year study, financed jointly by the Sports Council and the Nature Conservancy Council, into the impact of recreation on wildfowl in Britain, was completed in 1981. It examined winter wildfowl count data together with recreational and other information from a large number of sites and concluded that, though some deleterious effects of certain activities were noted, the impact was (at present, at least) not substantial. The study did, however, pinpoint the species most affected, particularly Teal, Shoveler and Goldeneye. Among the main reasons for this apparent lack of impact were that the most disturbing activities – those involving entry of boats onto water – were conducted outside the main wintering period for wildfowl. This situation is, of course, changing with the increasing use of wetsuits and especially the growing popularity of sail-boarding. We should, therefore, remain watchful lest this favourable situation changes.

The 1980 summer breeding survey was conducted specifically to examine the impact of recreation in summer, but here also few really significant effects were picked out on a national scale. Again, this may to some extent be due to the fact that sailing, at least in larger boats, needs relatively deep water and does not affect shallows favoured by the birds. The increasing use of sail-boards may cause concern in future.

A major factor in lessening the impact of man has been the sympathetic management of waters by the Water Authorities and other controlling agencies. Most of the larger reservoirs have some form of zoning of activities. Sailing is often restricted to the deeper water and in some cases also to the summer months. Such zoning, coupled with some form of nature reserve, have been spectacularly successful in such reservoirs as Grafham and Rutland Water, now among the top ten inland sites for wintering wildfowl.

Similarly, on gravel pits, demand from birdwatchers and conservationists has resulted in the creation of nature reserve waters. Since the requirement of wildfowl for secluded shallows, and those of many sports for expanses of open and deep water, do not entirely overlap it has not been difficult in the larger gravel complexes to provide for both. Two of the country's largest gravel companies have indicated their commitment to conservation by funding substantial programmes of research and conservation management.

Therefore, we can conclude that these artificial habitats have provided some compensation for the loss of our natural wetlands. We must not forget, however, that much of this contribution has not come automatically, but has been achieved through compromise and co-operation between the needs of the birds and of other users of water space. Although pressure from these other users continues to increase, I am sure we should be optimistic that these habitats will continue to provide important refuges for our wetland birds.

SOURCES: Appleton (1982); Archer (1972); Atkinson-Willes (1969); Olney (1963); Owen and Atkinson-Willes (in press); Tanner (1979); Tuite (1981).

Wetlands – threats, problems and opportunities

KENNETH SMITH

To most birdwatchers the term 'wetland' conjures up images of the Ouse Washes, the Somerset Levels or the coastal marshes of north Norfolk – wide expanses of wet grassland and marshes interspersed with reed and osier beds and pools. In fact, the definition of wetlands is somewhat broader than this: they have been defined in the Ramsar Convention (1971) as all areas of marsh, fen, peatland or water, fresh or salt, including marine water up to a depth of 6 m. This definition therefore includes intertidal flats and marshes, many lakes, reservoirs, rivers, bogs, fens and wet grasslands. In a short article it is not possible to consider all these examples in detail and, in fact, estuaries and reservoirs are fully covered elsewhere in this chapter. In this section only threats and problems to rivers and their associated marshes and grasslands are considered in any detail.

Although the major interest of the birdwatcher is clearly the birds, it should be remembered that wetlands represent a series of unique habitats holding characteristic and increasingly restricted communities of plants and animals. The birds are usually the most obvious and easily observed members of the community but any threat to the birds is no less threat to the other animals and plants.

HISTORY

Throughout recorded history, and probably before, man has sought to modify wetlands to suit his own purposes and to safeguard himself and his property from flooding. In a desire to prevent flooding, and also to exploit the watercourse for transport and power, rivers have been deepened and embanked and elaborate systems of weirs built. Associated marshlands and fens, thought to be of little use to man, have been drained and the land put to agricultural use. Examples of man's impact are to be seen everywhere but perhaps the most outstanding are the once extensive fenlands of East Anglia, which were drained during the last three centuries (Thomas 1981). The land is now largely under intensive arable cultivation and the wetland flora and fauna are limited to a few relict areas of fen occupying approximately 1% of the former area.

In most river valleys flooding could not be avoided and occurred every winter – often during the summer as well. The agricultural use of extensive areas of lowland valleys was therefore restricted to summer grazing and hay-making. In fact in some chalk valleys complex systems of water meadows were created where grasslands were systematically flooded with stream water; in early spring the slightly elevated temperature and nutrient levels of this water were sufficient to produce an early flush of growth. Such management has now largely died out, although the areas are often still grazed.

CURRENT PROBLEMS

All the current threats to our wetlands stem from the increasing demands we are placing on our land and rivers. We now have the knowledge and resources to make very radical changes to these habitats – changes that can be made so rapidly that wildlife has little time to respond.

Rivers

These provide an important habitat for birds. Steep banks are used by nesting Kingfishers and Sand Martins, whilst emergent vegetation gives cover to Little Grebes, Moorhens, Coots, Sedge Warblers and Reed Warblers. Trees and scrub on the bank are also important for a wide range of birds. On upland rivers there is often less emergent vegetation and the Dipper, Common Sandpiper and Grey Wagtail are important breeding species.

The management of all major rivers in England and Wales is the responsibility of ten Regional Water Authorities. These authorities are responsible for water supply, sewage disposal and all maintenance and works on what are termed 'main rivers' – usually most major rivers. In Scotland similar responsibilities are held by the Scottish Development Department and the Regional Councils. The current annual expenditure by water authorities is approximately £100 millions, of which, some 60% is devoted to urban and agricultural flood protection and land drainage improvement. A significant proportion is supported by grant aid from MAFF. Although, in recent years, constraints on government spending have led to a fall in water authority expenditure, in the last decade a vigorous programme of 'improvement' and maintenance works has been completed. Most major rivers have been subject to some works and precious few have been unaffected.

Smaller watercourses are under the control of a variety of organisations, including local authorities, individual landowners and Internal Drainage Boards. The latter are restricted to England and Wales and are bodies responsible for all aspects of land drainage within their designated areas. There are over 250 IDBs in this country, covering areas varying from 200 ha to more than 40,000 ha. Many were first constituted in the 19th century and all cover areas with historically poor or difficult land drainage. Members of a drainage board are elected, mainly by agricultural ratepayers, and the finance is raised by drainage rates on land and property within the district. Most improvement works are supported by grants from MAFF. At present the annual expenditure by IDBs is some £18 millions.

River improvement works have largely been concentrated in the lowlands. In a typical scheme the capacity of the river will be increased by dredging, the banks cleared and reshaped, features such as gravel banks and bends removed, and water levels reduced by lowering weirs and bridge inverts. To allow heavy machinery access, trees and scrub are cleared from one or both banks. The overall effect of these works is to remove the majority of features used by birds and to turn the river into a virtual canal. Although some recovery of the vegetation will occur after major works, the frequent need for maintenance prevents any full recovery (Williamson 1971). The justifications for such works are complex and vary from scheme to scheme. They include the prevention and alleviation of flooding to buildings (often unwisely built in the floodplains), and the reduction of flooding and waterlogging of farmland. In addition, changes upstream, such as increased urbanisation, better land drainage and improved river channels, can result in higher peak flows and therefore require higher standards of flood protection in the lower reaches. Extensive stretches of rivers have already been 'improved' and a great deal of valuable habitat lost. At the time of writing (1982) there are many more schemes, both large and small, in the planning stage. For instance, major schemes will affect the River Soar in Leicestershire and Nottinghamshire, the River Nene in Northamptonshire, and the Hampshire Avon. The Thames Water Authority is at present reconsidering its plans for an extensive improvement to the River Stort after objections from conservation bodies and both Hertfordshire and Essex County Councils.

The Regional Water Authorities have taken some notice of protests from conservation organisations and the general public, and consultations now take place at the planning stage of most schemes (Williams 1980). Guidance notes have also been published by the Water Space Amenity Commission (WSAC 1980). However, consultation arrangements with IDBs are far less satisfactory and many of them have had little regard for nature conservation. Under section 48 of the Wildlife and Countryside Act 1981 both water authorities and IDBs are obliged '. . . so far as may be consistent with the purposes of this (Water) Act and of the Land Drainage Act 1976, to exercise their functions . . . as to further the conservation and enhancement of natural beauty and the conservation of flora, fauna and geological or physiographical features of special interest.' For the first time both water authorities and IDBs are now required by law to further the aims of conservation where this is possible. A guidance note has recently been issued by the Department of Environment outlining these responsibilities where Sites of Special Scientific

Interest are concerned (DoE 1982).

Rivers attract many leisure activities, including boating, fishing and walking. Boating is limited to the major waterways, but is increasing with the general increase in leisure activities. Where the boat traffic is heavy then serious problems can arise from the wash and disturbance caused, but as yet this is not a widespread problem. The major leisure activity on our rivers is, of course, fishing: there are over two million active coarse fishermen in England and Wales! Fishermen cause some damage to vegetation and disturbance to birds but (fortunately) the close season for coarse fishing corresponds with the breeding season of the birds. Some regions have abandoned the close season and there are proposals to abandon it elsewhere; this is certainly detrimental and any further extensions will be opposed by the conservation organisations. A number of rivers in southern Britain and the uplands are maintained for salmon and trout fishing; often these are among the most outstanding rivers for birds.

At present the major problems associated with fishing are caused by discarded tackle and lead shot. Birds can become entangled in line and swallow hooks and, if not rescued, can suffer a lingering death. In addition, discarded lead shot is taken up by wildfowl as grit; when the shot is embedded in the gizzard it causes poisoning and ultimately the death of the bird. In some regions, such as the River Thames and the Warwickshire Avon, Mute Swan populations are suffering badly from lead poisoning (Hardman 1980, Birkhead 1981) and the problem has been the subject of a special NCC Working Group (Goode 1981). It is hoped that over the next few years a safe substitute material will be developed which will allow the use of lead shot fishing weights to be phased out.

Marshes and wet grasslands

These may hold particularly important bird communities – flocks of wildfowl and plovers in winter, and in summer breeding birds such as Redshank, Snipe, Lapwing, Yellow Wagtail and various wildfowl. In addition, because of their traditional, low intensity management for grazing or haymaking they are often very rich botanically. Most wet grasslands show evidence of old drainage works, but modern machinery and techniques allow new and deeper drainage to be installed very easily. In total, some 80,000 ha of agricultural land are drained annually in England and Wales and it is estimated that approximately 10% (8,000 ha) is new drainage of wetlands (FWAG 1982). In southern Britain drainage improvements are now proceeding at such a rate that there will soon be precious few wetland sites outside nature reserves. Even the existing nature reserves are being affected adversely by the lowering of the water table on surrounding land.

It is not only the lowlands that are being affected. In the straths and glens of the Scottish Highlands land drainage, promoted by individual landowners, is proceeding at an alarming pace (Green 1980). Rough grazing is being converted to arable and much good wader and wildfowl breeding habitat lost.

Usually it is impossible to separate river improvement works and the effects on adjacent marshes and meadows. In fact, the financial justification of many river improvements is often based on the potential agricultural benefits to adjacent land. Lower river levels will lower the surrounding water table and also allow the installation of deep field ditches and underdrains. The alleviation or reduction of winter and spring flooding allows the farmer to grow arable crops or to improve his existing grass sward. The problems which must be addressed by conservationists and farmers when dealing with wet grasslands and marshes are extremely complex and raise a number of issues fundamental to conservation in this country. The sites have long been farmed and often their current wildlife interest depends on the continuance of the traditional patterns of use. Encouraged by generous grants, subsidies and guaranteed prices, and under pressure to obtain a satisfactory return on investment, the farmer often wishes to intensify his use of wetlands. Unlike river improvements, there appears to be little room for compromise in these cases: if a site is drained its principal wildlife interest will be lost, while if a site is retained the individual farmer must accept lower financial returns.

At present the system of agricultural grants and subsidies and our legislative framework are designed to encourage intensification. This system has largely built up since World War II when it was recognised that a strong, efficient agriculture could make great strides towards self-sufficiency. Undoubtedly British farming has come a long way since then. However, in the case of our remaining wet grasslands, we are now talking about bringing the remaining small pockets of very marginal land into more efficient production. Is it not time to keep these areas as havens for wildlife? But how can this be achieved without penalizing the individual farmer?

Under the provisions of the Wildlife and Countryside Act 1981 the NCC is obliged to notify all landowners of Sites of Special Scientific Interest of the particular interest of the site and of activities which would be detrimental to this interest. If the landowner wishes to carry out any of these activities he must inform the NCC which, if it objects, can then negotiate some form of management agreement. This may involve compensation payments for any financial loss experienced by the farmer. Ultimately, if no agreement can be reached, the NCC has powers of compulsory purchase. The idea of compensation payments to a farmer to continue his traditional land use may be the way forward but there are a number of serious drawbacks. The first is that this is a substantial drain on the resources of the NCC, both of cash and manpower, at a time when the government is attempting to reduce its budget. Without adequate financial resources the NCC will be unable to operate the system. Compensation payments do not provide any long-term safeguard for the sites and long periods of negotiation can be expected each time a new agricultural change is proposed. Of course the system applies only to SSSIs – for other sites we must rely on the voluntary restraint of landowners. Ultimately, the only way to provide long-term safeguard of important sites is purchase by one of the conservation organisations and the maintenance of traditional management. This will certainly require a large financial input either from those with an interest in conservation or from central government.

Drainage and agricultural improvement schemes are being carried out on an enormous scale at present. Stacks of plastic drainage pipes in the corner of a meadow, awaiting installation, are an all too familiar sight. It is just not possible to catalogue all these schemes in a short article. There are, however, a number of major sites which are threatened at present, some of which merit mention. The extensive coastal grazing marshes of North Kent continue to be drained and converted to arable so that at present only about half remains as grassland (Williams *et al.* 1982). In Yorkshire there are a number of proposals to install pumped drainage on the Derwent Ings, which hold internationally important wintering wildfowl populations and are also major breeding areas for wildfowl and waders. In Northamptonshire there are plans to improve the evacuation of water from the Nene Washes which will allow further conversion of the area to arable and loss of waders and wildfowl. In Norfolk the Yare marshes form an important block of damp grazing marsh which hold numbers of breeding and wintering wildfowl and waders; these already have pumped drainage, but there are proposals to replace the present ageing pumps with new ones which will allow lower water levels to be maintained and accelerate the conversion of much of the land to arable. Probably the most extensive areas of wet grassland remaining in Britain are in the Somerset Levels; several comprehensive river management and flood alleviation schemes are being planned which threaten large areas.

These are just a few of the major proposals affecting our marshes and wet grasslands. Negotiations are still taking place on all the schemes and it is to be hoped that the important wetland areas can be retained. However, the piecemeal drainage schemes which are occurring throughout the lowlands are likely to destroy the wildlife interests of many small damp pockets, restricting riparian wildlife to just a few major sites. Although the Wildlife and Countryside Act and compensation payments may be of some help in retaining small sites, there is a fundamental conflict between the interests of agriculture and conservation which will only be resolved by an integrated strategy for the conservation of our remaining wetlands.

Threats to estuaries

A. J. PRATER

For many years the wide open spaces of estuaries have attracted engineering proposals for barrages; certainly serious consideration was given to a barrage on the Severn estuary as long ago as 1933. The reasons put forward for development have been many, such as water storage, tidal power generation and improvement of road or rail links.

There is no shortage of water falling on England and Wales but its distribution is uneven, with the bulk of it falling where there are fewest people. In the mid-1960s concern about future water supplies was based on two predicted values: population level and total demand. Recalculations ten years later estimated short-fall of supplies to be reduced to 53·3%, and such a decrease lessens the immediate prospect of massive water storage schemes at all estuarine sites. Projections are, however, at best a guide and at worst wholly misleading!

Initially, plans for estuarine storage were expansive. Barrages were considered for the Severn, Solway, Morecambe Bay and the Wash, but were soon ruled out on several counts. In each case a barrage would have meant a massive initial expenditure on a technology which was not yet proven in Britain. In the Severn and Solway schemes the costs of transporting water were also considered to be prohibitive. By 1970 attention was switched to smaller and ecologically less (though still significantly) damaging bunded reservoir projects.

Bunded reservoirs are simply reservoirs which are enclosed by an artificial bank (or bund); they have no natural freshwater inflow and depend on a pumped supply, hence their alternative name of pumped storage reservoirs. They would be placed at some distance beyond the existing sea-wall to ensure that any back seepage would not affect present land areas. Experimental bunds incorporated into the feasibility study on the Wash have shown that it would be technically possible to build a reservoir on the higher intertidal flats. Between the inner bund and the existing sea-wall there would be high level flats or a saltmarsh. Increased sedimentation would be expected to occur if no development of the area took place. In practice, in order to allow full access to the reservoir, some development is likely. This polder zone could be used for agriculture, industrial development, nature reserves or for leisure activities.

The Dee crossing and reservoir scheme was one of the first full feasibility studies undertaken. Subsequent to the publication of the feasibility study, the shape of the reservoirs was shown by a hydraulic model not to be ideal, and the Shotton Steelworks has been run down, not expanded. Accordingly, a supplementary report was published incorporating new features. In particular, one or two small reservoirs were proposed for part of the estuary which had been set aside for the expansion of the steel works. The bund shapes of the now reduced (but still large) reservoirs in the middle of the estuary were realigned to minimise siltation. The report by the Water Resources Board (1975) recommended that staged development of the Dee should be part of the national water strategy; the implementation of the first stage should also take place by 1990.

The Morecambe Bay embayment, incorporating the estuaries of the rivers Wyre, Lune, Kent and Leven, was the second British estuary to come under scrutiny for water storage in recent years, although suggestions had been put forward for a barrage from Morecambe to Barrow as long ago as the 1890s. After the feasibility study report, relatively little was heard about development of water storage here. This was mainly because alternative estuary storage sites, the Dee and the Wash, were being considered by detailed feasibility studies. However, since the re-organisation of the water industry in 1974, further plans have been proposed and a reappraisal undertaken by the North Western Water Authority. The suggested designs involve much smaller, although still large, bunded reservoirs in sensitive areas. Water storage is not the only threat to Morecambe Bay; recently, outline proposals have mentioned the possibility of a major gas terminal being sited on the Lune/Wyre estuary.

The Wash storage scheme originally involved a complete barrage across the Wash from Bennington to Snettisham, but the desk study concentrated on smaller bunded reservoirs which could be built on the foreshore of the inner Wash. Initial plans were for a four-stage development, but soon the proposals were restricted to the south-east of the Wash. All bunded reservoirs would be 1–3 km away from the present sea-wall. The polder area between the bund and the sea-wall could have an area of 3–10 km^2, depending upon design. The investigations narrowed down to assessing alternatives for a two-staged development with a smaller first stage and a larger second stage.

The biological studies for the Wash feasibility project were the most intensive yet made for any such investigation. As a result, many of the processes involved and the descriptive and predictive aspects are known in detail.

When stage one (a $6\frac{1}{2}$ km^2 reservoir) and the larger (an additional 10 km^2) stage two are combined there would be a very large effect. All schemes, including the preferred Westmark and Hull Sand reservoirs, would displace 45,000 or more waders and involve at least five species of international importance. The numbers of birds involved are somewhat smaller than in the Morecambe Bay reservoir proposals, but so is the area. The conclusion of the feasibility study was that, despite the practicability of building bunded reservoirs on the Wash, they would not be needed before the end of this century, nor would they present a viable economic alternative to other methods of obtaining water.

Tidal power proposals

Tidal power generation was first proposed for the Severn in 1933. Since then, innumerable schemes have been put forward for the development of this estuary, each of these raising a different set of environmental problems.

There are three barrage designs for generating electricity from tidal movements: (i) a simple barrage with turbines driven by the ebb tide; (ii) a simple barrage with turbines powered by both the flood and ebb tides; and (iii) a complex barrage with a secondary basin kept at a different water level so that continuous generation of power is possible. In the simpler schemes the production of electricity would be periodic, in the case of (i) perhaps as little as eight effective hours per day, while in (ii) there would be still two slack periods per tide around low and high water. The power would only periodically be available at the time of peak demand and, unless power could be stored elsewhere, the scheme would be relatively inefficient. Surprisingly, a type (i) scheme is presently preferred.

At this stage very little hard data is available to enable an environmental impact statement to be drawn up, but a Committee has been formed by the Department of Energy to supervise the feasibility study, which will include ecological research. It is hoped this will lead to a much clearer assessment.

RECLAMATIONS

Large-scale reclamation of upper shore for industrial development, and the continual attrition from many small reclamations, present the most serious overall threats to estuaries. Although the word 'reclamation' is used here to describe the process of converting intertidal land to terrestrial land, it is an incorrect term. Reclamation of the estuarine habitat should only be used for the recovery of land lost to the sea; virtually no intertidal flats fall into that category, except on a geological timescale. The correct definition is really the claiming of land. There should be a different philosophical approach to taking something one never had from recovering that which was lost!

Coastal sites appear to be attractive propositions to industrial developers, for they are relatively flat and there is relatively easy sea access. A number of large developments, particularly involving the petrochemical industry, have already made a noticeable impact on existing estuaries. Storage or refining plants have been built on the Thames (Canvey, Isle of Grain), Southampton Water (Fawley), Milford Haven, Teesmouth, Firth of Forth (Grangemouth), Cromarty Firth (Nigg Bay) and in the Shetlands (Sullom Voe). The policy of fully developing facilities at a few sites has certain advantages but nevertheless can have an immense impact on those chosen (see Fig. 5, p. 80).

Construction of maintenance yards for offshore oil developments have become a problem over recent years, especially in Scotland. The yard at Ardersier on the Moray Firth (for example) was given planning permission, but then there was an attempt to reclaim a larger area than was agreed; this was, however, discovered before reclamation was completed. Subsequently, planning permission was sought for an extension into the area which had already been excluded on environmental grounds. Other heavy industries have utilised coastal land, examples such as gas developments (present proposals for which in the Irish Sea include the Dee, Ribble or Morecambe Bay), steel (Dee, Severn), docks (Thames, Teesmouth, Southampton Water) and airports (Maplin and Severn) have or could have significant repercussions on estuarine bird populations. They are also potential pollution problems.

Agricultural reclamation

This process has been happening for a long time. On the Wash, where it has been a particularly important factor, 470 km^2 of land has been reclaimed since Saxon times, this being a larger area than the 314 km^2 of intertidal flats and saltmarsh that remain. Reclamation has traditionally involved the enclosure of high-level saltings by a sea-wall, then an interval of a few years for the leaching of salt from the ground, followed by cropping. The land so gained has a high silt content which provides a fertile soil, although it may grade to fairly sandy at the limit of reclamation. Much of the intensive agricultural belt of East Anglia has been reclaimed from marshland and estuary. The reclamation of the higher saltmarshes, i.e. those which would be covered by higher spring tides, introduces an imbalance into the dynamics of sediment deposition; the result, if there is sufficient material in the system, is further deposition on the remaining lower marsh and previously uncolonised mudflats. Thus the process of reclamation provides the right conditions for further reclamation many years later. Quite how far this process of reclamation can go is not clear as deeper water and more marine influences are approached. Recent studies on the Wash have shown two alarming developments. Firstly, the low-water mark is now no longer moving seaward and all reclamation is a net loss of intertidal habitat; secondly, very little organic sediment is now being brought in from the North Sea.

To date in most cases, such reclamation has not caused great concern to conservation bodies. Yet two recent instances have rather modified attitudes. Firstly, new techniques enabled large reclamation projects to be carried out on the Wash in the mid-1970s and others are projected for Gedney Drove End and other Lincolnshire marshes. Secondly, a proposal was put forward for a massive reclamation on the Ribble estuary. Although saltmarshes seem to be extensive on our major estuaries, they only cover about 450 km^2 in total; thus they are a relatively scarce natural habitat. They support nationally significant numbers of many breeding species, provide valuable feeding areas for many wildfowl in winter and are good roosting areas for waders. Also, they are essential in providing organic material on which intertidal invertebrates feed, so providing the food for waders. We cannot be complacent as to their future by simply saying more will accrete, especially if immature marshes can be reclaimed by modern methods.

Of course, few estuaries have vast saltmarshes where such dramatic reclamation can take place. In many smaller ones, limited reclamations have been made, although subsequently the land is usually only suitable for rough grazing. Indeed, many attempts have been foiled by the sea breaking back through the defences and the areas reverting to saltmarsh.

Small reclamations

So far we have considered the effects of large developments. Few massive schemes have gone ahead, no doubt primarily due to the huge expenditure needed rather than to prevent the loss of wildlife. Perhaps much more insidious are the many small developments which beset virtually all estuaries. Such reclamations take many forms, from the infill of a creek for a road, housing, small industry, a refuse tip or sewage works, to the siting of a yachting marina, slipways, quays, etc. It may be that only a few hundred square metres are involved, although small creeks of up to a hundred hectares can be included. It is rare that such a development can be opposed successfully on the grounds that it supports x% of the international or even national population. Each removal, however, goes towards reducing the total area available as feeding grounds. The cumulative effect is undoubtedly considerable, and very worrying.

POLLUTION

Like every other part of our environment, estuaries are subjected to many types of pollution. Some are already showing noticeable effects while others remain as potential threats for the moment. Four of the main types are organic nutrients, heavy metals, oil and thermal.

SHELLFISH FISHERIES

Commercial exploitation of shellfish in Britain is limited to a few species and a few areas. Three species are involved: the cockle *Cerastoderma edule*, the mussel *Mytilus edulis* and the oyster *Ostrea edulis*. Cockles are (or were) found in considerable quantities on the Wash, Thames and Burry Inlet, although other estuaries such as Morecambe Bay and the Dee have had small industries in the past. Where birds eat shellfish, conflicts do arise!

THE FUTURE

The overwhelming majority of people would be aghast if tens of thousands of birds were deliberately killed for another development or more land. This is precisely what will happen if we do not build conservation consideration into our actions. Change is inevitable, but surely progress should be on all fronts, so embracing cultural and aesthetic as well as economic grounds.

There are many threats to the estuarine habitat, some large, some small, but taken together they form a massive assault. The pressures are now just as great on the intertidal flats as they are on saltmarshes and reclaimed land. The counts of birds for the Estuaries Enquiry, the Wetlands Enquiry and the Wildfowl Counts have provided detailed information as to what is where, and when, in Britain and Ireland. The international counts have achieved similar information for other European countries. We have seen clearly that in winter, Britain and Ireland support in the order of half of all waterfowl in western Europe. As a result, our conservation efforts for this habitat must rank among national priorities. Certainly the Nature Conservancy Council, the Institute of Terrestrial Ecology and the Natural Environmental Research Council have recognised this by providing funding for both additional survey and detailed ecosystem research.

Are we doing enough? Or to put it another way – are we allowed to develop a reasonable approach to estuarine conservation? The framework does exist for a national policy to protect estuaries but it needs to be developed further. Some of those wishing to develop estuaries have shown appreciation of the national significance of the habitat but most do not care. The *ad hoc* assessment should be changed so that everyone can be more certain of the status of each estuary. Inevitably this will mean that money will have to be found but the alternative of piecemeal loss, with prime conservation areas being isolated and then destroyed, would present a much greater loss to the country as a whole.

Seabird problems

W. R. P. BOURNE

Britain and Ireland provide breeding places for something over three million pairs of seabirds; or, including immatures who have not yet started to breed, roughly ten million birds. They disperse throughout the North and South Atlantic (and may even reach Australia at times) and are replaced by many winter visitors from all round the northern parts of the Atlantic and adjacent arctic waters. They include a majority of the world population of the Northern Gannet and probably of the Storm Petrel, and of races of the Fulmar, Manx Shearwater, Common Guillemot (or Murre), Great Skua, Herring and Lesser Black-backed Gulls, of the European population of the Roseate Tern, and a major part of the European population of fifteen other species, amounting to between a quarter and a third of all European seabirds. They have always been considered one of the most remarkable features of the wildlife of these islands. And they present some problems.

The first problem has always been how to count the birds, for they spend most of their lives moving about at sea and come ashore only irregularly, often in large masses in remote and sometimes inaccessible or dangerous places. In its early years the BTO sponsored a number of attempts to count some of the more conspicuous species such as the Gannet, Fulmar, Kittiwake and Black-headed Gull, all of which proved to be increasing, probably because they had been protected and had started to feed on human wastes (Fisher and Lockley 1954). With the development of coastal bird observatories, initially intended to facilitate observations of landbird migration, it was also found possible to obtain much interesting new information on seabird breeding behaviour and movements.

At the annual Bird Observatories Conference in 1966, the Trust joined with the other national ornithological societies to sponsor the foundation of a Seabird Group, to promote further developments. Initially the new group concentrated on the observation of seabirds passing along the shore, known as 'sea-watching', while considering other options. The observations were organised by Garth Pettit and recorded on bird observatory-type forms provided by the BTO. The earlier results were recorded in seven cyclostyled *Seabird Bulletins*, which are still of interest. They soon revealed a very complicated picture, including the presence of unprecedented numbers of supposedly scarce species such as the rarer shearwaters and even albatrosses, and also a curious tendency for all the birds to fly out into the Atlantic, presumably to compensate for previous drift inshore with the prevailing westerly winds (Bourne 1982a). The enquiry in time became swamped by its own data, which clearly requires analysis by computer. Observations have since continued at the better sites.

Meanwhile, arrangements were also being made with the Royal Society for the Protection of Birds to revive their long-established pioneer surveys of dead birds on beaches, which it was hoped would provide more information about the birds present offshore. This enquiry was just getting under way when the 112,000-tonne oil tanker *Torrey Canyon* was wrecked off the coast of Cornwall in March 1967. The Seabird Group and BTO organised joint investigations by marine research vessel and helicopter, followed by surveys of the dead birds on the beaches and breeding censuses, to assess the damage. The Group was later given some of the excess money subscribed for the relief of the oiled birds, which enabled it to develop the decennial censuses of individual species (which had been organised for the Trust by James Fisher) into a comprehensive national census of all species in 1969–70. This Fisher christened 'Operation Seafarer', after the Old English poem containing the first descriptions of the birds. Unfortunately, he did not live to see its completion (Cramp *et al.* 1974).

The winter beached bird survey and summer sample breeding censuses have since been developed into regular enterprises by the RSPB (Stowe 1981). They reveal a fairly steady level of chronic oil pollution of bird bodies found on beaches (whose numbers appear to be influenced mainly by the weather) and the occurrence of local pollution incidents, and also a variety of other problems, including poisoning by toxic chemicals and the micro-

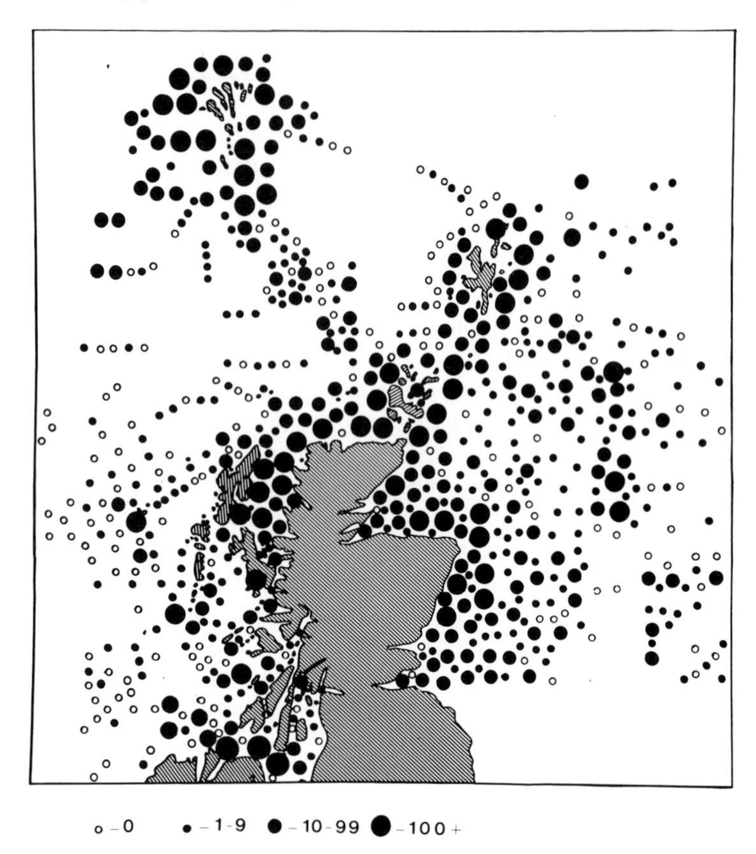

Fig 38 Number of auks seen during half-hour periods in Scottish waters 1970–75 (average taken for overlapping observations).

organisms responsible for red tides and botulism, and encounters with drifting rubbish which may either be eaten by the birds or ensnare them, notably when they use fragments of nylon fish-net for nest material (Bourne 1976). Botulism is probably of most immediate importance as a factor limiting the otherwise uncontrollable natural increase of gull populations (Mudge and Fearns 1982). It is doubtful whether the numbers of birds killed is of any long-term importance, especially at a time when most of them are increasing (Dunnet 1982).

The occurrence of toxic chemicals also has a wider significance. Persistent organochlorine pesticides introduced in the late 1940s were first identified as a threat to terrestrial birds by a pioneer committee, including a representative of the BTO, in the 1950s. A special unit set up by the former Nature Conservancy at Monks Wood found that they were also present in seabird eggs and began to monitor these in 1963. The results attracted little attention

Fig 39 Infra-red satellite photograph of Scottish waters. The pale areas of cool water along the coast are fairly stable; but the eddies north-west of the Hebrides had changed since the previous day; there is some cloud to the west and north-east.
(Photograph supplied by the Department of Electrical Engineering and Electronics, Dundee University, taken with Figure 38 from Bourne 1982b; compare with figures in Swallow et al. 1981).

until raised levels of a variety of compounds, including heavy metals, pesticide residues and polychlorinated biphenyls (PCBs) used by industry were found in starving Guillemots and Razorbills washed up around the Irish Sea and Firth of Clyde after bad weather in the autumn of 1969. Subsequent investigations have shown that low levels of some of these compounds are found in seabirds almost everywhere, although they only become serious in limited areas of contamination. Even the most contaminated species, the Great Skua, is increasing rapidly (NERC, in press). Clearly, this situation needs watching.

The onset of North Sea oil development next led to increased support for research on seabirds: first by the Natural Environment Research Council, and then by British Petroleum, at Aberdeen University, followed by a variety of people elsewhere.

The Trust carried out much analysis of ringing returns of seabirds. All this has led to a much-improved understanding of their ecology. Firstly, surveys of bird distribution at sea and satellite imaging has demonstrated that bird concentrations tend to develop over patches of cool surface water where turbulence develops in the current flowing north up the coast of Europe and clockwise around the British Isles. This results from mixing with cold, deep water rich in nutrient salts which supports a growth of plankton attractive to fish (Bourne 1982b, Figs 38, 39). Mixing starts where deep water impinges on the edge of the continental shelf and banks offshore to give rise to upwelling, becomes more marked where the stratified oceanic water gives way to the well-mixed coastal current at a well-defined front associated with further upwelling offshore, and reaches a climax where the effect of tidal movements is added around islands and headlands and in straits and inlets. Here, large seabird colonies are found (Bourne 1980, Swallow *et al.* 1981).

Secondly, there appear to be long-term fluctuations in the conditions at sea, possibly related to changes in the strength of the water circulation. These affect seabirds through their influence on the quality of the food supply (Southward *et al.* 1975, Harris and Hislop 1978). Over the course of time these may help explain (i) a decline in northern species, usually attributed to the persecution which led to the first British bird protection acts of 1869; (ii) a subsequent increase usually attributed to protection at the end of the last century; (iii) another decline (of auks) usually attributed to oil pollution although it started earlier in about 1910 (*Scot. Nat.* 1913: 235–236, 260); and (iv) a subsequent increase despite continuing pollution since the 1960s. It is notable that another tropical seabird, the Roseate Tern, has shown exactly the opposite pattern of fluctuation, ending with a recent decrease made worse by trapping by small boys in its winter quarters.

Thirdly, over the course of time seabirds have also been affected in a variety of ways by the human fishing industry (Bourne 1972, Martin 1981). Initially, fishermen were also hunters who made free use of birds for meat, oil, eggs, bait, feathers and even manure; probably this reached a climax when the proliferating human population reached a crisis in which they were faced with emigration or starvation in the west, following the failure of the potato crop in the late 1840s (Andrews 1860). Crofters still take some seabirds in the Hebrides, but it is now unusual elsewhere in Britain and it seems much of the recent increase of the birds may involve a recovery from over-exploitation in the past. In recent times more damage has probably been caused by losses in nets, which were already considerable in Scotland by the end of the last century (McIntosh 1903) and have become worse with the introduction of inconspicuous monofilament nylon drift-nets in Ireland (Whilde 1980). Although these are illegal in Scotland, a certain number are said to be used at sea undetected, and some birds are also caught in fixed salmon nets along the coast (Melville 1973).

Fourthly, human fishing activities may also have had an indirect effect on the birds' food-supply, both by removing competitors with the provision of additional food in the form of offal, and more recently by taking both the offal and smaller fish to make fish-meal. This process probably started with the reduction of large seal populations in prehistoric times, but only began to attract attention when first the elimination of whales and then the expansion of fisheries over the last 250 years was accompanied by a progressive increase in the numbers of aerial seabirds which followed fishing-boats. This applies especially to the Northern Fulmar, which has spread all round the temperate North Atlantic (Fisher 1953). While there has recently been some concern lest the rapid development of industrial fisheries might lead to a reversal of this trend, the general pattern of a decline of the auks in the west does not agree with that of the greatest development of industrial fisheries in the east, where the birds are all increasing (Bailey and Hislop 1978).

The main current question relates to the extent to which birds may come into competition with man for food. Originally posed by Buckland *et al.* (1878) as whether birds are harmful to fisheries, it was restated a century later by Furness (1978) – who calculates that birds must consume 29% of the fish production around Foula – as whether fisheries are harmful to birds. This reveals a curious sense of proportion, since if (for example) we take a rather larger and more realistic area, it seems rather unlikely that there were much more than 5,000 tonnes of birds feeding in the North Sea in 1971 when men took nearly 3,000,000 tonnes of fish. About a third of these were potential competitors with birds for food and the rest potential prey, so that the effect on birds must at least have balanced out. Thus it seems rather unlikely, as pointed out by McIntosh in 1903, that birds can have much effect on man, and little more likely that his activities are harmful to them, especially when he produces nearly enough offal to feed them all twice over (Bourne 1983).

Hence, in general, while man may once have exploited British and Irish seabirds excessively, exterminating the Great Auk in the process, it seems likely that his activities are now mainly beneficial to them. In most cases they have even ceased to show natural fluctuations in their numbers, although these are still evident in the group which is least affected – the remaining auks. While pollution has recently received a great deal of publicity and undoubtedly has disastrous local effects, its overall impact has probably been exaggerated (Royal Commission on Environmental Pollution 1981). It now seems likely that an excessive increase of gulls may prove to be limited naturally by botulism; and the other obvious current problem, excessive human disturbance of the more accessible breeding colonies, often by birdwatchers, is gradually being dealt with by the creation of a growing number of reserves. Perhaps it is time we spared more concern for the state of the rest of the world.

Gulls: populations and problems

PATRICIA MONAGHAN

> I do not at present condemn the Herring Gull as vermin nearly to the same extent as the other (the Lesser Black-back), but it will depend most truly upon whether certain legislation (not always operative, for a blessing), does not change their habits and haunts in time.
>
> J. A. HARVIE-BROWN

The above statement was made in 1904, shortly after the introduction of protection of birds acts at the end of the last century. It accurately predicted the subsequent population increase in the Herring Gull, changes in its distribution and habits, and the environmental problems which have resulted from the change in mortality patterns which followed protection. The comparative success of gulls is due to their being, in general, characterised by a lack of specialisation: being neither committed herbivores nor carnivores, neither pelagic nor terrestrial, they are omnifarious both in diet and in habitat. In relation to their environment, they are for the most part opportunistic and adaptable, and the recent population increases have been accompanied by the colonisation of new breeding sites and the exploitation of new food sources.

These qualities have brought many gulls into conflict with man, resulting in several species being regarded as pests by farmers, townsfolk and conservationists alike. Of the six species which commonly nest in the British Isles, only the rarest and most common have escaped censure: the scattered and restricted distribution of the Common Gull and the more pelagic habits of the Kittiwake rarely give cause for complaint. Where problems have arisen, as for example with the mess created by Kittiwakes nesting on the harbour wall at Lowestoft, willing helpers have regularly cleared up the offending excretions in order to prevent the birds from being disturbed. This is in sharp contrast to the treatment usually meted out to the other four species – the Great Black-backed, Herring, Lesser Black-backed and Black-headed Gulls.

The populations of gulls breeding in Britain have undergone marked changes in recent times. A period of intense persecution during the last century, when large numbers were shot by gamekeepers, sportsmen and for the millinery trade, resulted in considerable declines. The Lesser Black-backed Gull in particular, the most inland nester of the large gulls, met with great hostility, often being treated as 'the most destructive winged vermin in the district' (Adair 1898). However, persecution of gulls and other seabirds gradually relaxed following the introduction of acts to protect seabirds in 1869, and birds in general between 1880 and 1896. Overall numbers have increased greatly since then (Parslow 1967). Changes in Black-headed Gull numbers were noticed by BTO members and resulted in Trust surveys of its breeding colonies in 1938 (Hollom 1940) and 1958 (Gribble 1962); these showed that some 175 new colonies had been formed since 1889, and between the two censuses an increase of over 27% had occurred. The Black-headed Gull appears to have continued to increase, though in some inland areas recent and dramatic declines have been noted (Mitchell 1979). The rate of population increase has been particularly striking in the Herring Gull throughout most of its range. While several authors have documented localised changes in Herring Gull numbers (Brown 1967, Harris 1970, Parsons 1971), the large gulls in general have not been fully censused as breeding birds. The full extent of the Herring Gull increase was not realised until 'Operation Seafarer', the national census of breeding seabirds in 1969 (Cramp *et al.* 1974). Using the Seafarer data, Chabrzyk and Coulson (1976) showed that the increase in the Herring Gull appeared to have been taking place at an average annual rate of between 12 and 13 per cent per annum since at least 1930; in effect, the numbers had been doubling within each six-year period. The availability of an abundant food supply at refuse tips, though not in itself responsible for the decrease in mortality rate, has probably affected the extent to which the populations have been able to expand. The ringing, census and survey work of the BTO has contributed greatly to our understanding of gull movements and population dynamics. The Trust has also provided information of considerable use to those dealing with environmental problems arising from too many gulls, or gulls in the wrong places; this relates to both their breeding and wintering habits.

In addition to the formation and expansion of vast new coastal gulleries, for example at Walney Island (Cumbria), large gulls nesting on moorland have increased, to the horror of gamekeepers (Duncan 1981), as have the numbers nesting in towns, to the horror of environmental health officers! The habit of nesting on inhabited buildings, rare amongst gulls prior to 1940, has increased considerably (Cramp 1971). In 1976, another Trust-aided investigation into the status of large gulls nesting on buildings in Britain and Ireland was carried out (Monaghan and Coulson 1977); although the urban nesting population was underestimated in some places (Bourne 1979), it was found that the number of rooftop nesting Herring Gulls had risen from at least 1,200 pairs in 1969 to over 3,000 pairs in 1976. The known urban colonies were expanding at an average annual rate of 13%; furthermore, the rate of colony formation in towns (9·3% per annum) was such that the overall increase in the number of known urban nesting Herring Gulls was 17% per annum between 1969 and 1976. Urban nesting Lesser Black-backs, though less numerous and less widespread than Herring Gulls, increased by an average of 28% per annum in the same period to 323 pairs. The increase in towns reflects the overall population changes in gulls and the comparative saturation or near-saturation of many of the more traditional breeding sites. It may be that, to a gull at least, the outline of buildings in a town resembles the irregular rocky outcrops characteristic of their former coastal haunts.

Though involving only a small percentage of the total gull breeding population in Britain, the problems which result from urban nesting are many and varied and several local authorities have undertaken culling or other preventative measures. Noise tends to be a major cause for complaint – the early-morning trumpeting calls frequently meet with considerable opposition from the somewhat irate human occupants with whom the nest site is shared. The use of roofing material as surrogate grass for pulling in territorial disputes, coupled with the acidic droppings, causes damage to the fabric of buildings; gutters and downcomers may become choked with conglomerations of nest debris, carcasses and faeces, causing floodings and unpleasant smells. Fouling of pavements, and the people who walk on them, with regurgitated food and droppings also does little to improve their popularity, nor does their dive-bombing behaviour in defence of their eggs and chicks. The latter has even resulted in whole streets in some towns being closed due to gull chicks on the road, vigorously defended by their apparently marauding parents. On the other hand there are, albeit a minority, some people who take great pleasure in the opportunity to observe the nesting activities of a large bird at relatively close quarters, often from the comfort of their own home or office! Gulls also remain popular with fishermen who, in addition to using them as a cue in the location of fish shoals (Martin 1981), often attach legendary significance to much of their behaviour – viewing them as an integral part of the coastal environment. Indeed, for most of us, the plaintive cries of gulls evoke soulful images of sand and sea.

Gull colonies in the more traditional places are not without their attendant problems, largely due to the prodigious expansion which has taken place. Though gulls and other birds – for examples, Black-headed Gulls and Sandwich Terns, large gulls and Eiders – can and do nest together in comparative harmony, gulls are often considered to be the undisputable enemies of other seabirds, relentlessly pirating their eggs and young. Such predation is of course greatest in areas subject to human disturbance, often due to over-zealous birdwatchers. Herring and Lesser Black-backed Gulls have also taken over breeding sites formerly occupied by nesting terns. While it is not clear to what extent the gulls have ousted the terns, they probably do prohibit their return. Large, dense gull colonies also contribute to changing vegetation patterns (Sobey and Kenworthy 1979), as on the Isle of May in the Firth of Forth, where the typical *Armeria* and fescue swards have been replaced by plant communities dominated by so-called coarse grass and weeds.

Problems arise not only with breeding gulls, but also with wintering concentrations and feeding flocks. The increasing numbers inland often feed at refuse tips or in urban areas and loaf on conveniently situated pastureland by day and water storage reservoirs by night. Ringing studies carried out in a large-scale co-operative project at Durham and Glasgow Universities have shown that individual Herring Gulls regularly move between different kinds of feeding places, coastal and inland, and that (contrary to popular belief) these gulls are by no means sedentary. Long-range movements take place between breeding and wintering grounds in many areas, often involving rapid transit over several hundred kilometres. Large numbers of Scandinavian Herring and Great Black-backed Gulls overwinter in eastern Britain, and also in the London area (Stanley *et al.* 1981). There has recently been a great deal of interest in the development of methods for identifying the origins of winter visitors based on biometrics, coloration and wing-tip patterns. The relatively small-scale daily movements between roosting and feeding sites near airports or in low-flying areas results in the gulls being a potential hazard to aircraft, particularly during low-flying manoeuvres or landing and takeoff. The Royal Air Force estimates that more than half of their bird strike problems involve gulls. This is partly due to birds coming to feed and loaf on the airfields, and also to flocks flighting across airfields en route to feeding sites elsewhere. This problem formed the subject of an intensive survey carried out (under BTO auspices) on gull roosting and feeding sites in Yorkshire, which clearly demonstrated the need for pilots to be alerted to established gull flight lines, and that more care should be given in this context to the siting of refuse tips.

The behaviour and ecology of gulls brings them into close proximity to man, his pathogens, domestic animals, foodstuffs and water supplies. The extensive movements which gulls undertake, coupled with their comparatively unsavoury feeding habits, gives them considerable potential in the dissemination of disease. In particular they have been associated with the Salmonellae and Campylobacters, which are causative agents of enteric disease in man; for example, 28 serotypes of Salmonellae were isolated from gull faeces in Scotland between 1978 and 1980, in 13 incidents in which gulls were implicated in the spread of infection. The evidence that gulls are involved in the spread of such infections is at present largely circumstantial; however, a recent incident in Scotland highlights their possible involvement. A man, already ill, arrived in Thurso from Malaysia in August 1980; *Salmonella zanzibar*, a serotype new to Scotland, was identified as the cause of his illness; the man was clear of infection by the end of September, and returned to Malaysia in November 1980. A few weeks later, *S. zanzibar* was isolated in a bulk milk sample from a farm near Thurso; there was no illness in the cows, but since 1972 a variety of Salmonellae had been isolated from this dairy herd and from gull faeces on the pastureland. Herring Gulls which fed at sewage outfalls in Thurso were known to roost regularly on a small loch on the farm. In April 1981, *S. zanzibar* was isolated from a calf on another farm in the area and in January 1982 turned up again in the milk on the first farm (Johnston *et al.* 1982). Are the sewage-feeding Herring Gulls the vectors in this case? Can they harbour these pathogens for long periods of time and thereby act as reservoirs of infection? The circumstantial evidence is strong, but the birds themselves have not been investigated. There is a great deal that we do not know about the capacity of gulls to act as vectors in disease transmission, and this is currently under investigation. Ringing is providing information on the nature and extent of movements typical of the birds concerned.

Gulls have also been implicated in the pollution of water supplies, mainly due to their habit of roosting on inland water storage and service reservoirs in winter. This problem, though most often associated with winter roosts, can occur in other contexts. For example, the water run-off from the large gullery in the Lancashire Pennines has created serious pollution problems for the North West Water Authority (Fennel *et al.* 1974), and was the reason behind control attempts being undertaken at this colony. Inland roosting by gulls was first noted at the end of the last century and has been well documented by BTO surveys conducted at ten-year intervals since 1953 (Hickling 1954, 1967, 1977); the last survey showed that nearly three times as many gulls were wintering inland as recorded in 1953. This increase most probably reflects the population expansion which has taken place, rather than a behavioural change involving a shift of birds away from coastal areas. The next of these wintering gull surveys will take place in 1983. Trust-aided investigations into the winter status of the Lesser Black-backed Gull, documenting a phenomenon of considerable biological interest, took place in the winters of 1949/50, 1950/51 and 1959/60 (Barnes 1952, 1961); these showed the numbers to have increased to almost 3,000, the rate of increase being particularly high in the London Area and the West Midlands.

In addition to contributing to our understanding of the ecology of gulls, these winter surveys are particularly relevant to the water pollution problem. For example, the reservoirs at Milngavie (near Glasgow) have been used as a nocturnal roost by increasing numbers of gulls over the past 30 years at least. They supply over 900,000 consumers and the water quality was initially so good that facilities were constructed late last century which now permit only marginal chlorination and pH correction. The bacteriological quality of the stored water has been steadily declining, and the pattern of contamination – high in winter and low in summer – mirrored the pattern of reservoir use by roosting gulls. During the 1980/81 and 1981/82 winters, these reservoirs have been kept free of roosting gulls by controlled and judicious use of taped distress calls. A marked improvement in water quality has resulted, the faecal indicator organisms having decreased from over 2,000/100 ml when the gulls were present to less than 50/100 ml. In addition to solving the problem for the Strathclyde Regional Water Authority, and thereby saving the expenditure of tens of millions of pounds in upgrading the treatment plant, this work has demonstrated clearly that roosting gulls were the source of the problem (Benton *et al.*, in press).

With regard to the control of gulls and the problems they create, a variety of methods have been tried, ranging from tying fireworks on the end of broom handles and pointing them at urban nesting gulls, to hardboiling their eggs in an attempt to reduce their breeding success. In general, attempts to control breeding gull numbers by egg or nest destruction have met with little success. This does not remove the breeding adults, who will rebuild the nest and lay a replacement clutch, if not in the same year then at least in the next. Furthermore, we know from ringing studies that there is considerable intercolony dispersal (Duncan and Monaghan 1977); even if breeding success is kept low in one area, recruits from elsewhere will move in to swell the numbers. Culling, a very unpleasant task, is now the method most often used for breeding birds. The first organised and officially approved gull culls began in the 1960s, moving on to the large-scale culling which now seems to have become almost an annual event in several places, notably the Isle of May. However, while population decreases have been effected, recruitment still continues; in some areas the disturbance caused by culling may have dispersed the birds over a wider area. It is not always clear what the aim of these culls is: to reduce the number of breeding birds to some so-called acceptable (but rarely defined) level, or to maintain the colony at its existing size, or to wipe it out completely. Since the damage which the gulls cause has rarely been quantified, any improvement after culling is difficult to assess. Since we know, again from ringing studies, that a great deal of movement takes place in winter, any culling outwith the breeding season is unlikely to have much effect; the turnover of birds may be too great. Scaring flocks can be successful, being applicable mainly to roosting but possibly also to some feeding sites. This may depend upon how easily the gulls can move to alternative sites. Recent increases in the incidence of botulism, particularly amongst the large gulls (Lloyd *et al.* 1976, Bourne 1977) may have brought about localised declines in some areas; for how long this continues remains to be seen. In general, gulls are well adapted to a changing environment and well equipped to resist or evade control measures.

Studying gulls does offer a great deal of scope for both the professional and amateur ornithologist. They are large, easy to see and identify and they are accessible. Gulls have long been used as subjects in basic ecological and ethological research; indeed much of the pioneering work in the science of ethology by Nobel prizewinner Professor Niko Tinbergen was concerned with the social behaviour of gulls. Information collected on gulls is also likely to have many practical applications. The recently established Gull Study Group provides a forum for the exchange of ideas and for co-operation between those who study gulls from different viewpoints. Judging by the success of this group, gulls do still have their enthusiasts.

8: The Trust in the future

S. M. Taylor

The Trust's first task was to acquire basic information about bird communities, breeding biology and movements. The last twenty years saw growing emphasis on monitoring, and this will continue, but it will be backed by increasing efforts to understand the relationships between birds and their habitats and environment. With long series of data available from the ringing, nest record and CBC schemes, we have begun to investigate how weather, general habitat features and population levels affect breeding success and winter survival. This work will accelerate; by allowing the monitoring data to be interpreted in greater depth, it will give us a better picture of the general health of the bird populations and of the environment we share with them. This will make it more than ever important to maintain the long-term schemes in operation. The general overview given by the breeding-season Atlas will need to be brought up to date every twenty-five or thirty years.

Besides these large-scale studies we shall expand our work on the relation between birds and the details of their habitat, to give information directly useful in conservation and land management. For example, what are the likely effects of hedgerow removal? How can they best be mitigated? Are small copses or patches of scrub a worthwhile replacement? How do the size and structure of a wood affect the numbers and species of birds present? To answer such questions needs detailed habitat data, recorded in a consistent yet easily interpretable way. We shall have to develop techniques allowing amateurs with simple equipment to do this, perhaps with a progressive training programme and annual courses, like those for ringers. To study the related question, of just how the countryside is changing, we can expect to make more use of the CBC habitat maps, remapping old plots that have ceased to be censused. We shall need to keep census workers abreast of changes in agricultural practice, to ensure proper recording of land use.

Now that our special surveys are based, like the Atlas projects, on 10-km grid squares, we shall find ourselves making more effective use of samples. It will be feasible to recheck sub-samples of squares, perhaps for several species at once, and so to plan our full-scale repeats with maximum effect. To aid the organisation of fieldwork we shall encourage the more widespread use of '10-km stewards' – members of the BTO or of local societies who undertake to do or to arrange all fieldwork within a given square, whether for a BTO project or for local studies. They are an important link at the working level between the Trust and local organisations, and by noting and reporting major changes in land use they could also be a means of bringing the Habitats Register up to date and maintaining it.

In the 1960s our first attempts to use computers foundered because the resources at our disposal fell short of our needs. Now powerful facilities of our own have revolutionised the handling of our data. The large-scale analyses needed for the developments mentioned above are now possible, and so is the handling of more information from our fieldwork, so making it more productive. The timed counts of the Winter Atlas, and the coded habitat keys of the Waterways Bird Survey are examples. Future developments along these lines can safely be predicted. Two other things are certain. One is that no matter how complicated the technical developments ahead, the first crucial step will remain the field skills of our observers, and their willingness to dedicate their time and effort to the task. The second is that the pleasure to be gained from meeting the challenge and from close and detailed acquaintance with the birds and their habitats will not grow less.

References

Anon (1959). *From Fisherman's Paradise to Farmer's Pride*. Netherlands Govt. Information Service.

Adair, P. (1898). Notes on the birds of Etterick. *Ann. Scott. Nat. Hist.* 1898: 21–27.

Alexander, W. B. (1932). The bird population of an Oxfordshire farm. *J. Anim. Ecol.* 1: 58–64.

Andrews, W. (1860). Notes on the birds of the south-west coast. *Proc. Nat. Hist. Soc. Dublin* 1: 80–85.

Appleton, T. P. (1982). Rutland Water Nature Reserve: concept, design and management. *Hydrobiologia* 88: 211–224.

Archer, A. A. (1972). Sand and gravel as aggregate. Mineral Resources Division. *Inst. Geol. Sci. Mineral Dossier* 4. London (H.M.S.O.)

Arnold, G. W. (in press). The influence of ditch and hedgerow structure, length of hedgerows and area of woodland and garden on bird numbers on farmland. *J. App. Ecol.*

Atkinson-Willes, G. L. (1969). Wildfowl and recreation: a balance of requirements. *British Water Supply* 11: 5–15.

Axell, H. E. (1966). Eruption of Bearded Tits during 1959–65. *Brit. Birds* 59: 513–543.

Bailey, R. S. (1967). An index of bird population changes on farmland. *Bird Study* 14: 195–209.

Bailey, R. S. (1968). An index of bird population changes in woodland. *Bird Study* 15: 171–180.

Bailey, R. S. and J. R. G. Hislop (1978). The effects of fisheries on seabirds in the northeast Atlantic. *Ibis* 120: 104–105.

Barham, K. E. I., P. J. Conder and I. J. Ferguson-Lees (1956). Bee-eaters nesting in Britain, 1955. *Bird Notes* 28: 34–43.

Barnes, J. A. G. (1952). The status of the Lesser Black-backed Gull. *Brit. Birds* 45: 3–17.

Barnes, J. A. G. (1961). The winter status of the Lesser Black-backed Gull, 1959–60. *Bird Study* 8: 127–147.

Baxter, E. V. and L. J. Rintoul (1918). The birds of the Isle of May: a migration study. *Ibis* (10) 6: 247–287.

Baxter, E. V. and L. J. Rintoul (1953). *The Birds of Scotland*. Edinburgh (Oliver & Boyd).

Bell, B. D., C. K. Catchpole and K. J. Corbett (1968). Problems of censusing Reed Buntings, Sedge Warblers and Reed Warblers. *Bird Study* 15: 16–21.

Bell, B. D., C. K. Catchpole, K.J. Corbett and R. J. Hornby (1973). The relationship between census results and breeding populations of some marshland passerines. *Bird Study* 20: 127–140.

Benson, G. B. G. and K. Williamson (1972). Breeding birds of a mixed farm in Suffolk. *Bird Study* 19: 34–50.

Benton, C., F. Kahn, P. Monaghan, W. N. Richards and C. B. Shedden (in press). The contamination of a major water supply by gulls (*Larus* sp.): a study of the problem and remedial action taken. *Water Research*.

Bibby, C. J. (1973). The Red-backed Shrike: a vanishing British species. *Bird Study* 20: 103–110.

Birkhead, M. (1981). How fishermen kill the swans. *New Scientist* 1247: 14–15.

Bonham, P. F. and J. C. M. Robertson (1975). The spread of Cetti's Warbler in north-west Europe. *Brit. Birds* 68: 393–408.
Bourne, W. R. P. (1972). Threats to seabirds. *Bull. Internat. Council Bird Pres.* 11: 200–218.
Bourne, W. R. P. (1976). Seabirds and pollution. Pp. 403–502 in: R. Johnston (ed.), *Marine Pollution*. London (Academic Press).
Bourne, W. R. P. (1977). The epidemiology of botulism. *Marine Poll. Bull.* 8: 28–29.
Bourne, W. R. P. (1979). Herring Gulls nesting on buildings in eastern Scotland. *North East Scotland Bird Rept.* 1978.
Bourne, W. R. P. (1980). The habitats, distribution and numbers of northern seabirds. *Trans. Linn. Soc. NY.* 9: 1–14.
Bourne, W. R. P. (1982a). The manner in which wind drift leads to seabird movements along the east coast of Scotland. *Ibis* 124: 81–88.
Bourne, W. R. P. (1982b). The distribution of Scottish seabirds vulnerable to oil pollution. *Marine Poll. Bull.* 13: 270–273.
Bourne, W. R. P. (1983). Birds, fish and offal in the North Sea. *Marine Poll. Bull. 14* (in press).
Brown, P. and G. Waterston (1962). *The Return of the Osprey*. London (Collins).
Brown, R. G. B. (1967). Breeding success and population growth in a colony of Herring and Lesser Black-backed Gulls, *Larus argentatus* and *L. fuscus*. *Ibis* 109: 502–515.
Buckland, F., S. Walpole and A. Young (1878). *Report on the Herring Fisheries of Scotland*. H.M.S.O.
Buker, J. B., L. S. Buurma and E. Osieck (1975). Post-juvenile moult of the Bearded Tit in Zuidlijk Flevoland, Netherlands. *Beaufortia* 23 (306).
Bull, A. D., C. J. Mead and K. Williamson (1976). Bird-life on a Norfolk farm in relation to agricultural changes. *Bird Study* 23: 163–182.

Cadbury, C. J. (1980). The status and habitats of the Corncrake in Britain 1978–79. *Bird Study* 27: 203–218.
Campbell, B. (1953). A comparison of bird populations upon 'industrial' and 'rural' farmland in South Wales. *Cardiff Nat. Soc. Repts. & Trans.* 81: 4–65.
Campbell, B. (1954). The breeding distribution and habitats of the Pied Flycatcher in Britain. *Bird Study* 1: 81–101.
Cawthorne, R. A. and J. H. Marchant (1980). The effects of the 1978/79 winter on British bird populations. *Bird Study* 27: 163–172.
Chabrzyk, G. and J. C. Coulson (1976). Survival and recruitment in the Herring Gull *Larus argentatus*. *J. Anim. Ecol.* 45: 187–203.
Chapman, W. M. M. (1939). Bird population of an Oxfordshire farm. *J. Anim. Ecol.* 8: 286–299.
Clafton, F. R. (1959). Green Sandpiper breeding in Inverness-shire. *Brit. Birds* 52: 430–433.
Clarke, W. E. (1912). *Studies in Bird Migration*. London.
Colquhoun, M. K. and A. Morley (1941). The density of downland birds. *J. Anim. Ecol.* 10: 35–46.
Cornwallis, R. K. (1954–56). The pattern of migration at the east coast observatories. *Brit. Birds* 47: 423–431; 48: 429–446; 50: 105–118.
Cornwallis, R. K. (1956). Autumn migration on the east coast of Britain in relation to weather. *Ardea* 44: 224–231.
Cornwallis, R. K. (1961). Four invasions of Waxwings during 1956–60. *Brit. Birds* 54: 1–30.
Cornwallis, R. K. and A. E. Smith (1960). The bird in the hand. *BTO Field Guide* no. 6.

Cornwallis, R. K. and A. D. Townsend (1968). Waxwings in Britain and Europe during 1965/66. *Brit. Birds* 61: 97–118.
Cramp, S. (1949). The birds of Kensington Gardens and Regent's Park. *London Bird Rept.* 13 (1948): 37–45.
Cramp, S. (1971). Gulls nesting on buildings in Britain and Ireland. *Brit. Birds* 64: 476–487.
Cramp, S. (1975). The influence of cleaner air on the breeding birds of Inner London. *London Bird Rept.* 38 (1973): 65–72.
Cramp, S., W. R. P. Bourne and D. Saunders (1974). *The Seabirds of Britain and Ireland.* London (Collins).
Cuisin, M. (1980). Nouvelles donnees sur la repartition du Pic noir en France et comparison avec la situation dans d'autres pays. *Oiseau* 50: 23–32.

Davidson, J. and R. Lloyd (eds.) (1977). *Conservation and Agriculture.* Chichester (John Wiley).
Davies, J. L. (1949). The breeding of the Starling in West Wales. *Brit. Birds* 42: 369–375.
Davis, B. N. K. (1967). Bird feeding preferences among different crops in an area near Huntingdon. *Bird Study* 14: 227–237.
Davis, P. (1966). The movements of Pied Wagtails as shown by ringing. *Bird Study* 13: 147–162.
Dobinson, H. M. (1963). The Inland Observation Points. *Bird Migration* 2: 272–275.
DoE (1982). Land drainage and conservation: guidance notes of procedures for Water Authorities, Internal Drainage Boards, Nature Conservancy Council and Countryside Commission. DoE October 1982.
Duncan, N. (1981). The Abbeystead and Mallowdale gull colony before control. *Bird Study* 28: 133–138.
Duncan, N. and P. Monaghan (1977). Infidelity to the natal colony by breeding Herring Gulls. *Ringing & Migration* 1: 166–172.
Dunnet, G. M. (1982). Oil pollution and seabird populations. *Phil. Trans. Roy. Soc. Lond.* B 297: 413–427.
Durman, R. (ed.) (1976). *Bird Observatories in Britain and Ireland.* Berkhamsted (Poyser).
Dybbro, T. (1976). *De Danske Ynglefugles Udbredelse.* Copenhagen (Dansk Orn. Forening).

Evans, G. (1976). Gibraltar Point. Pp. 133–157 in: R. Durman (ed.), *Bird Observatories in Britain and Ireland.* Berkhamsted (Poyser).
Everett, M. J. (1971). Breeding status of Red-necked Phalaropes in Britain and Ireland. *Brit. Birds* 64: 293–302.

Farming and Wildlife Advisory Group (FWAG) (1982). FWAG Newsletter, summer 1982.
Fennel, H., D. B. James and J. Morris (1974). Pollution of a storage reservoir by roosting gulls. *Water Treatment & Examination* 23: 5.
Fisher, J. (1953). The Collared Turtle Dove in Europe. *Brit. Birds* 46: 153–181.
Fisher, J. (1953) *The Fulmar.* London (Collins).
Fisher, J. and R. M. Lockley (1954). *Seabirds.* London (Collins).
Fitter, R. S. R. (1949). *London's Birds.* London (Collins).
Fitter, R. S. R. and R. A. Richardson (1952). *Collins Pocket Guide to British Birds.* London (Collins).
Flegg, J. J. M. (1975). Bird population and distribution changes and the impact of man. *Bird Study* 22: 191–202.

Fowler, J. A., J. D. Okill and B. Marshall (1982). A retrap analysis of Storm Petrels tape-lured in Shetland. *Ringing & Migration* 4: 1–7.
Fuller, R. J. (1982). *Bird Habitats in Britain*. Calton (Poyser).
Fuller, R. J. and R. E. Youngman (1979). The utilisation of farmland by Golden Plovers wintering in southern England. *Bird Study* 26: 37–46.

Gibb, J. A. (1962). L. Tinbergen's hypothesis of the rôle of specific search images. *Ibis* 104: 106–111.
Glegg, W. E. (1929). *A History of the Birds of Essex*. London (Witherby).
Glue, D. (ed.) (1982). *The Garden Bird Book*. London (Macmillan).
Godwin, H. E. (1975). *History of the British Flora*. 2nd edn. Cambridge (University Press).
Goode, D. A. (1981). Lead poisoning in swans. Report to NCC Working Group.
Grant, P. J., J. G. Harrison and K. Noble (1974). The return of birdlife to the inner Thames. *London Bird Rept.* 37 (1972): 61–64.
Green, G. H. (1980). Changing agricultural practice in Scotland and breeding waders. *Wader Study Group Bull.* 29: 5.
Gribble, F. C. (1962). Census of Black-headed Gull colonies in England and Wales 1958. *Bird Study* 9: 56–71.

Hale, W. G. (1980). *Waders*. London (Collins).
Hardman, J. A. and D. R. Cooper (1980). Mute Swans on the Warwickshire Avon: a study of a decline. *Wildfowl* 31: 29–36.
Harris, M. P. (1970). Rates and causes of increases of some British gull populations. *Bird Study* 17: 325–335.
Harris, M. P. and J. R. G. Hislop (1978). The food of young Puffins *Fratercula arctica*. *J. Zool. Lond.* 185: 213–236.
Harrison, C. J. O. (1961). Woodlark population and habitat. *London Bird Rept.* 24 (1959): 71–80.
Harvey, W. G. (1977). Cetti's Warbler in east Kent in 1975. *Brit. Birds* 70: 89–96.
Harvie-Brown, J. A. and H. A. Macpherson (1904). *A Fauna of the North West Highlands and Skye*. Edinburgh.
Hickling, R. A. O. (1954). The wintering of gulls in Britain. *Bird Study* 1: 129–148.
Hickling, R. A. O. (1967). The inland wintering of gulls in England 1963. *Bird Study* 14: 104–113.
Hickling, R. A. O. (1977). Inland wintering of gulls in England and Wales. *Bird Study* 24: 79–88.
Hinde, R. A. and A. S. Thom (1947). The breeding of the Moustached Warbler in Cambridgeshire. *Brit. Birds* 40: 98–104.
Hollom, P. A. D. (1940). Report on the 1938 survey of Black-headed Gull colonies. *Brit. Birds* 33: 202–221, 230–244.
Hoskins, W. G. (1977). *The Making of the English Landscape*. London (Book Club Associates).
Hudson, R. (1965). The spread of the Collared Dove in Britain and Ireland. *Brit. Birds* 58: 105–139.
Hudson, R. and G. A. Pyman (1968). *A Guide to the Birds of Essex*. Chelmsford (Essex B.W.P.S.).
Hutchinson, C. (1979). *Ireland's Wetlands and their Birds*. Dublin (Irish Wildbird Conservancy).

Johnston, W. S. (1982). Sequelae to imported *Salmonella zanzibar*. *CDS Rept.* 82/17: ix–x.

Kent, A. K. (1964). The breeding habitats of the Reed Bunting and Yellowhammer in Nottinghamshire. *Bird Study* 11: 123–127.
Kist, J. (1957). Schlegel en onze huidige avifauna. *Ardea* 45: 2–24.

Lack, D. (1943–44). The problem of partial migration. *Brit. Birds* 37: 122–130; 38: 143–150.
Lack, D. (1959). Migration across the North Sea studied by radar. Part 1. *Ibis* 101: 209–234.
Lack, D. (1960). The influence of weather on passerine migration: a review. *Auk* 77: 171–209.
Lack, D. (1965). *Enjoying Ornithology*. London (Methuen).
Lack, E. (1950). Breeding season and clutch size of the Wood Warbler. *Ibis* 92: 95–98.
Lamb, P. J. (1982). Persistence of sub-Saharan drought. *Nature* 299: 46–48.
Lloyd, B. (1950). Further notes on the breeding status of the Starling in West Wales. *Brit. Birds* 43: 142–143.
Lloyd-Evans, T. (1971). Numbers and movements of gulls in an inland area of Yorkshire. Unpubl. Rept. on BTO/RAF Yorkshire Gull Project.
Lloyd, E. S., G. J. Thomas, J. W. Macdonald, E. M. Borrland, K. Standing and J. L. Smart (1976). Wild bird mortality caused by botulism in Britain in 1975. *Biol. Conserv.* 10: 119–129.
Lodge, G. E. (1946). *Memoirs of an Artist Naturalist*. London & Edinburgh.
London Natural History Society (1957). *Birds of the London Area since 1900*. London (Collins).
Lovegrove, R. (1978). Breeding status of Goosanders in Wales. *Brit. Birds* 71: 214–216.

Mabey, R. (1980). *The Common Ground*. London (Hutchinson).
McIntosh, W. C. (1903). The effects of marine piscatorial birds on the food fishes. *Ann. Mag. Nat. Hist.* (7) 11: 551–553.
Macpherson, H. A. (1892). *Fauna of Lakeland*. Edinburgh.
Macpherson, H. A. and W. Duckworth (1886). *The Birds of Cumberland*. Carlisle.
Marchant, J. H. (1982). Bird population changes for the years 1980–81. *Bird Study* 29: 143–148.
Marchant, J. H. and P. A. Hyde (1979). Population changes for waterways birds 1974–78. *Bird Study* 26: 227–238.
Marchant, J. H. and P. A. Hyde (1980). Aspects of the distribution of riparian birds on waterways in Britain and Ireland. *Bird Study* 27: 183–202.
Martin, A. (1981). *The Ring-net Fisherman*. Edinburgh (John Donald).
Mead, C. J. (1974). Bird ringing. *BTO Guide* 16.
Mead, C. J. and J. D. Harrison (1979). Sand Martin movements within Britain and Ireland. *Bird Study* 26: 73–86.
Meek, E. R. and B. Little (1977). The spread of the Goosander in Britain and Ireland. *Brit. Birds* 70: 229–237.
Mellanby, K. (1970). *Pesticides and Pollution*. 2nd edn. London (Collins).
Melville, D. (1973). Birds and salmon nets. *Seabird Rept.* 3: 47–50.
Mitchell, F. S. (1885). *The Birds of Lancashire*. London.
Mitchell, J. (1979). The Black-headed Gull: its rise and decline as a breeding species on Loch Lomondside and neighbouring areas. *Loch Lomond Bird Rept.* 8.
Monaghan, P. and J. C. Coulson (1977). Status of large gulls nesting on buildings. *Bird Study* 24: 89–104.
Montier, D. (1968). A survey of the breeding distribution of the Kestrel, Barn Owl and Tawny Owl in the London Area in 1967. *London Bird Rept.* 32 (1967): 81–92.

Moore, N. W. (1957). The past and present status of the Buzzard in the British Isles. *Brit. Birds* 50: 173–197.

Moore, N. W. (1967). A synopsis of the pesticide problem. *Adv. Ecol. Res.* 4: 75–129.

Moore, N. W. (1974). Ecological effects of pesticides. In: A. Warren and F. B. Goldsmith (eds.), *Conservation in Practice.* London (Wiley).

Moore, N. W., M. D. Hooper and B. N. K. Davies (1967). Hedges. 1: introduction and reconnaisance studies. *J. Appl. Ecol.* 4: 201–220.

Moreau, R. E. (1961). Problems of Mediterranean-Saharan migration. *Ibis* 103a: 373–427, 580–623.

Moreau, R. E. (1972). *The Palaearctic-African Bird Migration Systems.* London (Academic Press).

Morgan, R. A. and D. E. Glue (1981). Breeding survey of Black Redstarts in Britain 1977. *Bird Study* 28: 163–168.

Morgan, R. A. and R. J. O'Connor (1980). Farmland habitat and Yellowhammer distribution in Britain. *Bird Study* 27: 155–162.

Moriarty, F. (1975). *Pollutants and Animals.* London (Allen & Unwin).

Mudge, G. P. and P. N. Ferns (1982). Breeding populations of gulls in the inner Bristol Channel 1980. *Seabird Rep.* 6: 48–49.

Murray, R. D. (1979). Colonisation of Scotland by northern birds 1820–1977. *Scott. Birds* 10: 158–174.

Murton, R. K. (1971). *Man and Birds.* London (Collins).

N.E.R.C. (in press). Contaminants in marine top predators. London (Natural Environment Research Council).

Newton, I. (1972). *Finches.* London (Collins).

Nicholson, E. M. (1957). The rarer birds of prey: their present status in the British Isles – Marsh Harrier. *Brit. Birds* 50: 142–143.

Nicholson, E. M. and I. J. Ferguson-Lees (1962). The Hastings rarities. *Brit. Birds* 55: 299–382.

Norris, C. A. (1945). Summary of a report on the distribution and status of the Corncrake. *Brit. Birds* 38: 142–148, 162–168.

Norris, C. A. (1947). Report on the distribution and status of the Corncrake. *Brit. Birds* 40: 226–244.

Oakes, C. (1949). Status of the Green Woodpecker in Lancashire. *Brit. Birds* 42: 186–187.

O'Connor, R. J. (1979). Population dynamics of some farmland species. *BTO News* 98: 9–10.

O'Connor, R. J. (1980a). Pattern and process in Great Tit (*Parus major*) populations in Britain. *Ardea* 68: 165–183.

O'Connor, R. J. (1980b). The effect of census date on the results of intensive Common Birds Census surveys. *Bird Study* 27: 126–136.

O'Connor, R. J. (1980c). Ornithology in Ireland. *Brit. Birds* 73: 85–92.

O'Connor, R. J. and R. K. Hicks (1980). The influence of weather conditions on the detection of birds during Common Birds Census fieldwork. *Bird Study* 27: 137–151.

O'Connor, R. J. and C. J. Mead (in press). The Stock Dove in Britain, 1930–1980. *Brit. Birds.*

Olney, P. J. S. (1963). Artificial habitats for wildfowl. Pp. 307–314 in: G. L. Atkinson-Willes (ed.), *Wildfowl in Great Britain.* London (H.M.S.O.).

Olsson, V. (1971). Studies of less familiar birds: Serin. *Brit. Birds* 64: 213–223.

O'Meara, M. (1979). Distribution and numbers of Corncrakes in Ireland in 1978. *Irish Birds* 1: 381–405.

Osborne, P. (1982). Some effects of Dutch elm disease on nesting farmland birds. *Bird Study* 29: 2–16.
Owen, M. (1976). Solway-Spitsbergen Barnacle Geese. *Wildfowl News* 75: 13–14.
Owen, M. and G. L. Atkinson-Willes (in press). *Wildfowl in Great Britain*. 2nd edn. Calton (Poyser).

Parrinder, E. R. (1964). Little Ringed Plovers in Britain 1960–1962. *Brit. Birds* 57: 191–198.
Parrinder, E. R. and E. D. Parrinder (1975). Little Ringed Plovers in Britain in 1968–1973. *Brit. Birds* 68: 359–368.
Parslow, J. L. F. (1967). Changes in status among breeding birds in Britain and Ireland. Part 3. *Brit. Birds* 60: 177–202.
Parslow, J. L. F. (1973). *Breeding Birds of Britain and Ireland*. Berkhamsted (Poyser).
Parsons, J. (1971). The breeding biology of the Herring Gull *Larus argentatus*. Unpubl. PhD thesis, University of Durham.
Picozzi, N. and D. Weir (1976). Dispersal and causes of death of Buzzards. *Brit. Birds* 69: 193–201.
Pollard, E., M. D. Hooper and N. W. Moore (1974). *Hedges*. London (Collins).
Potts, G. R. (1980). The effects of modern agriculture, nest predation and game preservation on the population ecology of partridges *Perdix perdix* and *Alectoris rufa*. *Adv. Ecol. Res.* 11: 1–79.
Prater, A. J. (1981). *Estuary Birds in Britain and Ireland*. Calton (Poyser).

Rabøl, J. (1969). Reverse migration in the course of westward vagrancy by four *Phylloscopus* warblers. *Brit. Birds* 62: 89–92.
Rackham, O. (1976). *Trees and Woodland in the British Landscape*. London (Dent).
Ramsar Convention (1971). E. Carp (ed.), *Proc. Internat. Conf. Conserv. Wetlands & Waterfowl, Ramsar (Iran) 1971*. Slimbridge (I.W.R.B.).
Ratcliffe, D. A. (ed.) (1977). *A Nature Conservation Review*. Cambridge (University Press).
Ratcliffe, D. A. (1980). *The Peregrine Falcon*. Calton (Poyser).
Redman, P. S. and W. D. Hooke (1954). Firecrests in Britain 1952–53. *Brit. Birds* 47: 324–335.
Riddiford, N. and P. Findley (1981). Seasonal movements of summer migrants. *BTO Guide* 18.
Rintoul, L. J. and E. V. Baxter (1935). *A Vertebrate Fauna of Forth*. Edinburgh.
Robson, W. and K. Williamson (1972). The breeding birds of a Westmorland farm. *Bird Study* 19: 203–214.
Royal Commission on Environmental Pollution (1981). Eighth Report: Oil Pollution of the Sea. London (H.M.S.O.).

Sage, B. L. and J. D. R. Vernon (1978). The 1975 national survey of rookeries. *Bird Study* 25: 64–86.
Sharrock, J. T. R. (1974). *Scarce Migrant Birds in Britain and Ireland*. Berkhamsted (Poyser).
Sharrock, J. T. R. (1976). *The Atlas of Breeding Birds in Britain and Ireland*. Tring (BTO) and Berkhamsted (Poyser).
Sharrock, J. T. R. (1976). Cape Clear Island. Pp. 66–80 in: R. Durman (ed.), *Bird Observatories in Britain and Ireland*. Berkhamsted (Poyser).
Sharrock, J. T. R. (et al) (1980). Rare breeding birds in the United Kingdom in 1978. *Brit. Birds* 73: 5–26.
Sharrock, J. T. R. (et al) (1981). Rare breeding birds in the United Kingdom in 1979. *Brit. Birds* 74: 17–36.

Sheail, J. (1971). *Rabbits and their History*. Newton Abbot (David & Charles).
Shrubb, M. (1970). Birds and farming today. *Bird Study* 17: 123–144.
Silva, E. T. (1949). Nest records of the Song Thrush. *Brit. Birds* 42: 97–111.
Sitters, H. P. (1982). The decline of the Cirl Bunting in Britain 1968–1980. *Brit. Birds* 75: 105–105.
Snow, D. W. (1965). The relationship between census results and the breeding population of birds on farmland. *Bird Study* 12: 287–304.
Snow, D. W. (1966). The migration and dispersal of British Blackbirds. *Bird Study* 13: 237–255.
Snow, D. W. and H. Mayer-Gross (1967). Farmland as a nesting habitat. *Bird Study* 14: 43–52.
Sobey, D. G. and J. B. Kenworthy (1979). The relationship between Herring Gulls and the vegetation of their breeding colonies. *J. Ecol.* 67: 469–496.
Southward, A. J., E. I. Butler and L. Pennycuick (1975). Recent cyclic changes in the abundance of marine life. *Nature, Lond.* 253: 714–717.
Southward, T. R. E. (1961). The number of species of interest associated with various trees. *J. Anim. Ecol.* 30: 1–8.
Spencer, R. (1976). Introduction. Pp. 11–28 in: R. Durman (ed.), *Bird Observatiories in Britain and Ireland*. Berkhamsted (Poyser).
Spencer, R. and G. H. Gush (1973). Siskins feeding in gardens. *Brit. Birds* 66: 91–99.
Spencer, R. and R. Hudson (1978). Report on Bird Ringing for 1977. *Ringing & Migration* 2: 57–62.
Spencer, R. and R. Hudson (1979). Report on Bird Ringing for 1978. *Ringing & Migration* 2: 161–165.
Stanley, P. I., T. Brough, M. R. Flectcher, N. Horton and J. B. A. Rochard (1981). The origins of Herring Gulls wintering inland in south-east England. *Bird Study* 28: 123–132.
Stowe, T. J. (1982). Beached bird surveys and surveillance of cliff-breeding seabirds. R.S.P.B. Report. Sandy.
Svärdson, G. (1957). The 'invasion' type of bird migration. *Brit. Birds* 50: 314–343.
Svensson, L. (1970). *Identification Guide to European Passerines*. Stockholm (Riksmuseum).
Swallow, J. C., R. I. Currie, A. E. Gill and J. H. Simpson (eds.) (1981). Circulation and fronts in continental shelf seas. *Phil. Trans. Roy. Soc. Lond.* A 302: 511–689.

Tanner, M. F. (1979). Wildfowl, reservoirs and recreation. *Water Space Amenity Commission Rept.* 5. London (W.S.A.C.).
Tatner, P. (1982). Factors influencing the distribution of Magpies in an urban environment. *Bird Study* 29: 227–234.
Taylor, S. M. (1965). The Common Birds Census – some statistical aspects. *Bird Study* 12: 268–286.
Teixeira, R. M. (1979). *Atlas van de Nederlandse Broedvogels*. 's-Graveland, Netherlands.
Thomas, G. J. (1972). A review of gull damage and management methods at nature reserves. *Biol. Conserv.* 4: 117–127.
Thomas, G. J., D. A. Allen and M. P. B. Grose (1981). The demography and flora of the Ouse Washes, England. *Biol. Conserv.* 21: 197–229.
Thomson, A. L. (1926). *Problems of Bird Migration*. London (Witherby).
Thomson, A. L. (1936). *Bird Migration: a short account*. London (Witherby).
Thomson, A. L. (1964). *A New Dictionary of Birds*. London (Nelson).
Tuite, C. H. (1981). The impact of water-based recreation on the waterfowl of enclosed inland water in Britain. Report to the Sports Council and Nature Conservancy Council. Slimbridge (Wildfowl Trust).

Voous, K. H. (1960). *Atlas of European Birds.* London (Nelson).

Warren, A. and F. B. Goldsmith (eds.) (1974). *Conservation in Practice.* London (John Wiley).

Water Space Amenity Commission (1980). Conservation and land drainage guidelines. London (W.S.A.C.).

Watson, A. (1973). Shore Larks summering and possibly breeding in Scotland. *Brit. Birds* 67: 505–508.

Whilde, A. (1980). Auks trapped in salmon drift nets. *Irish Birds* 1: 370–376.

Williams, G. (1980). Swifter flows the river. *Birds* 8 (2): 19–22.

Williams, G., A. Henderson, L. Goldsmith and A. Spreadborough (1982). The effects on birds of land drainage improvements in the North Kent marshes. Unpubl. MSS.

Williamson, K. (1965). *Fair Isle and its Birds.* Edinburgh.

Williamson, K. (1967). The bird community of farmland. *Bird Study* 14: 210–226.

Williamson, K. (1969). Weather systems and bird movements. *Quart. J. Roy. Met. Soc.* 95: 414–423.

Williamson, K. (1969a). Habitat preferences of the Wren on English farmland. *Bird Study* 16: 53–59.

Williamson, K. (1969b). Bird communities in woodland habitats in Wester Ross, Scotland. *Quart. J. Forestry* 63: 306–368.

Williamson, K. (1971). A bird census study of a Dorset dairy farm. *Bird Study* 18: 80–96.

Williamson, K. (1975). Birds and climatic change. *Bird Study* 22: 143–164.

Williamson, K. (1976). Recent climatic influences on the status and distribution of some British birds. *Weather* 31: 362–384.

Williamson, K. and R. C. Homes (1964). Methods and preliminary results of the Common Birds Census. *Bird Study* 11: 240–256.

Williamson, K. and R. Spencer (1960). Ringing recoveries and the interpretation of bird movements. *Bird Migration* 1: 176–181.

Winstanley, D., R. Spencer and K. Williamson (1974). Where have all the Whitethroats gone? *Bird Study* 21: 1–14.

Witherby, H. F., F. C. R. Jourdain, N. F. Ticehurst and B. W. Tucker (1938–42). *The Handbook of British Birds.* 5 vols. London (Witherby).

Wyllie, I. (1976). The bird community of an English parish. *Bird Study* 23: 39–50.

Yeatman, L. (1971). *Histoire des Oiseaux d' Europe.* Paris (Bordas).

Yeatman, L. (1976). *Atlas des Oiseaux Nicheurs de France.* Paris (Ministère de la Qualité de la Vie).

Facts and figures

1: Ringing and recovery rates 1960–1980

Ringed birds may be 'recovered' in numerous ways, examples being 'found dead', 'shot', 'came down chimney', 'caught and released'. In the following table all forms of recovery have been combined.

The proportions of ringed birds which are later recovered varies greatly from species to species. For example, it is always higher in big birds than in small; and for species which frequent towns and villages compared with rural species, as typified by Pied and Yellow Wagtails respectively.

Recovery rates may also alter with the passage of time, and for a variety of reasons. For example, the proportion of Sandwich Terns recovered has increased markedly in each decade, apparently because of a growing habit amongst people in their winter quarters of capturing them for food. Fewer Cormorants are recovered because they are shot less, the bounty on them having been lifted. For many species, e.g. Blackcap and Whitethroat, the recovery rate has remained remarkably stable over a period of 30 years.

The recovery rate is the number of recoveries per hundred birds ringed – i.e. a percentage. Italic figures indicate that because fewer than 100 individuals were ringed the recovery rate is probably not very reliable in a statistical sense. Each entry is the mean recovery rate up to the year given, i.e. 1909–1960, 1909–1970, 1909–1980.

	1960	*1970*	*1980*
Red-throated Diver		*10·0*	5·2
Great Northern Diver			*12·5*
Little Grebe	5·1	3·6	4·2
Great Crested Grebe		5·8	9·5
Red-necked Grebe			*11·1*
Slavonian Grebe			*10·0*
Fulmar	1·4	1·2	1·2
Manx Shearwater	1·1	1·4	1·4
Storm Petrel	0·2	0·4	1·0
Leach's Petrel	0·6	1·3	0·8
Gannet	4·3	5·5	6·1
Cormorant	23·8	19·6	18·5
Shag	9·7	8·0	7·7
Bittern		*15·5*	*17·5*
Grey Heron	15·7	15·6	14·8
Mute Swan	11·8	32·6	33·4
Bewick's Swan		4·1	7·4
Whooper Swan		*13·6*	10·0
Bean Goose		*100·0*	*50·0*
Pink-footed Goose	19·0	28·1	29·4
White-fronted Goose	22·6	32·6	32·5

	1960	*1970*	*1980*
Greylag Goose	25·8	21·6	24·1
Canada Goose	10·0	16·0	21·0
Barnacle Goose		12·1	10·5
Brent Goose		*14·3*	13·4
Shelduck	5·8	7·8	9·4
Mandarin			*9·4*
Wigeon	19·1	16·8	17·4
Gadwall	22·7	16·9	11·4
Teal	17·0	18·3	18·0
Mallard	14·3	17·0	17·0
Pintail	21·1	13·9	15·0
Garganey	13·7	15·3	16·3
Shoveler	21·5	22·3	17·8
Red-crested Pochard		*27·0*	*20·8*
Pochard	19·6	19·0	10·2
Ring-necked Duck			*33·0*
Tufted Duck	21·8	16·0	12·5
Scaup		24·8	22·8
Eider	4·8	9·0	11·3
Long-tailed Duck		*25·0*	*18·8*
Common Scoter		*11·0*	*12·1*

	1960	*1970*	*1980*
Velvet Scoter		*25·0*	*25·0*
Goldeneye		*17·0*	*14·1*
Red-breasted Merganser		*5·5*	*10·0*
Goosander		16·4	15·8
Ruddy Duck			*6·0*
Red Kite		*3·7*	6·5
Marsh Harrier	11·6	11·8	11·0
Hen Harrier	11·7	10·3	8·3
Montagu's Harrier	14·7	13·9	13·8
Goshawk			8·8
Sparrowhawk	15·2	12·9	10·0
Buzzard	5·5	6·5	7·9
Rough-legged Buzzard		*100·0*	*50·0*
Golden Eagle		*6·1*	6·4
Osprey		*15·4*	10·6
Kestrel	12·4	12·4	11·5
Merlin	14·2	12·2	9·4
Hobby		7·0	3·2
Peregrine	14·1	10·4	7·6
Red Grouse	11·4	11·4	11·5
Black Grouse		10·6	10·6
Red-legged Partridge		13·5	7·2
Grey Partridge	3·3	5·9	4·9
Quail		*6·3*	*4·5*
Pheasant		*7·8*	5·8
Water Rail	3·4	2·6	2·3
Corncrake	1·7	1·5	1·4
Moorhen	3·1	4·5	4·3
Coot	9·5	10·1	8·4
Oystercatcher	4·9	5·5	6·1
Avocet		*4·5*	5·1
Stone-Curlew	5·5	5·6	6·3
Little Ringed Plover	3·1	2·1	2·0
Ringed Plover	1·6	1·8	1·8
Dotterel		*1·4*	2·8
Golden Plover	3·3	3·4	2·5
Grey Plover		2·7	3·0
Lapwing	2·0	2·2	1·9
Knot	0·7	1·4	2·3
Sanderling	2·7	1·0	1·8
Little Stint	*1·8*	2·0	1·7
Curlew Sandpiper		1·3	1·0
Purple Sandpiper		8·5	1·7
Dunlin		1·2	1·4
Buff-breasted Sandpiper		*20·0*	*11·1*
Ruff	4·0	3·5	3·3
Jack Snipe	3·1	4·0	2·7
Snipe	4·3	5·2	4·3
Woodcock	7·7	7·9	7·8
Black-tailed Godwit		1·8	2·5
Bar-tailed Godwit		2·1	2·3
Whimbrel		2·5	2·1
Curlew	4·1	4·9	4·6
Spotted Redshank		5·8	4·3
Redshank	2·6	3·3	2·9
Greenshank		2·2	3·0
Green Sandpiper	2·9	2·7	2·9
Wood Sandpiper		0·4	0·3
Common Sandpiper	0·77	1·0	1·1
Turnstone	1·2	1·6	2·8
Pomarine Skua		*33·0*	
Arctic Skua	2·6	2·7	2·3
Great Skua	2·1	2·3	2·8
Little Gull		7·7	2·1
Black-headed Gull	5·0	4·6	4·6
Common Gull	4·2	4·0	3·1
Lesser Black-backed Gull	4·2	4·3	6·0
Herring Gull	3·9	4·1	6·2
Glaucous Gull		*6·6*	*3·7*
Great Black-backed Gull	6·0	6·8	5·0
Kittiwake	1·9	2·5	2·2
Sandwich Tern	1·7	2·3	2·7
Roseate Tern	0·63	1·7	1·7
Common Tern	1·9	1·8	1·8
Arctic Tern	1·3	1·5	1·3
Little Tern	1·4	1·3	1·3
Guillemot	3·4	4·1	2·5
Razorbill	2·8	3·2	3·0
Black Guillemot	0·93	1·2	1·4
Little Auk		*6·6*	5·9
Puffin	0·61	1·0	0·74
Rock Dove	4·1	3·8	4·2
Stock Dove	7·0	6·9	5·5
Woodpigeon	6·7	9·9	9·3
Collared Dove		4·7	4·2
Turtle Dove	4·0	4·0	3·6

	1960	*1970*	*1980*
Cuckoo	2·9	3·3	3·0
Barn Owl	13·8	16·0	17·0
Snowy Owl			7·7
Little Owl	8·5	8·7	7·5
Tawny Owl	6·8	7·8	8·5
Long-eared Owl	5·4	8·1	7·6
Short-eared Owl	7·4	8·3	7·1
Nightjar	2·2	2·5	2·2
Swift	2·4	2·2	2·0
Kingfisher	3·7	3·7	4·2
Wryneck	1·9	1·3	1·0
Green Woodpecker	2·9	4·9	4·9
Great Spotted Woodpecker	4·6	5·2	4·3
Lesser Spotted Woodpecker		1·3	1·4
Woodlark	0·4	0·2	0·2
Skylark	0·7	0·2	0·7
Shore Lark		*2·2*	*1·3*
Sand Martin	0·6	2·3	2·0
Swallow	0·7	0·8	0·8
House Martin	0·7	0·7	0·6
Tree Pipit	0·2	0·2	0·2
Meadow Pipit	0·8	0·9	0·8
Rock/Water Pipit	0·7	0·8	0·7
Yellow Wagtail	0·9	0·9	0·8
Grey Wagtail	0·6	1·1	0·9
Pied/White Wagtail	1·7	2·2	2·0
Waxwing	3·4	3·5	5·6
Dipper	1·1	1·2	1·1
Wren	0·6	0·6	0·5
Dunnock	1·3	1·3	1·0
Robin	2·3	2·2	1·8
Nightingale	0·4	0·5	0·5
Bluethroat	1·1	0·7	0·9
Black Redstart	2·3	2·0	1·7
Redstart	0·4	0·6	0·6
Whinchat	0·4	0·4	0·4
Stonechat	0·7	0·8	0·7
Wheatear	0·4	0·5	0·5
Ring Ousel	1·7	2·0	1·6
Blackbird	3·3	3·9	3·9
Fieldfare	2·2	2·1	1·8
Song Thrush	2·5	2·9	2·7
Redwing	1·0	1·4	1·0

	1960	*1970*	*1980*
Mistle Thrush	2·8	3·6	3·5
Cetti's Warbler			0·9
Grasshopper Warbler	2·5	0·2	0·3
Sedge Warbler	0·2	0·3	0·5
Marsh Warbler			0·44
Reed Warbler	0·5	1·0	1·1
Icterine Warbler		0·8	0·4
Dartford Warbler		0·6	1·0
Barred Warbler			0·2
Lesser Whitethroat	0·5	0·6	0·5
Whitethroat	0·4	0·4	0·4
Garden Warbler	0·1	0·3	0·3
Blackcap	0·5	0·5	0·5
Yellow-browed Warbler		0·3	0·6
Wood Warbler	0·5	0·3	0·2
Chiffchaff	0·2	0·3	0·3
Willow Warbler	0·2	0·3	0·2
Goldcrest	0·1	0·2	0·3
Firecrest		0·1	0·3
Spotted Flycatcher	0·7	0·7	0·5
Pied Flycatcher	0·3	0·4	0·6
Bearded Tit	0·8	3·5	3·8
Long-tailed Tit	0·6	0·8	0·6
Marsh Tit	0·9	0·8	0·7
Willow Tit	0·2	0·5	0·5
Coal Tit	1·3	1·0	0·7
Blue Tit	1·9	1·5	1·1
Great Tit	1·7	1·5	1·1
Nuthatch	2·6	2·5	1·9
Treecreeper	0·2	0·5	0·4
Golden Oriole			*2·7*
Lesser Grey Shrike		*22·0*	*20·0*
Red-backed Shrike	0·8	0·8	0·7
Great Grey Shrike		1·9	2·0
Woodchat Shrike			*1·2*
Jay	7·3	8·7	7·6
Magpie	4·4	5·7	5·3
Chough	4·8	7·4	6·9
Jackdaw	5·3	6·2	5·7
Rook	6·4	5·6	5·4
Carrion/Hooded Crow	6·1	6·8	6·3
Raven	9·3	10·0	9·2
Starling	3·9	3·8	3·6

	1960	*1970*	*1980*
House Sparrow	1·4	1·7	1·7
Tree Sparrow	0·4	0·5	0·4
Chaffinch	1·1	1·1	0·9
Brambling		0·64	0·65
Greenfinch	1·6	2·2	2·1
Goldfinch	1·3	1·0	1·1
Siskin	0·9	1·5	1·7
Linnet	0·7	0·8	0·6
Twite	0·4	0·6	0·6
Redpoll	1·1	1·1	1·0
Common Crossbill	1·0	1·0	0·6
Bullfinch	2·0	2·0	1·6
Hawfinch	1·0	1·3	2·0
Snow Bunting	0·7	0·7	0·6
Yellowhammer	0·8	0·8	0·7
Cirl Bunting		0·4	0·9
Reed Bunting	0·4	0·7	0·6
Corn Bunting	2·0	1·1	0·8
Rustic Bunting			*4·0*

2: The most distant ringing recoveries

The list which follows shows the distance, in kilometres, of the most distant recovery so far reported from British and Irish ringed birds of each species. The three columns give the age of the bird and recovery method (see longevity list for explanation) and maximum distance between ringing and recovery places. Not all the recoveries are processed for the BTO computer and a very few most distant recoveries may not yet have come to light from within our files of more than a third of a million records. In any case, as recoveries keep coming to us at the rate of some hundreds a week, this list will always need modification as new records are achieved.

Obviously species with many birds ringed and recovered will have movements logged which are very close to the maximum expected of the species: for instance the Starling at 3,376 km. This may be true for some species with only a few marked – for instance the Stone-Curlew at 4,833 km was in the extreme south of the species' known winter range. Other records will be of short distances compared even to the normal migration range of the species simply because so few are ringed or none have been reported from the wintering area – all British Grasshopper Warblers probably winter south of the Sahara but the furthest recovery is still in France although more than 7,000 have been ringed.

Both passerines with records of more than 10,000 km were reported from South Africa – a Spotted Flycatcher and several Swallows. The Storm Petrel (again one of several) and the Sandwich and Common Terns are also from South Africa but the two most distant birds (Manx Shearwater at 16,675 and Arctic Tern at 18,056) are from Australia. The Arctic Tern had travelled from Anglesey to New South Wales and was only a bit more than 2,000 km from reaching the conjugate point of its ringing site – going exactly to the opposite side of the world!

Massive movements east and west in the northern hemisphere are, of course, not so distant as the record north–south ones documented above. For example the Mallard found in Alberta, Canada, had moved just over 7,000 km and the Pochard far to the east in Siberia only slightly further. Many of the winter visitors amongst the wildfowl and waders show record movements between 4,000 and 7,000 km, penetrating well into central and eastern Siberia. The recent record of a Canada Goose from Scotland well into Siberia (3,857 km) was an amazing addition to this category. The distant records of Redwing, Fieldfare, Starling, Siskin and Brambling are all of birds reaching rather closer parts of the Soviet Union at distances of some 3,000 or 4,000 km.

Many resident species have not, so far, been recorded moving more than a few dozen kilometres. This is what one would expect of many of our populations of species which regularly move long distances on the Continent. Dippers and Great Spotted Woodpeckers, for example, are regular visitors from Scandinavia but we have yet to receive any ringing returns from birds of these populations marked in Britain and getting back to their homelands. However such records as the Dunnock at 1,813 km, the Great Tit at 1,446 and the Chaffinch at 2,238 are evidence of return movements of Continental birds which have reached Britain.

	Age when ringed	*Method of recovery*	*Distance travelled km*
Red-throated Diver	1	×	1,549
Little Grebe	3	×	435
Great Crested Grebe	4	×	175
Fulmar	1	×	4,686
Manx Shearwater	1	×	16,675
Storm Petrel	4	( )	10,850
Leach's Petrel	4	v	481
Gannet	1	×	5,300
Cormorant	1	v	2,120
Shag	1	×	1,443
Bittern	1	+	637
Grey Heron	1	+	2,666
Mute Swan	4	×	993
Bewick's Swan	6	×	3,504
Whooper Swan	5	×	1,390
Pink-footed Goose	4	+	1,823
White-fronted Goose	5	+	4,359
Greylag Goose	4	+	1,172
Canada Goose	4	+	3,857
Barnacle Goose	4	+	2,687
Brent Goose	6	/?/	5,443
Shelduck	1	v	1,458
Wigeon	4	+	4,891
Gadwall	3	( )	2,346
Teal	5	+	4,588
Mallard	3	+	7,012

	Age when ringed	*Method of recovery*	*Distance travelled km*
Pintail	4	+	5,512
Garganey	3	+	4,471
Shoveler	4	+	4,103
Pochard	3	+	7,217
Ring-necked Duck	4	+	2,557
Tufted Duck	6	+	4,043
Scaup	4	+	4,554
Eider	1	×	1,384
Goldeneye	3	+	1,431
Red-breasted Merganser	3	( )	821
Goosander	1	+	2,007
Red Kite	1	×	300
Marsh Harrier	3	×	4,260
Hen Harrier	1	+	1,413
Montagu's Harrier	1	+	1,516
Sparrowhawk	3	×	1,217
Buzzard	1	+	436
Golden Eagle	1	×	120
Osprey	1	+	4,928
Kestrel	1	×	2,590
Merlin	1	×	1,244
Hobby	1	×	584
Peregrine	1	×	1,700
Red Grouse	2	+	26
Black Grouse	5	×	40
Red-legged Partridge	2	+	68

	Age when ringed	*Method of recovery*	*Distance travelled km*
Grey Partridge	5	×	40
Quail	4	+	1,047
Water Rail	4	×	1,204
Corncrake	4	×	6,730
Moorhen	5	×	1,151
Coot	4	+	2,757
Oystercatcher	2	×	2,831
Avocet	1	+	1,841
Stone-Curlew	1	×	4,833
Little Ringed Plover	4	/?/	2,216
Ringed Plover	3	( )	5,159
Dotterel	2	( )	5,374
Golden Plover	1	+	2,343
Grey Plover	2	( )	5,156
Lapwing	1	+	4,381
Knot	4	v	9,697
Sanderling	4	v	9,706
Little Stint	2	+	2,256
Curlew Sandpiper	3	×	4,515
Purple Sandpiper	6	+	2,687
Dunlin	2	×	4,566
Ruff	4	+	7,831
Jack Snipe	2	+	1,944
Snipe	4	+	2,967
Woodcock	1	×	2,599
Black-tailed Godwit	1	+	1,915
Bar-tailed Godwit	1	+	4,889
Whimbrel	1	+	6,148
Curlew	2	+	2,458
Spotted Redshank	5	+	2,280
Redshank	4	+	4,241
Greenshank	3	+	1,543
Green Sandpiper	2	+	1,840
Wood Sandpiper	3	v	923
Common Sandpiper	4	+	4,710
Turnstone	4	+	6,270
Arctic Skua	1	( )	8,396
Great Skua	1	×	8,046
Little Gull	8	+	2,038
Black-headed Gull	1	×	3,853
Common Gull	4	×	2,853
Lesser Black-backed Gull	1	×	4,640
Herring Gull	1	/?/	2,538
Glaucous Gull	2	/?/	355
Great Black-backed Gull	8	×	1,781
Kittiwake	6	×	4,655
Sandwich Tern	1	×	10,363
Roseate Tern	1	/?/	5,755
Common Tern	4	×	10,704
Arctic Tern	1	×	18,056
Guillemot	1	×	2,279
Razorbill	1	( )	3,288
Black Guillemot	3	+	878
Puffin	1	×	4,074
Rock Dove	1	+	28
Stock Dove	1	+	1,121
Woodpigeon	1	+	1,025
Collared Dove	4	×	922
Turtle Dove	2	/?/	439
Cuckoo	1	+	5,368
Barn Owl	1	×	346
Snowy Owl	8	×	310
Little Owl	3	×	182
Tawny Owl	1	×	133
Long-eared Owl	2	×	3,279
Short-eared Owl	1	+	2,536
Nightjar	1	×	1,161
Swift	4	×	8,749
Kingfisher	3	v	555
Wryneck	1	×	1,785
Green Woodpecker	4	+	71
Great Spotted Woodpecker	3	×	256
Lesser Spotted Woodpecker	3	×	40
Skylark	4	( )	1,735
Sand Martin	4	×	4,715
Swallow	3	×	10,417
House Martin	4	×	2,397
Tree Pipit	2	×	4,109

	Age when ringed	*Method of recovery*	*Distance travelled km*
Meadow Pipit	2	/?/	2,914
Rock/Water Pipit	3	×	830
Yellow Wagtail	3	×	4,828
Grey Wagtail	2	×	874
Pied/White Wagtail	3	+	4,780
Waxwing	4	×	3,202
Dipper	3	×	57
Wren	3	v	1,173
Dunnock	4	v	1,813
Robin	4	+	2,246
Nightingale	4	×	1,919
Bluethroat	5	/?/	1,286
Black Redstart	2	+	1,648
Redstart	3	/?/	4,724
Whinchat	4	( )	3,395
Stonechat	1	+	1,924
Wheatear	3	+	3,620
Ring Ousel	3	×	2,577
Blackbird	4	+	2,391
Fieldfare	2	+	2,848
Song Thrush	3	+	2,489
Redwing	4	+	4,300
Mistle Thrush	4	×	1,023
Grasshopper Warbler	3	×	856
Sedge Warbler	3	+	4,982
Reed Warbler	3	( )	5,228
Icterine Warbler	2	( )	136
Dartford Warbler	3	×	110
Barred Warbler	3	+	2,577
Lesser Whitethroat	3	×	3,855
Whitethroat	3	×	4,392
Garden Warbler	2	+	2,718
Blackcap	3	( )	4,838
Wood Warbler	2	/?/	2,219
Chiffchaff	2	( )	4,632
Willow Warbler	4	×	5,272
Goldcrest	2	v	1,292
Firecrest	2	( )	870
Spotted Flycatcher	3	×	10,018
Pied Flycatcher	4	( )	3,293
Bearded Tit	2	v	780

	Age when ringed	*Method of recovery*	*Distance travelled km*
Long-tailed Tit	2	v	340
Marsh Tit	3	×	55
Willow Tit	2	×	170
Coal Tit	2	v	753
Blue Tit	2	×	573
Great Tit	3	v	1,446
Nuthatch	1	×	16
Treecreeper	3	v	115
Red-backed Shrike	1	( )	2,720
Great Grey Shrike	3	×	893
Woodchat Shrike	4	v	475
Jay	2	×	218
Magpie	3	( )	59
Chough	1	×	142
Jackdaw	2	+	1,023
Rook	6	+	480
Carrion/Hooded Crow	1	+	130
Raven	1	×	304
Starling	4	×	3,376
House Sparrow	4	( )	445
Tree Sparrow	2	v	470
Chaffinch	4	×	2,238
Brambling	6	+	3,244
Greenfinch	3	×	1,251
Goldfinch	3	( )	1,853
Siskin	6	( )	2,481
Linnet	2	( )	2,156
Twite	1	+	1,293
Redpoll	4	×	2,143
Common Crossbill	2	×	686
Bullfinch	5	×	391
Hawfinch	4	×	293
Snow Bunting	6	( )	3,451
Yellowhammer	4	×	344
Cirl Bunting	3	v	625
Rustic Bunting	4	+	2,868
Reed Bunting	2	×	1,699
Corn Bunting	2	×	205

3: The fastest movements shown by ringing recoveries

For each species with at least one recovery reported at a speed of over fifty kilometres a day the fastest is listed. The age at ringing (see list of oldest birds), the elapsed time in days and speed in kilometres per day are given. The few fast recoveries over a period of an hour or two (mostly hirundines moving between roosts on the same evening) are not listed but, if the elapsed time is known accurately, the speed has been calculated using the times reported. For example the Arctic Tern from Fair Isle was found in Denmark 39 hours 35 minutes after it was ringed.

There are a number of species where these 'fastest' records probably represent something like the average speed on migration – in the table there are migrant species with long elapsed times (e.g. several of the waders). For others the speed is of a single stage on migration (e.g. hirundines and warblers). Naturally, birds which are most often caught in mid-winter rather than on passage (like the wildfowl) and those like many seabirds which are almost all ringed as nestlings, tend to be under-represented. However the remarkable Manx Shearwater from Wales to South America (almost 10,000 km in 17 days) shows that some species may migrate almost immediately they fledge. The speed entered is always based on elapsed time between capture and finding so that the Swift, which was known to have fledged nine days after it was ringed actually made the journey from Oxford to Spain at roughly 300 km/day. The fastest recovery of a BTO ringed passerine remains the Redwing from a Midlands garden in the cold spell of 1963 found on a boat in mid-Atlantic three days later – speed 815 km/day or about 34 kph. However a female Blackcap from Holland (near the Hague) which killed itself against a window in the Shetlands 1,000 km away the next day is faster. From British ringing the fastest record is the Teal from Abberton in Essex ringed one December morning between 9 and 10 o'clock and shot at dawn the next day in Lot et Garonne (France) – 893 km/day.

Many resident species are missing from the table, as are a few migrants, since no fast recoveries have yet been reported. The coincidence of ringing and finding after a short period *and* the bird moving is not too likely and these fast recoveries are a direct result of the huge numbers of birds ringed and recovered in Britain and Ireland. One of the most intriguing records on the list is the Blue Tit. It averaged 64 km/day over the four days between being ringed at St Agnes on Scilly and later found aboard a boat off the Tuskar Rock Lighthouse. This was one of the hoards of tits which moved into Britain from the Continent during the irruption of autumn 1957.

A few fast records may still be buried, undiscovered, in the files for not all the ringing recoveries have yet been entered on the computer. A few, with very short elapsed times may have a slightly inflated speed entered as they may have been ringed early in the morning of one day and found late in the evening a couple of days later. At worst, with a three day elapsed time, this would lead to the speed being over-estimated by roughly 15% and there may be cases of birds ringed in the evening and recorded again in the morning where the real speed has been under-estimated to a certain extent.

	Age at ringing	*Elapsed time in days*	*Speed in km/day*
Fulmar	4	26	131
Manx Shearwater	1	17	568
Storm Petrel	4	2	220
Gannet	3	15	191
White-fronted Goose	6	10	109
Gadwall	5	10	94
Teal	4	1	893
Mallard	2	3	50
Pintail	3	69	65
Shoveler	3	6	77
Sparrowhawk	6	4	91
Osprey	1	c.60	c.80
Merlin	2	23	77
Quail	4	12	135
Coot	4	5	137
Oystercatcher	3	5	117
Little Ringed Plover	3	8	117
Ringed Plover	4	3	106
Grey Plover	2	55	94
Knot	3	8	651
Sanderling	4	38	140
Little Stint	2	21	52
Curlew Sandpiper	4	1	244
Dunlin	3	4	363
Ruff	3	23	98
Jack Snipe	2	39	50
Common Snipe	2	9	119
Bar-tailed Godwit	3	12	59
Spotted Redshank	4	20	59
Redshank	3	3	70
Greenshank	4	3	227
Green Sandpiper	4	15	74
Common Sandpiper	4	4	297
Turnstone	6	37	130
Arctic Skua	1	150	53
Great Skua	1	53	70
Kittiwake	1	19	121
Sandwich Tern	1	45	122
Roseate Tern	1	27	97
Common Tern	3	35	137
Arctic Tern	3	2	437
Little Tern	3	6	231
Razorbill	6	12	132
Puffin	1	6	68
Turtle Dove	3	10	85
Cuckoo	4	6	68
Long-eared Owl	2	7	126
Swift	1	12	106
Sand Martin	3	4	310
Swallow	4	4	411
House Martin	3	9	115
Tree Pipit	2	72	57
Meadow Pipit	2	29	62
Yellow Wagtail	3	29	129
Pied Wagtail	4	26	101
Dunnock	4	6	128
Robin	4	3	203
Bluethroat	5	4	242
Black Redstart	3	24	50
Redstart	6	6	162
Whinchat	3	10	134
Wheatear	2	2	526
Ring Ousel	3	1	570
Blackbird	3	2	415
Fieldfare	4	4	113
Song Thrush	2	8	146
Redwing	2	3	815
Mistle Thrush	2	5	52
Sedge Warbler	3	1	500
Reed Warbler	3	4	278
Icterine Warbler	2	1	136
Barred Warbler	4	49	67
Lesser Whitethroat	2	14	70
Whitethroat	4	3	337
Garden Warbler	3	6	151
Blackcap	3	3	281
Chiffchaff	2	32	106
Willow Warbler	3	5	329
Goldcrest	4	1	145
Spotted Flycatcher	3	3	349
Pied Flycatcher	4	4	313
Blue Tit	2	4	64
Red-backed Shrike	3	27	83
Starling	5	2	501
Chaffinch	4	7	118
Brambling	4	2	124
Greenfinch	3	3	55
Goldfinch	3	2	98
Siskin	5	31	51
Linnet	2	5	153
Snow Bunting	3	14	81

4: Longevity

The files of the Ringing Office provide extensive records of longevity for British wild birds. The following are the oldest *recoveries* (reports of birds, usually dead, from members of the public) or *retraps* (later handlings by ringers) so far traced for birds ringed in Britain or Ireland. The age given is, in all cases, the elapsed time between ringing and recovery in years (to two decimal places). The first figure is the European age code of the bird when it was originally ringed:

1 = nestling; 2 = full-grown;
3 = bird of the year; 4 = hatched the previous year or earlier;
5 = hatched the previous year; 6 = hatched two years ago or earlier;
8 = hatched three years ago or earlier.

The symbol after the age is the indicated fate of the bird when it was reported:

× found dead
+ shot
v alive and released (mostly by ringers)
? unknown
( ) caught or found alive and NOT released

This table covers all species for which more than a handful of recoveries have been reported, and all recoveries received to the end of 1982 have been examined. Ringers were also sent a provisional list and many searched their personal retrap files to see if they could find particularly ancient individuals.

Longevity records depend not only on the survival of the species under consideration but also on the sample size. Particularly in captivity many of the species listed are capable of living much longer than the record ages given, for wild birds are subject to all sorts of accidents, predation, hunger and diseases which do not affect caged individuals. For most species, with large numbers ringed and recovered, the average life-span of an individual in the wild will be from a fifth to a tenth, or shorter, than the maximum shown here. For example, of the small passerines hatched each year, in typical circumstances most survive for less than twelve months from the time of hatching. The population level of such species is maintained by the laying of large clutches or by multiple breeding attempts. Each pair of Blue Tits may, on average, hatch eight chicks a year and each pair of Robins may have two broods of four young. For both these examples, of the ten birds alive one summer (eight chicks and two parents) only two need survive through to the next breeding season for the population to be maintained.

The oldest birds on the list are mostly from the larger species. In many cases ringing with hard metal rings, likely to last for the whole of the bird's life-span, has only been undertaken over the last twenty years and individuals with ages well in excess of the current records are eventually to be expected. For other small species the rings have, for many years, been sufficiently durable to last for the whole of the species' potential life-span and the records entered are not expected to be broken by a very wide margin.

Three species of non-passerine have passed the 25 year mark – a Manx Shearwater at 29·92, Fulmar at 27·00 and Arctic Tern at 26·96 years. All three birds were in study populations where the adults were being recaught by the ringers and, with the Fulmar at least, the oldest birds are simply the ones first ringed when the study started in the early 1950s. Amongst the passerines the oldest is a Rook – one of the largest British passerines – at 18·33 years. The Swallow, carefully investigated at the time, recorded as being retrapped 16 years after original ringing is so much in excess of the next oldest (under eight years) that there must be some doubt attached to it. Of small passerines the House Sparrow (12·04) and Skylark (11·89) hold the record. The oldest record of more than 100,000 Goldcrests ringed is only just over 4½ years!

Many of the birds listed are the oldest known for their species worldwide. There are, however, a number of species on the British list with older records elsewhere. The record is held by an Oystercatcher at 36 years and four other British species have exceeded 30 years (Arctic Tern, Guillemot, Black-headed Gull and Osprey). Amongst the passerines both Blackbird and Starling have reached 20 years. Perhaps the most astonishing record of longevity, still awaiting confirmation, is of a Dipper photographed by the ringer on the territory where it had last been seen more than fifteen years earlier. This bird was identified from its very faded colour rings and, if investigations show that there is no possibility of confusion of identity, this bird will clock in at 22·94 years and be the oldest recorded passerine anywhere in the world.

	Age at ringing	*Method of recovery*	*Maximum lapsed time in years*
Red-throated Diver	4	v	10·03
Little Grebe	3	v	5·91
Great Crested Grebe	4	×	11·85
Fulmar	4	v	27·00
Manx Shearwater	4	v	29·92
Storm Petrel	4	v	18·03
Leach's Petrel	4	v	19·11
Gannet	1	×	24·53
Cormorant	1	×	19·72
Shag	1	×	20·62
Bittern	4	×	4·25
Grey Heron	1	×	18·47
Mute Swan	6	×	21·73
Bewick's Swan	6	v	18·81
Whooper Swan	5	×	c8·0
Pink-footed Goose	4	×	22·14
White-fronted Goose	6	+	17·67
Greylag Goose	3	+	15·17
Canada Goose	4	v	17·01
Barnacle Goose	4	v	19·69
Brent Goose	4	×	7·64
Shelduck	6	×	14·63
Mandarin	4	v	4·33
Wigeon	4	×	18·28
Gadwall	3	+	12·33
Teal	4	+	14·08
Mallard	2	+	20·90
Pintail	4	+	16·61
Garganey	1	?	5·68
Shoveler	4	+	13·58
Pochard	6	+	11·92
Tufted Duck	4	×	14·38
Scaup	5	+	8·42
Eider	1	v	22·92
Common Scoter	4	+	7·16
Goldeneye	4	×	4·80
Red-breasted Merganser	1	×	4·44
Goosander	1	×	7·22
Red Kite	1	×	13·58
Marsh Harrier	1	×	3·04
Hen Harrier	1	×	12·80
Montagu's Harrier	1	+	7·95
Goshawk	1	×	4·65
Sparrowhawk	1	×	10·77
Buzzard	1	+	12·86
Golden Eagle	1	×	5·65
Osprey	1	v	13·17
Kestrel	1	×	14·46
Merlin	1	×	12·53
Hobby	1	+	3·95
Peregrine	1	×	9·63
Red Grouse	2	+	2·87
Black Grouse	3	+	3·80
Red-legged Partridge	3	×	7·58
Grey Partridge	3	+	5·20

	Age at ringing	Method of recovery	Maximum lapsed time in years
Pheasant	4	v	8·49
Water Rail	2	×	7·49
Corncrake	1	+	1·24
Moorhen	4	+	11·26
Coot	4	+	12·80
Oystercatcher	1	v	20·37
Avocet	3	×	6·93
Stone-Curlew	1	×	6·46
Little Ringed Plover	3	v	6·03
Ringed Plover	4	v	12·06
Dotterel	1	+	3·55
Golden Plover	4	×	12·08
Grey Plover	4	v	17·85
Lapwing	1	×	15·71
Knot	5	v	16·08
Sanderling	4	v	13·49
Little Stint	2	×	6·36
Curlew Sandpiper	3	v	4·89
Purple Sandpiper	3	v	9·99
Dunlin	4	v	15·03
Ruff	3	+	6·52
Jack Snipe	4	×	9·38
Snipe	4	+	12·32
Woodcock	1	+	12·33
Black-tailed Godwit	3	v	9·87
Bar-tailed Godwit	4	×	13·87
Whimbrel	4	+	12·00
Curlew	1	×	23·76
Spotted Redshank	3	+	6·08
Redshank	4	v	17·03
Greenshank	4	+	9·63
Green Sandpiper	2	v	11·60
Wood Sandpiper	3	v	7·96
Common Sandpiper	2	v	8·94
Turnstone	5	v	14·43
Arctic Skua	1	v	18·11
Great Skua	1	+	16·19
Little Gull	5	v	5·82
Black-headed Gull	1	×	21·17
Common Gull	5	v	15·54

	Age at ringing	Method of recovery	Maximum lapsed time in years
Lesser Black-backed Gull	1	+	21·88
Herring Gull	1	×	20·23
Great Black-backed Gull	1	+	20·49
Kittiwake	1	×	23·07
Sandwich Tern	1	×	21·39
Roseate Tern	1	×	15·92
Common Tern	1	×	24·96
Arctic Tern	1	v	26·96
Little Tern	1	v	11·95
Guillemot	1	×	24·85
Razorbill	6	×	20·33
Black Guillemot	1	v	19·93
Puffin	6	v	22·18
Rock Dove	1	+	6·32
Stock Dove	4	×	9·18
Woodpigeon	1	+	15·92
Collared Dove	2	×	13·69
Turtle Dove	6	+	11·21
Cuckoo	3	×	8·95
Barn Owl	1	×	13·12
Little Owl	1	×	9·07
Tawny Owl	1	×	16·93
Long-eared Owl	1	×	9·68
Short-eared Owl	1	×	6·65
Nightjar	1	v	6·13
Swift	4	×	15·90
Kingfisher	3	×	4·54
Wryneck	1	×	2·00
Green Woodpecker	2	×	5·59
Great Spotted Woodpecker	6	v	10·81
Lesser Spotted Woodpecker	3	v	6·38
Skylark	2	v	11·89
Sand Martin	3	v	7·85
Swallow	3	v	15·96
House Martin	4	×	6·11
Tree Pipit	1	?	6·25

	Age at ringing	*Method of recovery*	*Maximum lapsed time in years*
Meadow Pipit	3	×	7·05
Rock Pipit	2	×	8·90
Yellow Wagtail	4	v	6·97
Grey Wagtail	2	v	6·27
Pied Wagtail	3	v	9·91
Waxwing	4	×	2·91
Dipper	1	v	8·36
Wren	4	×	4·95
Dunnock	4	×	9·02
Robin	3	×	8·42
Nightingale	4	v	4·07
Black Redstart	1	×	4·96
Redstart	5	×	8·04
Whinchat	1	×	4·79
Stonechat	1	v	4·95
Wheatear	3	v	7·04
Ring Ousel	4	×	6·48
Blackbird	4	×	14·78
Fieldfare	4	×	9·49
Song Thrush	1	×	10·18
Redwing	4	v	6·81
Mistle Thrush	4	×	8·86
Cetti's Warbler	4	v	3·59
Grasshopper Warbler	4	×	4·05
Sedge Warbler	4	v	6·25
Marsh Warbler	4	v	3·83
Reed Warbler	4	v	10·82
Lesser Whitethroat	3	v	4·83
Whitethroat	4	+	7·60
Garden Warbler	3	×	5·69
Blackcap	3	v	6·97
Wood Warbler	1	+	2·15
Chiffchaff	3	×	5·68
Willow Warbler	2	×	6·73
Goldcrest	4	v	4·51
Firecrest	6	v	1·78
Spotted Flycatcher	1	+	9·23

	Age at ringing	*Method of recovery*	*Maximum lapsed time in years*
Pied Flycatcher	1	v	7·00
Bearded Tit	3	v	6·03
Long-tailed Tit	2	v	8·07
Marsh Tit	3	v	9·26
Willow Tit	1	v	8·90
Coal Tit	2	v	7·28
Blue Tit	4	×	11·25
Great Tit	4	×	9·28
Nuthatch	1	×	8·68
Treecreeper	3	v	7·16
Red-backed Shrike	1	v	7·01
Great Grey Shrike	3	v	1·39
Jay	3	+	15·80
Magpie	4	+	9·73
Chough	4	×	16·70
Jackdaw	4	×	14·01
Rook	4	×	18·33
Carrion Crow	1	×	13·53
Raven	1	×	12·47
Starling	3	×	16·48
House Sparrow	4	×	12·04
Tree Sparrow	2	v	6·96
Chaffinch	3	×	11·59
Brambling	5	×	7·39
Greenfinch	4	×	11·12
Goldfinch	3	×	7·17
Siskin	5	v	6·94
Linnet	3	v	8·22
Twite	3	v	6·09
Redpoll	3	?	7·17
Common Crossbill	5	v	3·19
Bullfinch	6	x	9·19
Hawfinch	4	v	6·96
Snow Bunting	4	v	4·12
Yellowhammer	2	×	9·51
Reed Bunting	3	v	9·97
Corn Bunting	4	v	9·96

5: Common causes of mortality of British and Irish birds, as measured by ringing recoveries (omitting wildfowl, gulls and species with fewer than 25 recoveries)

There are two ways in which ringed birds may be recovered: they may be found by a member of the public, in which circumstances they are usually dead, or they may be retrapped by another ringer. The technical term for this is 'controlled'. For some species all the information is reported by the public and no birds are controlled. For other species, very few indeed are ever found dead by the public so that 'controls' are of great importance.

Since this is a table about the way in which birds meet their deaths, all controls are excluded, and the first column, headed *Total No. of Recoveries* excludes all live recoveries by ringers. The eleven columns which follow split up these recoveries into their component parts, by percentages. The meaning of most of the column headings is self-evident, but some require an explanation. In French the word 'capturé' may be used of a bird which is shot, but the bird *could* have been hunted in some other way. A similar circumstance arises in Spain with the word 'capturado'. All such recoveries are included in the column headed % *shot/hunted.*

Birds sometimes enter buildings, fruit cages etc. from which they are not able to get out. All such recoveries are brought together under the heading *Inside something.* Birds which are killed by man, basically to prevent them from harming man's interests, appear under the heading *Deliberately taken* whereas birds caught inadvertently, for example a Cormorant found in a salmon net, are listed under the heading *Accidently taken by man.* The heading *Collision* includes collision with windows, overhead wires, tall structures (e.g. masts) etc. but excludes all forms of transport. The heading *Other predators* includes all forms of predation other than *Taken by cat.*

	Total of recoveries	*% Shot/ hunted*	*% Oiled*	*% Traffic accident*	*% Taken by cats*	*% Inside something*	*% Found dead*	*% Delib. taken*	*% Acc. taken by man*	*% Collision*	*% Other pred.*	*% Other causes*
Little Grebe	29	20·7	6·9	6·9	0	3·5	41·3	0	6·9	3·5	3·5	6·9
Fulmar	455	7·7	4·4	0	0	1·5	57·8	11·1	11·1	0	0·7	5·9
Manx Shearwater	2906	2·9	2·4	0·5	0·1	0·1	64·1	10·4	3·0	0·6	9·7	6·2
Storm Petrel	70	2·9	0	1·4	4·3	2·9	42·9	20·0	4·3	5·7	7·1	8·6
Gannet	2489	5·4	7·8	0·2	0	0	52·6	8·8	18·4	0·5	0·1	6·2
Cormorant	4941	39·5	2·4	0·2	0	0·0	44·5	0·7	10·9	0·6	0·2	1·8
Shag	5840	8·4	4·8	0·1	0	0·3	68·2	2·2	10·0	0·2	0·3	5·5
Grey Heron	1463	13·5	0·1	1·0	0	0	65·9	0·6	1·7	7·8	1·4	8·1
Hen Harrier	177	7·3	0	4·0	0	0	66·7	1·1	3·4	10·2	1·7	5·7
Montagu's Harrier	32	62·5	0	0	0	0	18·8	3·1	3·1	6·3	0	6·3
Sparrowhawk	765	18·2	0	8·1	0·5	3·0	44·8	3·0	2·9	8·1	9·2	2·2
Buzzard	213	9·9	0	8·9	0	0	61·0	4·2	6·6	4·2	0	5·2
Kestrel	1659	11·0	0·2	14·0	0·4	3·8	54·5	1·6	1·3	4·3	1·4	7·5
Merlin	199	21·1	0	7·5	1·0	3·5	41·7	5·5	1·5	5·5	2·5	10·1
Peregrine	63	22·2	0	6·4	0	0	50·8	0	7·9	4·8	1·6	6·4
Red Grouse	177	53·7	0	0·6	0·6	0	21·5	1·1	0	9·6	12·5	0·6
Grey Partridge	37	46·0	0	8·1	0	0	35·1	0	2·7	2·7	5·4	0
Water Rail	45	6·7	0	2·2	6·7	2·2	68·9	2·2	2·2	0	4·4	4·4
Moorhen	713	11·2	0·1	13·3	4·5	0·1	53·9	2·7	1·5	1·7	6·5	4·5
Coot	574	32·6	0·2	4·7	0·7	0·2	45·6	1·2	1·2	2·3	3·7	7·7
Oystercatcher	2901	18·7	0·6	3·6	0·3	0·1	66·0	0·6	1·8	2·2	2·1	4·0
Stone Curlew	26	50·0	0	3·9	0	0	30·8	0	0	3·9	0	11·5
Ringed Plover	216	33·3	0	0·9	1·9	0	47·7	2·3	1·9	1·9	5·6	4·6
Golden Plover	59	45·8	0	6·8	0	0	25·4	5·1	0	6·8	5·1	5·1
Grey Plover	65	38·5	0	0	0	0	56·9	3·1	0	0	1·5	0
Lapwing	2371	37·2	0	5·6	0·7	0	45·5	1·4	0·8	3·8	4·0	1·1
Knot	408	40·7	0·5	0·7	0·3	0	48·3	3·4	0·3	0·5	3·4	2·0

	Total of recoveries	*% Shot/ hunted*	*% Oiled*	*% Traffic accident*	*% Taken by cats*	*% Inside something*	*% Found dead*	*% Delib. taken*	*% Acc. taken by man*	*% Collision*	*% Other pred.*	*% Other causes*
Sanderling	106	36·8	0	0·9	0·9	0	52·8	2·8	0	0·9	4·7	0
Dunlin	913	37·8	0·6	1·0	0·3	0	46·1	3·6	1·5	1·4	5·0	2·6
Ruff	50	66·0	0	0	0	0	26·0	2·0	0	0	2·0	4·0
Jack Snipe	48	81·3	0	4·2	0	0	8·3	0	0	0	4·2	2·1
Snipe	858	80·9	0	1·3	1·5	0	12·9	0·7	0·1	0·5	0·8	1·3
Woodcock	528	87·1	0	0·8	0	0·2	7·8	0	1·5	2·1	0·2	0·4
Bar-tailed Godwit	41	36·6	2·4	0	0	0	56·1	0	0	0	2·4	2·4
Curlew	782	49·4	0	2·8	0·3	0	38·1	0·8	1·4	2·3	2·6	2·4
Redshank	985	27·1	0·4	2·9	1·1	0	55·6	0·7	1·9	1·9	4·2	4·0
Common Sandpiper	84	33·3	0	4·8	4·8	0	44·0	1·2	3·6	3·6	2·4	2·4
Turnstone	144	23·6	0	0·7	1·4	0	61·8	2·1	0·7	2·1	4·2	3·5
Arctic Skua	83	16·9	0	1·2	0	0	63·9	1·2	4·8	0	0	12·1
Great Skua	856	17·4	2·5	0·6	0	0	60·4	6·8	7·5	0·5	1·5	2·9
Kittiwake	1098	14·6	5·5	0·2	0	0·1	63·0	6·6	2·5	0·6	0·7	6·8
Sandwich Tern	2256	12·7	1·0	0·4	0	0·1	46·3	29·2	4·4	0·2	0·5	5·3
Roseate Tern	302	8·3	0·3	0	0	0	32·5	50·7	1·3	0·7	0·7	5·6
Common Tern	641	10·5	0·8	1·1	0·5	0	51·6	19·5	5·8	1·1	3·3	5·9
Arctic Tern	480	3·5	0	2·3	0	0	78·1	5·6	2·3	1·5	1·0	5·6
Little Tern	48	10·4	2·1	0	4·2	0	62·5	16·7	0	2·1	0	2·1
Guillemot	1306	14·9	27·5	0	0	0	43·0	0·8	8·8	0	0·7	4·2
Razorbill	1430	15·6	21·1	0	0·1	0	46·2	2·3	12·3	0	1·0	1·5
Black Guillemot	44	2·3	11·4	2·3	0	0	70·5	0	9·1	0	4·5	0
Puffin	718	3·8	14·1	0	0·4	0	62·5	1·1	4·2	0·1	11·6	2·2
Stock Dove	255	67·5	0	2·0	0·8	1·6	24·3	1·6	0	0·8	1·2	0·4
Woodpigeon	1836	74·1	0	1·6	0·5	0·3	18·4	1·9	0·3	0·1	1·0	1·8
Collared Dove	397	16·4	0	7·3	9·1	2·5	51·4	3·5	1·0	2·3	3·8	2·8
Turtle Dove	166	68·7	0	0	0	0·6	18·1	5·4	0	1·8	1·8	3·6
Cuckoo	97	18·6	0	6·2	5·2	3·1	48·5	4·1	2·1	4·1	2·1	6·2
Barn Owl	735	3·8	0	30·2	0	6·8	46·3	1·1	1·4	2·7	0·4	7·4
Little Owl	263	11·8	0	23·6	0	3·8	46·8	4·6	2·3	1·5	1·1	4·6
Tawny Owl	620	4·5	0·2	31·0	0·2	3·7	45·2	1·0	2·6	3·1	1·3	7·4
Long-eared Owl	104	5·8	0	24·0	0	0	60·6	0	1·9	2·9	1·0	3·9
Short-eared Owl	69	24·7	0	2·9	0	0	59·4	2·9	0	2·9	1·5	5·8
Kingfisher	274	1·8	0·7	15·7	8·0	2·2	47·5	1·8	2·6	2·6	11·3	5·9
Green Woodpecker	66	6·1	0	13·6	3·0	0	66·7	0	1·5	0	1·5	7·6
Great Spotted Woodpecker	151	6·6	0	9·3	7·3	3·3	52·3	1·3	3·3	6·0	2·7	8·0
Skylark	146	4·1	0	10·3	13·0	1·4	47·3	2·7	2·7	0	6·8	11·6
Sand Martin	768	5·9	0·1	18·9	3·7	3·5	49·5	4·0	2·5	4·2	2·1	5·7
Swallow	2838	2·5	0·1	9·8	4·3	18·4	43·8	6·8	0·8	5·0	1·4	7·1
House Martin	498	0·6	0	6·6	9·2	3·8	64·1	1·6	1·4	4·0	0·8	7·8
Meadow Pipit	555	17·3	0	4·5	3·6	0·9	40·0	19·3	0·5	2·9	5·1	6·0
Rock/Water Pipit	98	0	0	4·1	1·0	5·1	61·2	3·1	3·1	4·1	10·2	8·2
Yellow Wagtail	232	13·4	0·4	10·8	8·2	0	39·7	21·1	2·6	0·9	1·3	1·7
Grey Wagtail	73	1·4	0	15·1	12·3	8·2	39·7	4·1	2·7	1·4	1·4	13·7
Pied/White Wagtail	1810	3·8	0·1	8·4	8·4	10·3	52·3	4·3	1·4	3·8	1·4	5·9
Waxwing	38	5·3	0	10·5	5·3	0	68·4	2·6	2·6	2·6	0	2·6
Dipper	129	2·3	0	2·3	10·9	5·4	58·2	0·8	0	7·8	3·9	8·5
Wren	655	0·3	0	15·1	25·0	4·3	34·0	3·1	0·6	1·4	10·4	5·8
Dunnock	1546	1·4	0·1	11·1	24·5	1·6	51·9	1·2	1·6	1·6	1·8	3·4
Robin	5128	0·9	0·0	10·5	23·3	5·0	45·6	3·2	3·5	0·9	2·9	4·2
Redstart	183	14·8	0	7·1	6·6	3·8	36·6	25·1	2·2	0	0	3·8
Whinchat	74	17·6	0	13·5	5·4	0	33·8	21·6	1·4	1·4	2·7	2·7
Stonechat	76	14·5	0	11·8	2·6	0	50·0	10·5	0	0	4·0	6·6
Wheatear	175	21·7	0	6·9	0·6	0	42·9	16·0	2·9	2·3	2·9	4·0
Ring Ousel	81	53·1	0	2·5	1·2	0	33·3	7·4	1·2	1·2	0	0
Blackbird	30069	27·0	0·0	14·4	13·6	2·7	52·3	1·8	3·3	3·0	2·0	4·3
Fieldfare	425	32·5	0	3·1	2·8	0·5	42·1	4·7	1·9	4·0	2·1	6·4
Song Thrush	8242	4·8	0	17·7	12·3	1·7	47·8	1·9	3·2	3·9	2·3	4·4
Redwing	1010	31·1	0	3·3	5·6	0·3	35·3	11·1	0·6	1·5	2·1	9·2
Mistle Thrush	841	4·9	0	13·2	7·5	1·2	54·6	1·2	1·8	4·8	4·3	6·6
Sedge Warbler	315	2·5	0·3	18·4	17·8	1·6	42·2	5·7	4·4	2·2	3·5	1·3
Reed Warbler	462	20·6	0·2	9·1	10·2	1·3	39·2	9·1	1·5	1·7	5·2	2·0
Lesser Whitethroat	116	26·7	0	18·1	6·0	0	36·2	4·3	0	3·5	3·5	1·7
Whitethroat	482	16·2	0	22·8	9·1	0·6	36·5	6·4	1·9	1·7	2·3	2·5
Garden Warbler	69	23·2	0	13·0	8·7	2·9	34·8	8·7	0	2·9	4·4	1·5
Blackcap	359	18·9	0	12·5	10·0	0·6	41·2	8·6	0	2·5	3·9	1·7
Chiffchaff	168	15·5	0	7·1	6·6	1·2	45·3	15·5	2·4	1·8	3·6	1·2
Willow Warbler	466	14·0	0	12·9	10·5	1·3	45·5	7·1	0·6	1·3	4·3	2·6

	Total of recoveries	*% Shot/ hunted*	*% Oiled*	*% Traffic accident*	*% Taken by cats*	*% Inside something*	*% Found dead*	*% Delib. taken*	*% Acc. taken by man*	*% Collision*	*% Other pred.*	*% Other causes*
Goldcrest	257	0·4	0·4	4·7	18·3	0·8	38·9	5·8	0·8	0·4	25·3	4·3
Spotted Flycatcher	217	10·6	0	10·6	8·8	5·1	41·5	14·3	0·9	3·7	0·9	3·7
Pied Flycatcher	244	15·2	0	8·2	4·9	4·9	41·8	18·9	0	5·3	0·8	0
Bearded Tit	40	0	0	2·5	10·0	0	40·0	5·0	0	0	42·5	0
Long-tailed Tit	222	2·7	0	29·7	14·9	2·3	41·0	1·4	0	3·6	2·7	1·8
Marsh Tit	89	0	0	22·5	21·4	1·1	42·7	3·4	2·3	1·1	4·5	1·1
Willow Tit	89	2·3	0	13·5	19·1	5·6	43·8	2·3	1·1	3·4	6·7	2·3
Coal Tit	379	1·6	0	10·6	23·2	2·1	51·5	2·6	0·5	3·4	1·6	2·9
Blue Tit	8458	1·0	0·0	13·8	18·7	6·2	46·5	2·8	1·8	3·6	1·8	3·8
Great Tit	3361	0·8	0·0	9·9	23·6	4·2	44·6	2·6	3·9	4·5	2·3	3·5
Nuthatch	152	0	0	5·3	25·7	4·6	48·0	2·0	3·3	5·3	2·6	3·3
Treecreeper	58	0	0	6·9	19·0	1·7	51·7	6·9	1·7	6·9	5·2	0
Jay	548	52·7	0·2	4·9	1·3	0	32·5	2·0	2·0	0·9	0·9	2·6
Magpie	370	36·8	0	2·4	1·9	1·6	47·3	3·8	0·5	0·3	0	5·4
Chough	33	9·1	0	0	0	0	72·7	0	0	3·0	0	15·2
Jackdaw	974	30·2	0	2·6	0·7	4·9	45·8	8·2	0·8	1·1	0·9	4·7
Rook	1185	41·3	0	2·5	0	0·4	43·7	4·3	0·3	1·2	0·3	6·0
Carrion/Hooded Crow	532	44·9	0	2·6	0·2	0	43·4	2·6	0·9	0·9	0·8	3·6
Raven	269	19·7	0·4	1·1	0	0	64·7	5·6	2·2	0·7	1·5	4·1
Starling	25828	9·4	0·0	2·3	12·8	6·9	56·0	3·4	1·1	1·1	1·5	5·4
House Sparrow	3414	3·4	0·1	9·5	19·1	4·5	54·0	1·8	1·3	1·1	2·0	3·2
Tree Sparrow	460	4·6	0	14·1	12·6	7·4	49·8	1·5	0·4	2·8	4·4	2·4
Chaffinch	2678	1·7	0	15·2	10·0	2·1	49·7	6·7	1·5	5·9	2·2	5·0
Brambling	207	6·3	0	10·1	4·4	3·9	48·3	15·9	0	3·9	3·4	3·9
Greenfinch	10598	1·4	0·0	14·3	19·0	1·9	49·2	3·2	1·7	3·0	1·4	4·9
Goldfinch	734	13·8	0	17·0	5·3	1·0	36·1	19·9	0·4	1·5	1·5	3·5
Siskin	185	6·5	0	8·1	8·1	1·6	49·2	13·5	0	7·6	2·7	2·7
Linnet	1304	7·3	0	15·0	6·4	0·8	37·7	26·5	0·5	0·9	1·4	3·5
Twite	33	9·1	0	15·2	6·1	3·1	36·4	18·2	3·0	0	3·0	6·1
Redpoll	468	7·3	0	9·6	13·9	0·6	37·6	23·7	1·3	1·9	1·3	2·8
Bullfinch	1881	9·4	0	10·6	16·3	1·8	37·0	10·0	2·1	9·8	1·2	1·9
Snow Bunting	27	3·7	0	0	3·7	0	33·3	14·8	3·7	7·4	25·9	7·4
Yellowhammer	397	2·3	0	28·7	8·8	1·5	40·6	2·0	1·3	4·8	5·8	4·3
Reed Bunting	583	2·1	0·2	13·0	13·2	1·4	49·1	4·0	1·4	3·1	8·8	4·0
Corn Bunting	34	2·9	0	20·6	5·9	0	35·3	2·9	0	8·8	17·7	5·9

6: Woodland bird population densities

The table presents data on the frequency and density of occurrence of common woodland species recorded in the CBC data for 1980. For each species four figures are presented, giving frequency of occurrence (percentage of CBC woodland plots with the species present in 1980) plus median and spread of density (pairs per 100 km^2). Quartiles are used to indicate the extent of between-plot variation in density, since these variations have statistically skewed distributions. The *lower quartile* indicates a density level below which 25% of all plot densities fall; the *median* indicates the density below which (and above which) 50% of the densities fall; and the *upper quartile* indicates the value below which 75% fall. (Hence half of the observed values lie between the lower and the upper quartiles.)

Note that these figures are only approximate estimates of absolute density since (unlike the CBC index of changes) they vary with census efficiency: a difficult-to-census species will be under-estimated relative to more easily censused species.

	% in plots	*Lower quartile*	*Median*	*Upper quartile*
Cuckoo	50	4·2	6·75	10·3
Green Woodpecker	50	5·2	6·9	11·8
Great Spotted Woodpecker	62	4·4	6·75	8·75
Wren	99	54·2	89·0	166·0
Dunnock	91	16·1	46·3	72·9
Robin	99	75·0	111·8	176·6
Blackbird	99	49·7	75·3	131·1
Song Thrush	97	12·8	27·6	55·6
Mistle Thrush	82	5·3	10·0	14·9
Whitethroat	33	6·5	10·3	16·3
Garden Warbler	46	10·5	18·1	39·5
Blackcap	75	14·0	27·5	47·5
Chiffchaff	68	9·9	19·6	44·0
Willow Warbler	94	37·5	72·0	109·0
Goldcrest	60	10·7	22·0	36·6
Spotted Flycatcher	36	6·3	9·1	16·5
Long-tailed Tit	73	4·45	8·8	13·4
Marsh Tit	38	9·2	15·6	27·6
Coal Tit	38	9·2	19·0	42·2
Blue Tit	98	23·1	33·3	71·8
Great Tit	99	27·8	49·4	77·3
Nuthatch	44	6·7	14·8	21·0
Treecreeper	60	6·2	10·2	14·2
Jay	37	6·6	15·0	10·55
Magpie	70	8·6	11·9	16·0
Carrion Crow	74	6·6	10·8	15·5

	% in plots	*Lower quartile*	*Median*	*Upper quartile*
Starling	57	8·3	27·4	46·5
Chaffinch	98	36·5	71·4	123·8
Greenfinch	52	7·9	20·3	40·5
Linnet	38	4·0	18·1	25·3
Bullfinch	80	6·1	10·8	20·5
Yellowhammer	66	11·8	27·3	64·0

7: Farmland bird population densities

The table presents data on the frequency and density of occurrence of common farmland species recorded in the CBC data for 1980. For explanation of terms and calculation procedures see Table 6. Where a species appears in both tables (woodland, farmland) the densities and frequencies listed are those calculated from CBC plots of that habitat type.

	% in plots	*Lower quartile*	*Median*	*Upper quartile*
Mallard	68	1·8	3·2	6·3
Red-legged Partridge	28	1·6	2·8	5·2
Grey Partridge	40	1·8	2·4	4·0
Pheasant	54	1·9	3·0	5·3
Moorhen	59	2·4	5·2	8·4
Lapwing	39	2·2	4·0	5·6
Turtle Dove	26	1·8	2·9	4·6
Cuckoo	51	1·4	2·2	3·4
Skylark	86	8·8	15·0	30·4
Swallow	66	2·8	5·1	12·8
Pied Wagtail	64	1·5	1·9	3·8
Wren	99	13·2	25·8	44·9
Dunnock	95	10·0	16·4	24·5
Robin	94	11·2	20·4	41·2
Blackbird	99	19·9	31·6	48·1
Song Thrush	92	4·8	8·2	14·0
Mistle Thrush	69	2·1	3·6	5·6

	% in plots	*Lower quartile*	*Median*	*Upper quartile*
Sedge Warbler	35	2·4	4·2	13·3
Lesser Whitethroat	39	1·4	2·2	3·0
Whitethroat	66	1·8	4·0	6·0
Garden Warbler	33	1·1	1·6	3·7
Blackcap	59	2·7	4·2	6·5
Chiffchaff	43	1·8	4·8	12·8
Willow Warbler	82	4·0	9·5	21·1
Spotted Flycatcher	46	1·4	2·2	5·2
Long-tailed Tit	40	1·4	2·3	4·4
Blue Tit	98	8·4	15·9	27·1
Great Tit	57	5·1	10·0	16·6
Treecreeper	26	1·4	2·0	3·5
Magpie	75	2·6	4·6	8·0
Jackdaw	40	1·6	2·8	10·6
Carrion Crow	81	3·0	4·8	7·3
Starling	77	4·6	11·3	19·0
Tree Sparrow	48	0·8	3·0	4·2
Chaffinch	96	13·4	24·8	47·2
Greenfinch	78	2·8	7·1	12·0
Goldfinch	61	2·1	2·8	6·2
Linnet	78	2·8	5·4	12·0
Bullfinch	53	1·6	3·4	5·4
Yellowhammer	75	9·8	13·1	22·6
Reed Bunting	62	2·8	6·0	9·6
Corn Bunting	22	2·6	6·0	8·4

8: Breeding statistics for species nesting in Britain and Ireland

Note: Figures in brackets are the extreme ranges.
* The period before the bird is capable of precocious flight (gamebirds only). It takes considerably longer before these species are fully feathered.
F = Based on data collected outside Britain and Ireland.

	No. of broods	*Clutch size*	*Incubation period*	*Fledging period*
Red-throated Diver	1	1–2	24–29	(38) 39–45 (48)
Black-throated Diver	1	1–2	27–29	72 F
Little Grebe	2–3	(2) 4–6 (7)	20–21	44–48
Great Crested Grebe	1–2	(2) 3–4 (6)	27–29	71–79 (84)
Slavonian Grebe	1 (2)	(1) 4–5 (7)	22–25	55–60
Black-necked Grebe	1 (2)	(1) 3–5 (6)	20–22	?
Fulmar	1	1	(41) 52–53 (57)	(41) 46–51 (57)
Manx Shearwater	1	1	47–55	62–76
Storm Petrel	1	1	39–43 (50)	56–73
Leach's Petrel	1	1	41–42	60–70
Gannet	1	1	42–49	84–97
Cormorant	1	3–4 (6)	28–31	c50
Shag	1	(1) 3 (6)	30–36	48–58
Bittern	1	(3) 5–6 (7)	25–26	50–55
Grey Heron	1	(1) 4 (10)	(25) 27–28	50–55
Mute Swan	1	(3) 6 (8)	35–41	120–150
Whooper Swan	1	4–6	(31) 35 (42)	c60
Greylag Goose	1	(3) 6 (9)	29	56–60
Canada Goose	1	(3) 5–6 (11)	28–30	40–48
Egyptian Goose	1	(6) 8–9 (15)	28–30	70–75
Shelduck	1	(3) 8–10 (12)	29–31	45–50
Mandarin	1	9–12 (14)	28–30	40–45
Wigeon	1	(6) 8–9 (12)	24–25	40–45
Gadwall	1	(6) 8–12 (15)	24–26	45–80
Teal	1	(7) 8–11 (15)	21–23	25–30
Mallard	1	(4) 9–13 (18)	24–32	50–60
Pintail	1	(6) 7–9 (12)	22–24	40–45
Garganey	1	(6) 8–9 (14)	21–23	35–40
Shoveler	1	(6) 9–11 (14)	21–25	40–45
Pochard	1	8–10	24–28	50–55
Tufted Duck	1	(3) 8–11 (14)	23–28	50–55
Scaup	1	(6) 8–11 (15)	26–28	40–45
Eider	1	(1) 4–6 (8)	25–28	65–75
Common Scoter	1	(5) 6–8 (11)	27–31	45–50
Goldeneye	1	(5) 8–11 (13)	27–32	57–66
Red-breasted Merganser	1	(6) 8–10 (14)	28–35	60–65

	No. of broods	*Clutch size*	*Incubation period*	*Fledging period*
Goosander	1	(4) 8–11 (13)	28–35	60–70
Ruddy Duck	1	(5) 6–10 (12)	25–26	50–55
Honey Buzzard	1	2	30–35 (37)	40–44
Red Kite	1	2–3	31–32	50–60
Marsh Harrier	1	(3) 5–6 (8)	32–38	35–40 (47)
Hen Harrier	1	(3) 4–5 (6)	29–37	(30) 32–38 (42)
Montagu's Harrier	1	4–5	(27) 28–29 (30)	35–40
Goshawk	1	3–4	35–38	40–43
Sparrowhawk	1	(3) 4–6 (7)	32–36	(24) 26–30
Buzzard	1	3 (6)	(28) 33–35 (38)	(42) 50–55 (62)
Golden Eagle	1	(1) 2 (4)	43–45	(65) 70–77 (80)
Osprey	1	2–3	34–40	49–57
Kestrel	1	(1) 4–5 (7)	27–29	(27) 28–30 (34)
Merlin	1	(1) 4–5 (6)	28–32	25–32
Hobby	1	2–3 (4)	28	28–32
Peregrine	1	(2) 3–4 (6)	29–32 (34)	35–40 (42)
Red Grouse	1	(2) 6–9 (15)	19–25	12–14*
Ptarmigan	1	(3) 6–10	(22) 24–28	10–15*
Black Grouse	1	(4) 6–10 (15)	25–27	10–14 (20) *
Capercaillie	1	(5) 7–11 (16)	24–26	15–20*
Red-legged Partridge	1–2	10–15	23–24	c10*
Grey Partridge	1	10–20	23–25	c15*
Quail	1–2	(7) 8–13 (18)	17–20	c11*
Pheasant	1	(2) 8–15 (18)	23–28	c12*
Water Rail	2	5–9 (15)	(19) 21–23	20–30
Spotted Crake	1–2	8–12	18–21	?
Corncrake	1 (2)	(6) 8–12 (14)	16–19	34–38
Moorhen	2–3	(3) 5–9 (13)	21–22	60–65
Coot	1–3	3–11	23–25	55–60
Oystercatcher	1 (2)	(1) 3 (4)	24–28	28–31
Avocet	1	3–4	21–22	c40–45
Stone Curlew	1	(1) 2 (3)	25–27	c56
Little Ringed Plover	1 (2)	(3) 4 (5)	24–25	24–29
Ringed Plover	2–3	(1) 3–4 (5)	23–25	c24
Dotterel	1	2–3	(22) 25–28	26–30
Golden Plover	1	2–4	27–34	32–33
Lapwing	1	3–4	(24) 27 (34)	31–40
Temminck's Stint	1 (2)	2–4	21–22	15–18F
Dunlin	1	(2) 4	21–24	(18) 19–20 (25) F
Ruff	1	(3) 4	21	c 4 weeks
Snipe	1–2	(1) 4 (6)	18–21	(14) 19–21
Woodcock	1	(2) 4 (5)	(20) 22 (24)	14

	No. of broods	*Clutch size*	*Incubation period*	*Fledging period*
Black-tailed Godwit	1	(3) 4 (5)	22–24 (27)	30–32F
Whimbrel	1	3–4	24–28	c 4–6 weeks
Curlew	1	4	26–30	5–6 weeks
Redshank	1	(3) 4 (5)	21–25	25
Greenshank	1	2–4	23–26	25–31
Wood Sandpiper	1	3–4	22–23	c 4 weeks
Common Sandpiper	1	(3) 4 (5)	21–25	25
Red-necked Phalarope	1	(3) 4 (8)	17–19	17–21
Arctic Skua	1	1–2	25–26	29–30
Great Skua	1	1–2	28–32	46
Black-headed Gull	1	2–3	23–24	4–6 weeks
Common Gull	1	2–3	22–28	c 5 weeks
Lesser Black-backed Gull	1	2–3	(25) 28 (29)	c 7 weeks
Herring Gull	1	2–3	27–30	c 6–7 weeks
Great Black-backed Gull	1	2–3	26–28	c 7–8 weeks
Kittiwake	1	(1) 2 (3)	(21) 27 (30)	33–47
Sandwich Tern	1	1–2	21–25	22–28 (30)
Roseate Tern	1	1–2	(21) 22 (26)	c 3–4 weeks
Common Tern	1	2–3	(21) 22 (29)	21–26
Arctic Tern	1	1–2	22	18–26
Little Tern	1	2–3	19–22	15–17*
Guillemot	1	1	(28) 32–36	18–25
Razorbill	1	1	(26) 34–36	16–19
Black Guillemot	1	1–2	21–25 (30)	35
Puffin	1	1	39	34 (36–40) 44
Rock Dove	5	2	18	35–37
Stock Dove	2–5	2	16	25–28
Woodpigeon	1–2	2	17	16–28
Collared Dove	2–4	2	14–16	15–17
Turtle Dove	2	2	14	c20
Cuckoo	Parasitic	6–18	11–12	21
Barn Owl	1 (2)	(2) 4–6 (11)	(29) 30–31 (34)	51–63
Snowy Owl	1	5–7	33	35–42F
Little Owl	1	3–4	(25) 28–33	(30) 32–34 (35)
Tawny Owl	1	(1) 2–5 (7)	27–30	32–37
Long-eared Owl	1	(1) 3–5 (6)	25–30	21–24
Short-eared Owl	1 (2)	(2) 4–7 (14)	24–28	20–27
Nightjar	1	2	17	20–21
Swift	1	2–3	18–21	(37) 42–44 (48)
Kingfisher	2–3	(3) 6 (7)	20–21	23–26
Wryneck	1–2	7–10	12–14	19–21
Green Woodpecker	1	5–7	18–19	18–21
Great Spotted Woodpecker	1	4–7	16	18–21

	No. of broods	*Clutch size*	*Incubation period*	*Fledging period*
Lesser Spotted Woodpecker	1	4–6	14	21
Woodlark	2	3–4	14	11–13
Skylark	1–2	3–5	11	16F
Sand Martin	2	(2) 5 (6)	14	19–22
Swallow	2 (3)	3–6	15	20–22
House Martin	2 (3)	3–4	14–16	28–33
Tree Pipit	1–2	(2) 4–5 (6)	13	13
Meadow Pipit	2	(2) 4–5 (6)	13	13
Rock/Water Pipit	2	(2) 4–5 (6)	14	16
Yellow Wagtail	1–2	(3) 5–6 (7)	11–13	(10) 12 (16)
Grey Wagtail	2	(3) 5 (7)	11–15	(11) 13–14 (17)
Pied/White Wagtail	2–3	(3) 5 (8)	(10) 13 (16)	(11) 14 (15)
Dipper	2	(1) 4 (7)	(12) 16 (18)	(20) 22 (24)
Wren	2	5–6	14–17	15–17
Dunnock	2–3	3–5	12–13	12
Robin	2–3	(4) 5 (6)	13–15	12–13
Nightingale	1	(2) 4–5 (6)	13	11
Black Redstart	2	4–6	12–13	16–18
Redstart	1 (2)	5–7	(11) 13–14 (17)	(13) 14–15 (17)
Whinchat	1–2	(2) 5–6 (7)	13	13
Stonechat	2–3	(2) 5 (7)	14–15	12–16
Wheatear	1–2	5–7	15	15–16
Ring Ousel	1 (2)	(1) 4 (6)	(8) 12–14	15–16
Blackbird	2–3	3–5	13–14	13–14
Fieldfare	1–2	4–6	13	12–14
Song Thrush	2–3	(3) 4–5	(10) 13 (17)	12–15
Redwing	2	5–6	13	12–14
Mistle Thrush	2	3–5	13–14	14–16
Cetti's Warbler	2	4–5	16	14–16
Grasshopper Warbler	1–2	5–6	13–15	10–12
Savi's Warbler	1–2	4–6	c12	c12
Sedge Warbler	1–2	5–6	13–14	10–14
Marsh Warbler	1	4–5	c12	10–14
Reed Warbler	1–2	3–5	12	10–14
Dartford Warbler	1–2	(3) 4 (5)	12–13	10–14
Lesser Whitethroat	1–2	4–6	10 (14)	10–13
Whitethroat	1–2	4–5	(9) 11 (14)	(8) 10–12 (15)
Garden Warbler	1–2	4–5	10–12	9–12
Blackcap	1–2	4–5	(10) 11 (16)	(8) 11 (14)
Wood Warbler	1	(4) 5–7 (8)	13	11–12
Chiffchaff	1–2	(5) 7–8 (11)	16	18–20
Willow Warbler	1–2	6–7	13	13
Goldcrest	2	(5) 7–8 (11)	16	18–20

	No. of broods	*Clutch size*	*Incubation period*	*Fledging period*
Firecrest	1–2	(5) 7–12	14–15	17–20
Spotted Flycatcher	1–2	(1) 4–5 (6)	13–14	(12) 13–14 (15)
Pied Flycatcher	1	(4) 6–7 (9)	12–13 (17)	13–14 (17)
Bearded Tit	2–3	5–7	12–13	9–12
Long-tailed Tit	1	(8) 9–10 (12)	13–14	15–17 (20)
Marsh Tit	1	7–9	13–14	17–20
Willow Tit	1	6–9	13–14	17–20
Crested Tit	1	5–7	13–14	17–20
Coal Tit	1 (2)	7–11	13–14	17–20
Blue Tit	1	7–16	13–14	19
Great Tit	1 (2)	5–12	13–14	18–19
Nuthatch	1	(4) 5–7 (9)	14–15	23–25
Treecreeper	1 (2)	(2) 5 (7)	(12) 14 (20)	12–18
Golden Oriole	1	3–5	14–15	14–15
Red-backed Shrike	1	(1) 4 (7)	14–15	14
Jay	1	(1) 3–6	16	20
Magpie	1	(3) 4–7 (8)	18–23	22–27
Chough	1	(2) 4 (6)	18	38
Jackdaw	1	(2) 3–6 (7)	17–21	30–35
Rook	1	(1) 2–6 (7)	(16) 17 (21)	29–30
Carrion/Hooded Crow	1	(1) 2–5 (7)	(17) 19 (22)	26–35
Raven	1	(3) 5 (7)	21	35–40
Starling	1–2	(2) 4–6 (7)	12–13	20–22
House Sparrow	1–4	(2) 3–6 (7)	11–12	13–18
Tree Sparrow	2–3	(2) 4–5 (7)	11–13	12–15
Chaffinch	1	(2) 3–5 (7)	11–14	(11) 14 (18)
Greenfinch	1–2 (3)	(2) 5–6 (7)	12–14	(11) 14 (17)
Goldfinch	2 (3)	4–6	11–13	13–16
Siskin	1–2	3–5	11–13	13–17
Linnet	2–3	(3) 4–6	11–12	11–12
Twite	2	(3) 4–5 (6)	11–13	11–12 (13)
Redpoll	1–2	4–6	10–11	11–12
Common Crossbill	1 (2)	3–4	13–16	16–25
Scottish Crossbill	1 (2)	3–4	13–15	17–20
Bullfinch	1–2	3–6	12–14	15–17
Hawfinch	1	(3) 4–5 (7)	11–13	12–14
Snow Bunting	1 (2)	4–6	12–13	11–12
Yellowhammer	2	(2) 3–4 (5)	13	12–13
Cirl Bunting	2	3–4	11–13	11–13
Reed Bunting	1 (2)	3–6	12–14	10–13
Corn Bunting	1–2	(2) 4 (5)	11–13	9–12 (14)

9: Central England winter temperatures

Climatologists define winter as comprising the months of December, January and February, and there is evidence to show that very cold winters are associated with more bird deaths than are mild ones. It is not, however, known whether low average temperatures or low minimum temperatures are more important for birds. This table deals with average temperatures, and for central England only, although it reflects general trends. The columns show winter temperatures, listing the years in chronological order, and winters arranged from coldest to mildest. In all cases the figure given is the mean temperature in °C. Grateful acknowledgement is made to the Climatic Research Unit of the University of East Anglia.

Chronological order				*Coldest to mildest*			
	Mean temperature °C		*Mean temperature °C*		*Mean temperature °C*		*Mean temperature °C*
1933	4·1	1958	4·2	1963	−0·3	1954	4·1
1934	3·2	1959	3·6	1947	1·1	1958	4·2
1935	6·1	1960	4·7	1979	1·4	1966	4·3
1936	3·0	1961	4·8	1940	1·5	1944	4·3
1937	5·4	1962	3·6	1942	2·2	1971	4·4
1938	4·6	1963	−0·3	1982	2·3	1981	4·4
1939	4·7	1964	3·5	1951	2·6	1980	4·5
1940	1·5	1965	3·5	1941	2·6	1946	4·5
1941	2·6	1966	4·3	1977	2·8	1938	4·6
1942	2·2	1967	5·1	1969	2·9	1960	4·7
1943	5·9	1968	3·4	1956	2·9	1939	4·7
1944	4·3	1969	2·9	1936	3·0	1961	4·8
1945	3·7	1970	3·4	1934	3·2	1976	4·9
1946	4·5	1971	4·4	1970	3·4	1973	4·9
1947	1·1	1972	5·0	1968	3·4	1972	5·0
1948	5·1	1973	4·9	1953	3·5	1950	5·1
1949	5·6	1974	5·5	1965	3·5	1948	5·1
1950	5·1	1975	6·7	1955	3·5	1967	5·1
1951	2·6	1976	4·9	1964	3·5	1937	5·4
1952	3·9	1977	2·8	1959	3·6	1974	5·5
1953	3·5	1978	3·9	1962	3·6	1957	5·5
1954	4·1	1979	1·4	1945	3·7	1949	5·6
1955	3·5	1980	4·5	1978	3·9	1943	5·9
1956	2·9	1981	4·4	1952	3·9	1935	6·1
1957	5·5	1982	2·3	1933	4·1	1975	6·7

10: Breeding season rainfall, England and Wales (mm)

There are considerable regional differences in rainfall, precipitation in Britain generally being greater to the north and west, and in the mountains, and lower in the south and east. It is possible that the heavy rain associated with thunderstorms is a more serious threat to nesting birds than prolonged though lighter rain; but thunderstorms tend to be localised and it is impossible to give meaningful data. The rainfall figures given here are the homogeneous series compiled by the Climatic Research Unit of the University of East Anglia, to whom grateful acknowledgement is made. They are intended to provide a generalised picture of breeding season rainfall during the period covered by this volume.

	April	*May*	*June*	*Total*	*Driest to wettest*	*Total*
1933	37·9	59·7	56·3	153·9	1976	101·2
1934	73·1	39·5	45·8	158·4	1957	109·2
1935	103·6	33·4	91·6	228·6	1940	121·9
1936	55·2	31·8	97·0	184·0	1974	124·3
1937	80·4	78·4	42·3	201·1	1956	135·5
1938	6·5	72·9	57·7	137·1	1938	137·1
1939	67·4	33·1	62·1	162·6	1941	137·2
1940	60·9	39·2	21·8	121·9	1975	140·5
1941	38·8	65·5	32·9	137·2	1960	142·3
1942	42·5	103·4	20·7	166·6	1949	146·5
1943	37·4	84·3	60·3	182·0	1959	147·3
1944	56·5	38·1	64·5	159·1	1933	153·9
1945	44·7	81·3	81·4	207·4	1962	156·0
1946	46·1	79·3	83·2	208·6	1970	156·2
1947	74·9	59·2	68·4	202·5	1934	158·4
1948	54·5	71·1	93·1	218·7	1944	159·1
1949	61·6	65·4	19·5	146·5	1978	160·6
1950	70·1	54·3	46·1	170·5	1939	162·6
1951	71·6	78·3	34·7	184·6	1942	166·6
1952	61·6	65·3	53·8	180·7	1950	170·5
1953	70·7	62·7	62·4	195·8	1980	177·3
1954	16·4	81·6	92·1	190·1	1961	180·4
1955	32·5	102·9	86·8	222·2	1952	180·7
1956	41·4	22·4	71·7	135·5	1943	182·0
1957	9·2	46·4	53·6	109·2	1936	184·0
1958	31·5	83·7	108·3	223·5	1951	184·6
1959	77·6	26·4	43·3	147·3	1977	188·6
1960	44·8	46·6	50·9	142·3	1954	190·1
1961	102·8	38·2	39·4	180·4	1953	195·8
1962	71·2	67·4	17·4	156·0	1965	198·4
1963	80·8	48·2	85·7	214·7	1937	201·1

	April	*May*	*June*	*Total*	*Driest to wettest*	*Total*
1964	68·3	58·6	79·8	206·7	1947	202·5
1965	61·0	65·9	71·5	198·4	1964	206·7
1966	111·2	68·6	88·3	268·1	1945	207·4
1967	46·2	138·9	40·0	225·1	1971	208·4
1968	70·2	78·5	91·6	240·3	1946	208·6
1969	58·7	121·5	53·6	238·8	1973	212·1
1970	87·7	25·1	43·4	156·2	1963	214·7
1971	52·8	50·4	105·2	208·4	1948	218·7
1972	70·1	75·2	74·4	219·7	1972	219·7
1973	67·4	83·8	60·9	212·1	1955	222·2
1974	14·9	41·2	68·2	124·3	1958	223·5
1975	69·6	49·9	21·0	140·5	1967	225·1
1976	19·7	64·0	17·5	101·2	1935	228·6
1977	51·2	51·0	86·4	188·6	1979	231·0
1978	54·3	46·6	59·7	160·6	1969	233·8
1979	70·5	120·4	40·1	231·0	1968	240·3
1980	17·7	32·5	127·1	177·3	1966	268·1

11: Ubiquity of species breeding in Britain and Ireland

The Ordnance Survey maps of Britain and Ireland have a superimposed grid of 10-km squares, giving a total of 3,862 such squares. During fieldwork in the years 1968–1972 every one of these squares was visited at least once in the breeding season to discover which species were breeding or possibly breeding there. The results, published in *The Atlas of Breeding Birds in Britain and Ireland* (1976), offer a convenient measure of ubiquity. In the table below the figure in the first column is the number of squares in which the species was found to be present during the breeding season. The figure in the second column expresses that number of 10-km squares as a percentage of the total number of squares.

	Number of 10-km squares in which recorded		*Number of 10-km squares in which recorded*
Red-throated Diver	319 (8%)	Shoveler	571 (15%)
Black-throated Diver	212 (5%)	Red-crested Pochard	7 (0·2%)
Great Northern Diver	8 (0·2%)	Pochard	563 (15%)
Little Grebe	1,882 (49%)	Tufted Duck	1,622 (42%)
Great Crested Grebe	987 (26%)	Scaup	8 (0·2%)
Slavonian Grebe	20 (0·5%)	Eider	498 (13%)
Black-necked Grebe	12 (0·3%)	Common Scoter	57 (1%)
Fulmar	725 (19%)	Goldeneye	19 (0·5%)
Manx Shearwater	86 (2%)	Red-breasted Merganser	915 (24%)
Storm Petrel	79 (2%)	Goosander	412 (11%)
Leach's Petrel	10 (0·3%)	Ruddy Duck	20 (0·5%)
Gannet	19 (0·5%)	Honey Buzzard	12 (0·3%)
Cormorant	575 (15%)	Red Kite	35 (0·9%)
Shag	682 (18%)	Marsh Harrier	27 (0·6%)
Bittern	36 (0·9%)	Hen Harrier	543 (14%)
Grey Heron	2,461 (64%)	Montagu's Harrier	51 (1%)
Mute Swan	2,258 (58%)	Goshawk	35 (0·9%)
Whooper Swan	9 (0·2%)	Sparrowhawk	2,626 (68%)
Greylag Goose	208 (5%)	Buzzard	1,451 (38%)
Canada Goose	687 (18%)	Golden Eagle	395 (10%)
Wood Duck	11 (0·3%)	Osprey	24 (0·6%)
Egyptian Goose	18 (0·5%)	Kestrel	3,546 (92%)
Shelduck	1,023 (26%)	Merlin	843 (22%)
Mandarin	41 (1%)	Hobby	261 (7%)
Wigeon	283 (7%)	Peregrine	634 (16%)
Gadwall	171 (4%)	Red Grouse	1,503 (39%)
Teal	1,766 (46%)	Ptarmigan	195 (5%)
Mallard	3,549 (92%)	Black Grouse	603 (16%)
Pintail	94 (2%)	Capercaillie	182 (5%)
Garganey	138 (4%)	Red-legged Partridge	919 (24%)

	Number of 10-km squares in which recorded
Grey Partridge	2,261 (59%)
Quail	438 (11%)
Pheasant	3,105 (80%)
Golden Pheasant	29 (0·8%)
Lady Amherst's Pheasant	13 (0·3%)
Water Rail	911 (24%)
Spotted Crake	39 (1%)
Corncrake	1,489 (39%)
Moorhen	3,149 (82%)
Coot	2,256 (58%)
Oystercatcher	1,802 (47%)
Avocet	8 (0·2%)
Stone Curlew	94 (2%)
Little Ringed Plover	288 (7%)
Ringed Plover	1,229 (32%)
Dotterel	46 (1%)
Golden Plover	915 (24%)
Lapwing	3,264 (85%)
Kentish Plover	3 (0·1%)
Temminck's Stint	4 (0·1%)
Dunlin	537 (14%)
Ruff	14 (0·4%)
Snipe	3,130 (81%)
Woodcock	2,190 (57%)
Black-tailed Godwit	47 (1%)
Whimbrel	59 (2%)
Curlew	2,784 (72%)
Redshank	1,925 (50%)
Greenshank	254 (7%)
Green Sandpiper	2 (0·1%)
Wood Sandpiper	18 (0·5%)
Common Sandpiper	1,858 (48%)
Red-necked Phalarope	22 (0·5%)
Arctic Skua	139 (4%)
Great Skua	85 (2%)
Black-headed Gull	1,736 (45%)
Common Gull	1,054 (27%)
Lesser Black-backed Gull	867 (22%)
Herring Gull	1,152 (30%)
Great Black-backed Gull	870 (23%)
Kittiwake	383 (10%)

	Number of 10-km squares in which recorded
Sandwich Tern	181 (5%)
Roseate Tern	62 (2%)
Common Tern	893 (23%)
Arctic Tern	536 (14%)
Little Tern	232 (6%)
Black Tern	2 (0·05%)
Guillemot	382 (10%)
Razorbill	384 (10%)
Black Guillemot	540 (14%)
Puffin	248 (6%)
Rock/Feral Dove	1,904 (49%)
Stock Dove	2,503 (65%)
Woodpigeon	3,536 (92%)
Collared Dove	2,653 (69%)
Turtle Dove	1,287 (33%)
Cuckoo	3,532 (91%)
Barn Owl	2,279 (59%)
Snowy Owl	5 (0·1%)
Little Owl	1,381 (36%)
Tawny Owl	2,305 (60%)
Long-eared Owl	942 (24%)
Short-eared Owl	802 (21%)
Nightjar	656 (17%)
Swift	3,073 (80%)
Kingfisher	1,819 (47%)
Hoopoe	4 (0·1%)
Wryneck	48 (1%)
Green Woodpecker	1,623 (42%)
Great Spotted Woodpecker	2,053 (53%)
Lesser Spotted Woodpecker	889 (23%)
Woodlark	188 (5%)
Skylark	3,775 (98%)
Sand Martin	2,889 (75%)
Swallow	3,592 (93%)
House Martin	3,325 (86%)
Tree Pipit	1,793 (46%)
Meadow Pipit	3,632 (94%)
Rock/Water Pipit	1,028 (27%)
Yellow Wagtail	1,161 (30%)
Grey Wagtail	2,740 (71%)
Pied Wagtail	3,646 (94%)

	Number of 10-km squares in which recorded
White Wagtail	19 (0·5%)
Dipper	2,051 (53%)
Wren	3,755 (97%)
Dunnock	3,574 (93%)
Robin	3,591 (93%)
Nightingale	639 (17%)
Black Redstart	68 (2%)
Redstart	1,671 (43%)
Whinchat	1,868 (48%)
Stonechat	2,015 (52%)
Wheatear	2,408 (62%)
Ring Ousel	780 (20%)
Blackbird	3,718 (96%)
Fieldfare	35 (0·9%)
Song Thrush	3,659 (95%)
Redwing	111 (3%)
Mistle Thrush	3,395 (88%)
Cetti's Warbler	6 (0·2%)
Grasshopper Warbler	2,508 (67%)
Savi's Warbler	13 (0·3%)
Sedge Warbler	2,929 (76%)
Marsh Warbler	21 (0·5%)
Reed Warbler	778 (20%)
Dartford Warbler	31 (0·8%)
Lesser Whitethroat	1,098 (28%)
Whitethroat	3,198 (83%)
Garden Warbler	1,891 (49%)
Blackcap	2,185 (57%)
Wood Warbler	1,238 (32%)
Chiffchaff	2,912 (75%)
Willow Warbler	3,536 (92%)
Goldcrest	3,259 (84%)
Firecrest	20 (0·5%)
Spotted Flycatcher	3,332 (86%)
Pied Flycatcher	546 (14%)
Bearded Tit	45 (1%)
Long-tailed Tit	2,916 (76%)
Marsh Tit	1,366 (35%)

	Number of 10-km squares in which recorded
Willow Tit	1,218 (32%)
Crested Tit	46 (1%)
Coal Tit	3,250 (84%)
Blue Tit	3,473 (90%)
Great Tit	3,365 (87%)
Nuthatch	1,175 (30%)
Treecreeper	3,002 (78%)
Golden Oriole	10 (0·3%)
Short-toed Treecreeper	5 (0·1%)
Red-backed Shrike	111 (3%)
Jay	2,142 (55%)
Magpie	2,899 (75%)
Chough	244 (6%)
Jackdaw	3,387 (88%)
Rook	3,178 (82%)
Carrion Crow	2,310 (60%)
Hooded Crow	1,665 (43%)
Raven	1,697 (44%)
Starling	3,709 (96%)
House Sparrow	3,643 (94%)
Tree Sparrow	1,800 (47%)
Chaffinch	3,553 (92%)
Brambling	6 (0·2%)
Serin	6 (0·2%)
Greenfinch	3,318 (86%)
Goldfinch	3,018 (78%)
Siskin	863 (22%)
Linnet	3,345 (87%)
Twite	785 (20%)
Redpoll	2,818 (73%)
Common Crossbill	305 (8%)
Bullfinch	3,202 (83%)
Hawfinch	459 (12%)
Snow Bunting	14 (0·4%)
Yellowhammer	3,380 (88%)
Cirl Bunting	174 (5%)
Reed Bunting	3,431 (89%)
Corn Bunting	1,424 (37%)

The twenty-five most ubiquitous species in the years 1968–1972

	Number of 10-km squares in which recorded
Skylark	3,775 (98%)
Wren	3,755 (97%)
Blackbird	3,718 (96%)
Starling	3,709 (96%)
Song Thrush	3,659 (95%)
Pied Wagtail	3,646 (94%)
House Sparrow	3,643 (94%)
Meadow Pipit	3,632 (94%)
Swallow	3,592 (93%)
Robin	3,591 (93%)
Dunnock	3,574 (93%)
Chaffinch	3,553 (92%)
Mallard	3,549 (92%)
Kestrel	3,546 (92%)
Woodpigeon	3,536 (92%)
Willow Warbler	3,536 (92%)
Cuckoo	3,532 (91%)
Blue Tit	3,473 (90%)
Reed Bunting	3,431 (89%)
Mistle Thrush	3,395 (88%)
Jackdaw	3,387 (88%)
Yellowhammer	3,380 (88%)
Great Tit	3,365 (87%)
Linnet	3,345 (87%)
Spotted Flycatcher	3,332 (86%)

12: Bird weights in Britain and Ireland

This list of weights of most British birds gives a mean, range and sample size. Units are generally grams but kg are used for bigger species (e.g. Mute Swan). For many species the sample has been restricted to a particular time of the year – where possible the breeding season – and for some which show sexual dimorphism separate weights are shown for males and females.

Bird weights are subject to very wide fluctuations. Migrants may put on fat to fuel their long flights and double their normal weight; females in the breeding season, with well-developed gonads and carrying forming eggs, may weigh 50% more than they would after the young have fledged; winter birds may increase weight as an insurance against a succession of cold days. There is thus no real 'average' weight for a bird and the weight distribution for a population of birds will often be skewed (with a few exceptionally heavy birds) rather than normal. The values given should be treated as no more than useful working guidelines.

Our thanks are due to the many ringers and other research workers who made available sample weights from their records.

		Mean	*Range*	*Sample*	*Seasonal details*
Red-throated Diver		1,780	1,530–2,060	15	July
Little Grebe		201	91–290	50	any
G. C. Grebe		1,036	568–1,490	77	all – (BWP)
Fulmar		808	605–1,100	329	June–July
Manx Shearwater		453	335–515	50	May–June adults
Storm Petrel		25·2	20·3–31·1	1,770	June–August
Leach's Petrel		44·5	35·5–59·5	1,208	August
Gannet		3,010	2,300–3,600	89	all year – (Nelson)
Cormorant		2,319	1,810–2,810	124	April – (BWP)
Shag		1,814	1,445–2,210	43	June–July
Grey Heron		1,361	1,020–1,785	13	BWP
Mute Swan	♂	11·8	9·2–14·3 kg	59	winter wt
	♀	9·7	7·6–10·6 kg	35	
Bewick's Swan	♂	6,400	4,900–7,800	96	winter wt
	♀	5,700	3,400–7,200	95	
Whooper Swan		9,350	7·4–14·0 kg	12	adults (BWP)
Greylag Goose	♂	3,692	3,200–4,300	36	resident population
	♀	3,237	3,000–3,600	30	June
Canada Goose		3,784	2,900–4,000	34	July
Barnacle Goose	♂	1,870	(1,590–2,100)	20	Solway (Scotland)
	♀	1,702	(1,420–1,870)	13	February
Brent Goose		1,368		89	adult (AOF J) ++
Egyptian Goose	♂		1,900–2,250		(BWP)
	♀		1,500–1,800		
Shelduck	♂	1,261	(1,100–1,450)	11	April–May
	♀	1,043	(926–1,250)	5	

		Mean	*Range*	*Sample*	*Seasonal details*
Mandarin	♂	628	571–693		USSR, December
	♀	512	428–608		(BWP)
Wigeon	♂	ca. 750	600–1,000		USSR, May–October
	♀	ca. 650	530–910		(BWP)
Gadwall	♂	ca. 850	650–1,300		USSR, April–October
	♀	ca. 750	500–1,000		(BWP)
Teal	♂	340	200–425	354	Camargue, winter
	♀	306	185–430	333	(BWP)
Mallard	♂	1,135	859–1,572	41	adult, Czechoslovakia
	♀	1,022	750–1,320	25	winter (BWP)
Pintail	♂	851	680–1,150	183	adult, spring in Caspian
	♀	735	550–900	68	(BWP)
Garganey	♂	349	320–440	22	adult in breeding area USSR
	♀	338	290–420	14	(BWP)
Shoveler	♂	692	560–950		autumn, USSR
	♀	664	600–800		(BWP)
Pochard	♂	849	585–1,240	119	winter, Camargue
	♀	807	467–1,090	202	(BWP)
Tufted Duck	♂	719	400–950	363	winter, Camargue
	♀	677	335–920	730	(BWP)
Scaup	♂	1,177	850–1,372	27	winter, Scandinavia &
	♀	1,115	791–1,312	21	Netherlands (BWP)
Eider	♂	2,315	1,965–2,875	22	winter, Denmark
	♀	2,142	1,864–2,595		(BWP)
Long-tailed Duck	♂	748	680–910	10	winter, North Sea
	♀	705	575–792	20	(BWP)
Common Scoter	♂	1,144	878–1,380	31	winter, North Sea
	♀	1,014	622–1,233	23	(BWP)
Velvet Scoter	♂	1,710	1,173–2,104	15	autumn & winter, North
	♀	1,540	1,140–1,895	15	Sea (BWP)
Goldeneye	♂	1,045	727–1,245	27	autumn & winter, North
	♀	745	496–860	18	Sea (BWP)
Smew	♂	ca. 640	500–825		October, USSR
	♀	ca. 560	500–680		(BWP)
Red-breasted Merganser	♂	1,201	947–1,350	13	North Sea, autumn &
	♀	925	826–1,055	7	winter (BWP)
Goosander	♂	1,750	1,540–1,960	24	breeding ♂, England.
	♀	ca. 1,250			♀ ex USA (BWP)
Ruddy Duck	♂	610	540–795	8	USA (BWP)
	♀	510	310–650	13	
Honey Buzzard	♂	716	440–943	17	all:
	♀	706	450–1,050	16	(BWP)

		Mean	*Range*	*Sample*	*Seasonal details*
Red Kite	♂	957	780–1221	27	all:
	♀	1,158	960–1600	28	(BWP)
White-tailed Eagle	♂	4,095	3,019–5,430	22	all:
	♀	5,489	3,200–7,500	37	(BWP)
Marsh Harrier	♂	492	320–667	19	all:
	♀	763	540–1,269	25	(BWP)
Hen Harrier	♂	345	300–400	29	all:
	♀	508	298–708	84	(BWP)
Montagu's Harrier	♂	261	227–305	13	all:
	♀	370	319–445	6	(BWP)
Goshawk	♂	776	517–1,110	59	all:
	♀	1,232	820–2,054	51	(BWP)
Sparrowhawk	♂	144	103–196	110	all:
	♀	254	185–346	82	(BWP)
Buzzard	♂	781	427–1,183	214	all adults:
	♀	969	486–1,364	261	(BWP)
Rough-legged Buzzard	♂	847	600–1,128	152	all:
	♀	1,065	783–1,660	119	(BWP)
Golden Eagle	♂	3,572	2,840–4,550	15	all:
	♀	5,194	3,840–6,665	19	(BWP)
Osprey	♂	1,428	1,120–1,740	15	all:
	♀	1,627	1,208–2,050	14	(BWP)
Kestrel	♂	186	117–259	40	all:
	♀	217	137–299	57	(BWP)
Merlin	♂	161	125–234	19	all:
	♀	201	156–300	20	(BWP)
Hobby	♂		131–232		all:
	♀		141–340		(BWP)
Peregrine	♂		582–750		all:
	♀		925–1,333		(BWP)
Red Grouse	♂	693	659–705		August–September range
	♀	609	578–619		(*J. An. Ecol.* 32, 1963)
Ptarmigan			530–540		spring
Black Grouse	♂	1,355	1,265–1,460	12	April
	♀	1,049	930–1,160	12	
Capercaillie	♂	4·0	3·3–4·5 kg	*	November–January typical wt.
	♀	1·8	1·4–2·0 kg		
Red-legged Partridge		484	391–547	20	adults (BWP)
Grey Partridge		374	320–433	37	autumn (BWP)
Quail	♂	93·9	73–120	52	summer (BWP)
	♀	104·1	80–134	28	
Pheasant	♂	1,281	900–1,800	74	winter (BWP)
	♀	981	720–1,250	56	

		Mean	*Range*	*Sample*	*Seasonal details*
Water Rail		119·5	92–164	50	April–May
Spotted Crake		77·9	65–96	16	any
Corncrake		141	117–167·5	29	any
Moorhen		299	198–385	50	April–mid June
Coot		668	440–865	50	any
Oystercatcher		519	425–590	38	breeding adults, Wales
Avocet		ca. 300	219–435	28	Europe
Stone Curlew		459	290–535	13	Europe
Little Ringed Plover		39	30–52·5	95	Britain
Ringed Plover		70·5	50–93	531	spring adults on passage: Dee
Dotterel		106	89–142	26	summer & autumn: Europe
Golden Plover		177	140–275	139	breeding: Europe
Grey Plover		253	168–330	71	winter: England
Lapwing		228	173–292	162	autumn: Britain
Knot		152·4	—	2,824	winter adults: Wash (Britain)
Sanderling		57·0	47–72·5	45	breeding birds: Greenland
Little Stint		28·6	19–36	92	Swiss migrants (autumn)
Curlew Sandpiper		63·3	44·5–91	27	Arctic breeding birds
Purple Sandpiper		64·6	51–92	262	adults: Scotland in winter
Dunlin	♂	43·9	38·9–47·9	33	breeding birds in Outer Hebrides
	♀	50·9	46·3–58·0	25	
Ruff	♂	188·4	121–268	88	passage birds in Britain
	♀	123·1	70–168	121	
Jack Snipe		61·5	41–91	140	Europe (autumn & winter)
Common Snipe		119	100–167	50	breeding birds: St Kilda
Woodcock		316	210–405	546	Southern France, winter
Black-tailed Godwit	♂	262	160–400	26	spring birds in Europe
	♀	348	244–500	16	
Bar-tailed Godwit	♂	279	—	224	winter birds from the Wash
	♀	335	—	114	
Whimbrel		449	226–660	110	Europe, whole year
Curlew	♂	662	572–779	71	European (West) nesting birds
	♀	788	680–919	62	
Spotted Redshank		159	100–230	99	all year, UK
Redshank		159	122–211	92	winter, UK
Greenshank		192·1	135–270	284	passage, W. Europe
Green Sandpiper		79·4	67–104	25	Cambridgeshire, passage
Wood Sandpiper		61·5	46–95	415	Camargue, autumn
Common Sandpiper		56·7	38–84	437	UK, all ages, all year
Turnstone		110	79–149	50	Greenland, breeding
Red-necked Phalarope	♂	32·4	28–40	23	breeding birds, worldwide
	♀	37·4	29–48	17	

		Mean	*Range*	*Sample*	*Seasonal details*
Grey Phalarope	♂	51·8	41–68	90	breeding birds, worldwide
	♀	61·2	49–77	58	
Arctic Skua		443		1	single, incubating
Great Skua		1,415	1,650–1,180	42	late June
Little Gull		118	88–162	87	spring
Black-headed Gull		276	211–367	50	any
Common Gull		411	370–450	7	winter
Lesser Black-backed Gull		765	595–1,065	682	May–June
Herring Gull		951	690–1,240	1,497	May–June
Iceland Gull		863		1	one – autumn
Glaucous Gull		1,570	1,151–2,152	20	any
Great Black-backed Gull		1,854	1,350–2,355	14	May–June
Kittiwake		387	335–440	50	June–July
Sandwich Tern		242	208–262	19	any
Roseate Tern		110	92–133	345	mid June–July, USA (BWP)
Common Tern		116	92–150	26	any
Arctic Tern		94	76–118	41	any
Little Tern		57	50–63	30	summer (BWP)
Black Tern		64·8	51–75	55	autumn passage
Guillemot		1,002	850–1,130	106	June–July
Razorbill		620	505–765	67	June–July
Black Guillemot		413	340–490	23	July
Puffin		395	320–475	188	June–July
Rock Dove		270	238–302	2	Fair Isle, November & April
Stock Dove		400	243–567	17	all year
Woodpigeon		524	322–590	50	all year
Collared Dove		196	148–224	50	June–July
Turtle Dove		145	74–158	50	May–September
Cuckoo		114	90–144	50	May–June
Barn Owl		287	267–310	4	autumn
Little Owl		168	133–206	15	all year
Tawny Owl		545	370–680	50	all year
Long-eared Owl		289	220–360	27	all year
Short-eared Owl		305	270–353	4	all year
Nightjar		77·9		129	June–August, adults
Swift		39	33–49	50	July
Kingfisher		39	32–48	50	April/July
Wryneck		32	26–45	50	all year
Green Woodpecker		189	164–217	22	all year
Great Spotted Woodpecker		81·6	71–83	50	all year
Lesser Spotted Woodpecker		19·8	18–22	50	all year
Woodlark		29·3	23·6–36	5	all year
Skylark		38	27–52	50	all year

	Mean	*Range*	*Sample*	*Seasonal details*
Sand Martin	13·5	11·9–18	50	June–July
Swallow	18·7	16–25	50	May–mid August
House Martin	18·0	15–21	50	June–mid September
Water Pipit	24	21–30	20	all year
Tree Pipit	22·1	20–25	12	summer
Meadow Pipit	20	16–25	50	April/May
Rock Pipit	24	21–27	50	all year
Yellow Wagtail	17·1	16–22	34	all year
Grey Wagtail	19	15–23·4	40	September–February
Pied/White Wagtail	22	19–27	50	April–August
Waxwing	53·3	40·1–68·1	50	all year; mostly migrants
Dipper	65	56–76	758	all year
Wren	9·9	8·0–12·7	50	all year
Dunnock	21·3	19·5–24·4	50	breeding season, adults
Robin	19·3	16–22	50	breeding season, adults
Nightingale	22·1	18·0–26·9	50	breeding season, adults
Bluethroat	17·1	14·0–22·5	50	migrants
Black Redstart	16·9	13·7–19·5	50	spring migrants
Redstart	14·5	12·0–19·5	50	early April–August
Whinchat	12·8	16·4–23·7	50	all year
Stonechat	15·5	14–17	17	all year
Wheatear	26·2	17·1–41·5	50	adults May & June
Ring Ousel	108·6	88·4–132·0	50	spring migrants
Blackbird	95	79–107	50	May–June adults
Fieldfare	112	77–137	50	November–February adults
Song Thrush	76	66–91	50	April–July
Redwing	65	55–74	50	November–February
Mistle Thrush	130	107–140	50	all year
Cetti's Warbler ♂	15·9	14·5–17·5	13	all year – sexual
Cetti's Warbler ♀	12·6	11·3–16·6	18	dimorphism
Grasshopper Warbler	13·3	11·4–15·2	50	summer adults
Aquatic Warbler	11·6	9·8–15·5	47	autumn passage
Sedge Warbler	11·2	9·6–13·0	50	June–July
Reed Warbler	14	9·5–15·4	50	June–July
Icterine Warbler	14·6	9·5–22·8	46	passage weights – all ages
Melodious Warbler	12·6	9·4–15·8	32	passage weights – (August–September), all ages
Dartford Warbler	10·8	9·7–11·8	52	all year
Barred Warbler	26·8	21–36·7	50	passage
Lesser Whitethroat	11·7	9·7–16·6	56	June adults
Whitethroat	16·3	12·0–18·0	50	June–May
Garden Warbler	17·9	16–22·7	50	June
Blackcap	17·5	14–20·3	50	May–June

	Mean	*Range*	*Sample*	*Seasonal details*
Wood Warbler	9·9	6·2–13·5	50	autumn migrants
Chiffchaff	8·0	6·7–9·2	50	April – early July
Willow Warbler	8·6	7·7–10·0	50	June–July
Goldcrest	5·7	4·9–7·4	50	April–June
Firecrest	5·6	4·5–8·2	44	all year
Spotted Flycatcher	15·0	13·2–19·1	50	late June–August
Red-breasted Flycatcher	10·0	8·4–12·6	50	autumn migrants
Pied Flycatcher	13·5	9·0–16·9	50	breeding adults
Bearded Tit	15·7	12·5–20	50	May
Long-tailed Tit	8·2	7·8–9·5	50	April–June
Marsh Tit	10·6	9·5–12·3	50	all year
Willow Tit	10·2	8·6–11·5	50	all year
Coal Tit	9·1	7·8–10·1	50	March–June
Blue Tit	13·3	9·0–14·0	50	breeding season, adults
Great Tit	19	15·5–21·5	50	April–June
Nuthatch	22	19·5–24·0	30	April–June
Treecreeper	9·0	7·8–11·5	50	April–early June
Red-backed Shrike	29·9	22·5–47·3	27	passage, any age
Great Grey Shrike	63·9	53·0–79·5		all year
Jay	161	140–187	50	April–June
Magpie	237		52	April–May
Chough	324	260–375	20	October–November 'adults'
Jackdaw	246		196	March–May
Rook	488		75	March–April
Carrion Crow	570		126	April–May
Starling	82	74–91	50	April–June
House Sparrow	27	22–31·4	50	May–August
Tree Sparrow	22	18·9–25	50	May–July
Chaffinch	20	18·8–23·6	50	May–June
Brambling	24	21·8–31	50	November–February
Greenfinch	27·8	25·0–31·5	21	May–June (26–34: Newton)
Goldfinch	15·6	13·4–17·8	50	breeding season adults
Siskin	14·5	11·6–18·2	50	April–June: spring passage
Linnet	15·3	14·5–21	50	all year, adults
Twite	15·4	13·0–17·6	50	winter
Redpoll	11·5	9·9–13·7	50	early May–July
Common Crossbill	40·6	34–48	638	July–September
Bullfinch	21·8	21–27	34	late May–July
Hawfinch	54	48–62	50	all year, all ages
Snow Bunting	33·9	26·8–41		winter
Yellowhammer	26·5	24–31	50	breeding season
Reed Bunting	18·3	15–22	50	May–late July
Corn Bunting	46	38–55	37	all year

Names of bird species mentioned in the text

Red-throated Diver *Gavia stellata*
Black-throated Diver *Gavia arctica*
Great Northern Diver *Gavia immer*
Little Grebe *Tachybaptus ruficollis*
Great Crested Grebe *Podiceps cristatus*
Fulmar *Fulmarus glacialis*
Cory's Shearwater *Calonectris diomedea*
Manx Shearwater *Puffinus puffinus*
Storm Petrel *Hydrobates pelagicus*
Leach's Petrel *Oceanodroma leucorhoa*
Gannet *Sula bassana*
Cormorant *Phalacrocorax carbo*
Shag *Phalacrocorax aristotelis*
Bittern *Botaurus stellaris*
Grey Heron *Ardea cinerea*
Mute Swan *Cygnus olor*
Bewick's Swan *Cygnus columbianus*
Whooper Swan *Cygnus cygnus*
Bean Goose *Anser fabalis*
Pink-footed Goose *Anser brachyrhynchus*
White-fronted Goose *Anser albifrons*
Lesser White-fronted Goose *Anser erythropus*
Greylag Goose *Anser anser*
Snow Goose *Anser caerulescens*
Canada Goose *Branta canadensis*
Barnacle Goose *Branta leucopsis*
Brent Goose *Branta bernicla*
Shelduck *Tadorna tadorna*
Wigeon *Anas penelope*
Gadwall *Anas strepera*
Teal *Anas crecca*
Mallard *Anas platyrhynchos*
Pintail *Anas acuta*
Garganey *Anas querquedula*
Shoveler *Anas clypeata*
Pochard *Aythya ferina*
Tufted Duck *Aythya fuligula*
Scaup *Aythya marila*
Eider *Somateria mollissima*
Goldeneye *Bucephala clangula*
Red-breasted Merganser *Mergus serrator*
Goosander *Mergus merganser*
Ruddy Duck *Oxyura jamaicensis*
Red Kite *Milvus milvus*
Marsh Harrier *Circus aeruginosus*
Hen Harrier *Circus cyaneus*
Montagu's Harrier *Circus pygargus*
Goshawk *Accipiter gentilis*
Sparrowhawk *Accipiter nisus*
Buzzard *Buteo buteo*
Rough-legged Buzzard *Buteo lagopus*
Golden Eagle *Aquila chrysaetos*
Osprey *Pandion haliaetus*
Kestrel *Falco tinnunculus*
Merlin *Falco columbarius*
Hobby *Falco subbuteo*
Peregrine *Falco peregrinus*
Red Grouse *Lagopus lagopus*
Ptarmigan *Lagopus mutus*
Black Grouse *Tetrao tetrix*
Red-legged Partridge *Alectoris rufa*
Grey Partridge *Perdix perdix*
Pheasant *Phasianus colchicus*
Water Rail *Rallus aquaticus*
Corncrake *Crex crex*
Moorhen *Gallinula chloropus*
Coot *Fulica atra*
Oystercatcher *Haematopus ostralegus*
Black-winged Stilt *Himantopus himantopus*
Avocet *Recurvirostra avosetta*
Stone-Curlew *Burhinus oedicnemus*
Little Ringed Plover *Charadrius dubius*
Ringed Plover *Charadrius hiaticula*
Dotterel *Charadrius morinellus*
Golden Plover *Pluvialis apricaria*
Grey Plover *Pluvialis squatarola*
Lapwing *Vanellus vanellus*
Knot *Calidris canutus*
Sanderling *Calidris alba*
Little Stint *Calidris minuta*
Temminck's Stint *Calidris temminckii*
Purple Sandpiper *Calidris maritima*
Dunlin *Calidris alpina*
Ruff *Philomachus pugnax*
Jack Snipe *Lymnocryptes minimus*
Snipe *Gallinago gallinago*
Woodcock *Scolopax rusticola*
Black-tailed Godwit *Limosa limosa*
Bar-tailed Godwit *Limosa lapponica*
Whimbrel *Numenius phaeopus*
Curlew *Numenius arquata*
Spotted Redshank *Tringa erythropus*
Redshank *Tringa totanus*
Greenshank *Tringa nebularia*
Green Sandpiper *Tringa ochropus*
Wood Sandpiper *Tringa glareola*
Common Sandpiper *Actitis hypoleucos*
Turnstone *Arenaria interpres*

Red-necked Phalarope *Phalaropus lobatus*
Arctic Skua *Stercorarius parasiticus*
Great Skua *Stercorarius skua*
Little Gull *Larus minutus*
Black-headed Gull *Larus ridibundus*
Common Gull *Larus canus*
Lesser Black-backed Gull *Larus fuscus*
Herring Gull *Larus argentatus*
Great Black-backed Gull *Larus marinus*
Kittiwake *Rissa tridactyla*
Sandwich Tern *Sterna sandvicensis*
Roseate Tern *Sterna dougallii*
Common Tern *Sterna hirundo*
Arctic Tern *Sterna paradisaea*
Little Tern *Sterna albifrons*
Black Tern *Chlidonias niger*
Guillemot *Uria aalge*
Razorbill *Alca torda*
Black Guillemot *Cepphus grylle*
Puffin *Fratercula arctica*
Rock Dove *Columba livia*
Stock Dove *Columba oenas*
Woodpigeon *Columba palumbus*
Collared Dove *Streptopelia decaocto*
Turtle Dove *Streptopelia turtur*
Cuckoo *Cuculus canorus*
Barn Owl *Tyto alba*
Snowy Owl *Nyctea scandiaca*
Little Owl *Athene noctua*
Tawny Owl *Strix aluco*
Long-eared Owl *Asio otus*
Short-eared Owl *Asio flammeus*
Nightjar *Caprimulgus europaeus*
Swift *Apus apus*
Kingfisher *Alcedo atthis*
Wryneck *Jynx torquilla*
Green Woodpecker *Picus viridis*
Black Woodpecker *Dryocopus martius*
Great Spotted Woodpecker *Dendrocopos major*
Lesser Spotted Woodpecker *Dendrocopos minor*
Wood Lark *Lullula arborea*
Skylark *Alauda arvensis*
Shore Lark *Eremophila alpestris*
Sand Martin *Riparia riparia*
Swallow *Hirunda rustica*
House Martin *Delichon urbica*
Tree Pipit *Anthus trivialis*
Meadow Pipit *Anthus pratensis*
Rock Pipit *Anthus spinoletta*
Yellow Wagtail *Motacilla flava*
Grey Wagtail *Motacilla cinerea*
Pied/White Wagtail *Motacilla alba*
Waxwing *Bombycilla garrulus*
Dipper *Cinclus cinclus*
Wren *Troglodytes troglodytes*
Dunnock *Prunella modularis*
Robin *Erithacus rubecula*
Nightingale *Luscinia megarhynchos*
Black Redstart *Phoenicurus ochruros*
Redstart *Phoenicurus phoenicurus*
Whinchat *Saxicola rubetra*
Stonechat *Saxicola torquata*
Wheatear *Oenanthe oenanthe*
Ring Ousel *Turdus torquatus*
Blackbird *Turdus merula*
Fieldfare *Turdus pilaris*
Song Thrush *Turdus philomelos*
Redwing *Turdus iliacus*
Mistle Thrush *Turdus viscivorus*
Cetti's Warbler *Cettia cetti*
Fan-tailed Warbler *Cisticola juncidis*
Grasshopper Warbler *Locustella naevia*
Savi's Warbler *Locustella luscinioides*
Sedge Warbler *Acrocephalus schoenobaenus*
Marsh Warbler *Acrocephalus palustris*
Reed Warbler *Acrocephalus scirpaceus*
Dartford Warbler *Sylvia undata*
Lesser Whitethroat *Sylvia curruca*
Whitethroat *Sylvia communis*
Garden Warbler *Sylvia borin*
Blackcap *Sylvia atricapilla*
Arctic Warbler *Phylloscopus borealis*
Pallas's Warbler *Phylloscopus proregulus*
Yellow-browed Warbler *Phylloscopus inornatus*
Bonelli's Warbler *Phylloscopus bonelli*
Wood Warbler *Phylloscopus sibilatrix*
Chiffchaff *Phylloscopus collybita*
Willow Warbler *Phylloscopus trochilus*
Goldcrest *Regulus regulus*
Firecrest *Regulus ignicapillus*
Spotted Flycatcher *Muscicapa striata*
Pied Flycatcher *Ficedula hypoleuca*
Bearded Tit *Panurus biarmicus*
Long-tailed Tit *Aegithalos caudatus*
Marsh Tit *Parus palustris*
Willow Tit *Parus montanus*
Crested Tit *Parus cristatus*
Coal Tit *Parus ater*
Blue Tit *Parus caeruleus*
Great Tit *Parus major*
Nuthatch *Sitta europaea*
Treecreeper *Certhia familiaris*
Red-backed Shrike *Lanius collurio*

Great Grey Shrike *Lanius excubitor*
Jay *Garrulus glandarius*
Magpie *Pica pica*
Chough *Pyrrhocorax pyrrhocorax*
Jackdaw *Corvus monedula*
Rook *Corvus frugilegus*
Carrion/Hooded Crow *Corvus corone*
Raven *Corvus corax*
Starling *Sturnus vulgaris*
House Sparrow *Passer domesticus*
Tree Sparrow *Passer montanus*
Chaffinch *Fringilla coelebs*
Brambling *Fringilla montifringilla*
Greenfinch *Carduelis chloris*
Goldfinch *Carduelis carduelis*
Siskin *Carduelis spinus*
Linnet *Carduelis cannabina*
Twite *Carduelis flavirostris*
Redpoll *Carduelis flammea*
Common Crossbill *Loxia curvirostra*
Bullfinch *Pyrrhula pyrrhula*
Hawfinch *Coccothraustes coccothraustes*
Lapland Bunting *Calcarius lapponicus*
Snow Bunting *Plectrophenax nivalis*
Yellowhammer *Emberiza citrinella*
Cirl Bunting *Emberiza cirlus*
Reed Bunting *Emberiza schoeniclus*
Corn Bunting *Miliaria calandra*

Index